For Eddie   March 9, 1999

Best wishes

J.

GREAT IRISH HUMOR

GREAT IRISH HUMOR

Edited and introduced by
Peter Haining

BARNES
& NOBLE
BOOKS
NEW YORK

For
Gemma
who missed the last Irish jaunt!
With Love

There is a little Devil, that does watch 'em,
Would steal their Jackets, if she catch 'em;
And always has her Rods in pickle,
If they presume, their Ribs to tickle.

James Farewell, 'The Irish Hudibras' (1689)

CONTENTS

INTRODUCTION

'Release the clergy to mate and breed', by Frank Usher from *The Midnight Court* by Brian Merriman.

It had been a long, hot drive from Waterford to Dublin, not helped by the fact that the car my family and I hired had broken down near the Wicklow Mountains and the rest of the journey was by taxi with a driver who had his own sense of time. We knew there was just one remaining flight back to London that evening and the man behind the wheel seemed to be more interested in chatting to us than getting us to the airport in time.

The sun was still on the horizon as we reached the outskirts of Dublin, but instead of taking the convenient ring-road, our driver insisted we go across Phoenix Park. The minutes ticked by as he pointed out the various sights, and it seemed like an eternity before we at last emerged onto the road once again. After three turns in opposite directions which took the car into a series of increasingly narrow back-streets, it was evident our man from Wicklow was lost. Finally, he pulled into a dead-end road surrounded on both sides by small garages, and there was no choice but to stop. We all sat in silence as he turned to look at us. There was a wide grin on his face.

'The t'ing is,' he said without a hint of apology, 'I know me way best in the dark!'

It was a classic piece of Irish wit, the unintentional humour breaking the tension of the moment. We were going to be late now, of course, but what did *that* matter! It was worth it for such a remark.

But the story of our journey was not quite over. We did reach Dublin Airport just as the flight was scheduled to leave. The terminal building was crowded with people as I sprinted across to the check-in and breathlessly thrust my tickets at the girl sitting behind the desk.

'No hurry, sir,' she smiled in that effortless way of those whose equilibrium is never ruffled. 'Your flight has been delayed for an hour.'

In a way this book was born on that day. The memory of it is as clear in my mind now as it was then. And it confirmed, if I ever needed confirmation, that few other nations on the face of this earth have a sense of humour quite like the Irish.

I almost feel as if Vivian Mercier, the author of that excellent work, *The Irish Comic Tradition* (1962), which has been so useful in my research, must have experienced something similar— indeed, probably *did* several times over—to have written in his book, 'No aspect of life is too sacred to escape the mockery of Irish laughter. By the fullest exercise of this great human gift the Irish have remained true to one of the deepest impulses of all mankind.'

In the following pages the reader will discover just how true this statement is, for these short stories demonstrate to the full the special Irish gift for ribaldry, wit, parody and satire.

All these categories of humour have a long and enduring tradition in Ireland. Indeed, examples of the country's love of the comic can be found in writings from the very earliest times. Take these lines from an anonymous ninth-century poem, originally written in the old Irish language:

> Sad to see the sons of learning,
> In everlasting hell-fire burning;
> While he that never reads a line,
> Doth in eternal glory shine.

There are also wonderful lines of self-mockery contained in the poems of the ninth-century writer, Siadhal Mac Feradach (*c.* AD 820–880), who is better known under his Latin appellation of Sedulius Scotus.

> I read and write and teach, philosophy peruse,
> I eat and freely drink, with rhymes invoke the muse,
> I call on heaven's throne both night and day,
> Snoring I sleep, or stay awake and pray.
> While sin and fault inform each act I plan—
> Ah! Christ and Mary, pity this miserable man.

The reader need only turn to some of the classic Irish myths and sagas to find that the element of humour is an essential ingredient in them all. As Peter Berresford Ellis, the expert on Gaelic history and author of *A Dictionary of Irish Mythology* (1987), has pointed out, 'That mischievous element—poking fun at life—has become a tradition in the Irish language, in Irish literature and in Irish literature written in English. Humour is also the essential ingredient of the Irish drama tradition. The dramatic humorist endures from the plays of Dion Boucicault (1820–1890)—his best-known work being *The Shaughraun* (1875)—through those of Sean O'Casey, Brendan Behan and even Samuel Beckett, who has his own bleak sense of humour.'

By just looking briefly in the voluminous archives of Gaelic humour it is not hard to find several works of outstanding merit. Take the *Parliament na mBan* ('The Parliament of Women'), written in Cork by Domhnall O Colmain about 1670. In it, the women of Ireland, disgusted at the political mess their men have landed Ireland in, set up their own parliament to put things right. Coming immediately after Oliver Cromwell's plans to 'ethnically cleanse' the Irish nation, the humour is understandably bitter.

Perhaps more famous still is the *Cuirt na Mhean Oiche* ('The Midnight Court') by Brian Mac Giolla Meidhre (Brian Merriman, *c.* 1747–1805). It is a hilarious satire which became one of the most controversial pieces of Irish literature—often banned—for its forthright views on the subject of sex. 'The Midnight Court' also stands as one of the first 'Women's Lib' poems, in which one girl even complains about the celibacy of the priesthood when they above all men can afford to support a wife:

> Release the clergy to mate and breed
> That the land may teem with their sturdy seed,
> Do not deny the women redress
> Nor leave them to languish in this distress,
> See how the ground in crowds they cumber,
> And by three to one they the men outnumber.

In fact, the sexual restraints which have been placed on all Irish writing in English for the last two centuries are not to be found in the more liberal traditions of the Irish who wrote in Irish. That tradition has continued to the present day: a recent notable example is Padraig Ua Maoleoin's 1985 novel, *O Thuaidh* ('From the North') which tells of the ludicrous sexual adventures of an Ulsterman in the Kerry Gaeltacht (Irish-speaking district).

Although I have made no attempt in this book to trace in detail the origins of Irish ribaldry, wit, parody and satire, there are certain basic truths that become evident. Ribald humour, for example, has evolved from folklore and a love of the grotesque; while wit and wordplay come straight from native speech. Satire, in turn, would seem to have been a result of the prestige in which poets and writers were held, thus enabling them to publish critical views in an oblique though readily understandable manner; and parody represents the constant attempts by writers to further the techniques of humour.

This said, the purpose of this anthology is to try to offer some of the best examples of Irish humour in each of the four categories by the nation's leading writers. Compiling the book has given me many hours of enjoyment. Some of the stories caused me to laugh out loud, others to chuckle at their mischievous tone, and many made me smile at the truths revealed in an ostensibly comic remark.

It was that famous Irish writer and wit, Oscar Wilde, I believe, who defined the cynic as 'a man who knows the price of everything and the value of nothing'. Wit can indeed be absurd and true— as our driver to Dublin Airport ably demonstrated—and the Irish have certainly provided as many truths as any other nation, if not more, through their rich tradition of humorous literature.

Peter Haining
September 1994

1

BELLY LAUGHS

Ribald Yarns

'Phelim O'Toole's Courtship', by W. H. Brooke from *Traits and Stories of the Irish Peasantry* by William Carleton.

A NIGHT IN LIMERICK

Roddy Doyle

The origins of the ribald and picaresque tales for which the Irish are undeniably famous stem from the nation's folklore and people's interest in the grotesque and the macabre. Early Gaelic literature is full of stories in which figures of mythology find themselves in sinister situations and extricate themselves with a mixture of stoicism and humour. In Anglo-Irish literature the elements of bawdy—particularly sexual—have tended to be censored until modern times, although there have always been a few writers looking to generate a risqué scene or two for their readers. The nation's current master of ribald humour is Roddy Doyle (1958–   ), a former Dublin teacher who has been showered with critical acclaim for his trio of comic masterpieces, The Barrytown Trilogy, *and the semi-autobiographical novel,* Paddy Clarke Ha Ha Ha *(1993), which received the Booker Prize. Doyle's work is now carrying the flag of Irish humour into the most unlikely places:* Paddy Clarke *has recently been published in Japan (complete with a glossary of Dublin expressions), where it has been compared to James Joyce's* Dubliners.

*The 'Barrytown' books—*The Commitments *(which Doyle actually first published himself in 1987 under the imprint King Farouk, Dublin rhyming slang for 'book'),* The Snapper *(1990) and* The Van *(1991)—are all based on the Kilbarrack area of Dublin where Doyle was born, grew up and became an English teacher in the local school. In writing these stories, said Mick Brown in a recent interview for the* Telegraph Magazine, *'Doyle transformed Kilbarrack from dull, grey anonymity into a vibrant canvas of bawdy, ducking and diving, weeping and swearing picaresques.' At the heart of all three books are the Rabbitte family—Jimmy Sr, his wife, Veronica, Jimmy Jr, Sharon, Darren and the twins—who are* *surely one of the great comic creations of recent years. In fact, the family display the same stoic outlook on life and sense of humour that the mythic heroes of Gaelic fiction used as talismans against disaster—here Doyle continues a great Irish tradition. Despite the phenomenal success that has now embraced his work, Roddy Doyle still retains his passion for football (he once wanted to be a professional) and pubs—a fact which gives an added flavour to the following extract from* The Van *in which Jimmy Rabbitte Sr spends a night with his mates and as the drinks flow the yarns, as of old, turn more ribald . . .*

*   *   *

He had young Jimmy's fiver and two more quid Veronica'd given him so he could buy a round. If only Bimbo and Bertie were there the fiver would be enough and he'd be able to give Veronica her money back but if Paddy was there he'd need it. It was a quarter past ten, early enough to get three or four pints inside him and late enough to make sure that his turn to put his hand in his pocket didn't come round again before closing time.

He came off the Green, crossed the road. The street light here was broken again. The glass was on the path. It was always this one they smashed, only this one.

It was funny; he'd been really grateful when young Jimmy had given him the fiver, delighted, and at the same time, or just after, he'd wanted to go after him and thump the living shite out of him and throw the poxy fiver back in his face, the nerve of him; who did he think he was, dishing out fivers like Bob fuckin' Geldof.

He was grand now though. He had the fiver and he was out on a Monday night.

—There's Jimmy, said Malcolm, one of the Hikers' bouncers.

—Howyeh, Malcolm, said Jimmy Sr.

—Chilly enough.

—Who're yeh tellin'.

He pushed the bar door, and was in.

—The man himself, said Bimbo.

He was pleased to see him; Jimmy Sr could tell. He had a grin on him that you could hang your washing on. There was just himself and Bertie up at the bar, new pints in front of them. Bertie turned and saw Jimmy Sr.

—Ah, he said. —Buenas noches, Jimmy.

—Howyis, said Jimmy Sr.

There was nothing like it, the few scoops with your mates.

—A pint there, Leo, Bimbo shouted down the bar, —like a good man.

Leo already had the glass under the tap. Jimmy Sr rubbed his hands. He wanted to whoop, but he put his hands in his pockets and looked around.

He nodded to a corner.

—Who're they? he said.

—Don't know, compadre, said Bertie. —Gringos.

They were looking over at three couples, all young and satisfied looking.

—They look like a righ' shower o' cunts, said Jimmy Sr.

—You don't even know them, sure, said Bimbo.

Bimbo fell for it every time.

—I wouldn't want to fuckin' know them, Jimmy Sr told Bimbo. —Look at them. They should be upstairs.

The Lounge was upstairs.

—I speet on them, said Bertie.

—Yeh can't stop people from comin' in if they want, said Bimbo. —It's a pub.

—'Course yeh can, said Jimmy Sr.

—He's righ', compadre, Bertie told Bimbo.

—How is he? said Bimbo. —A pub is a pub; a public house.

Leo arrived with Jimmy Sr's pint.

—Now, said Leo.

—Good man, Leo, said Jimmy Sr. —Fuck me, it looks lovely.

They agreed; it did.

The head of the pint stood higher than the glass, curving up and then flat and solid looking. The outside of the glass was clean; the whole thing looking like an ad. Jimmy Sr tilted the glass a little bit but the head stayed the way it was. They admired it.

—My Jaysis, said Jimmy Sr. —Wha'.

They got down off their stools and headed for an empty table.

—Anyway, said Bimbo. —Anyone should be able to come into a pub if they want.

—No way, said Jimmy Sr.

They sat down at their table and settled themselves in; sank into the seats, hooshed up their trousers, threw the dried-up, twisted beermats onto the table beside them—they were dangerous.

There wasn't much of a crowd in.

—Come here, Bimbo, said Jimmy Sr. —Do yeh think annyone should be allowed in here? Annyone now?

—Eh—, said Bimbo.

He didn't want to answer, but he had to.

—Yeah.

—Then what's Malcolm doin' outside then?

He had him.

—In the fuckin' cold, said Jimmy Sr.

—Si, said Bertie. —Poor Malcolm.

—He's gettin' well paid for it, Bimbo told Bertie.

Then he got back to Jimmy Sr.

—That's different, he said. —He's only there to stop messers from comin' in. He's not goin' to stop them just cos he doesn't like them.

—Me bollix, said Jimmy Sr. —How does he tell tha' they're messers?

He had him again.

—He can tell.

—How?

—Si.

—Ah look it, lads, said Bimbo. —Anyone—not messers now, or drug pushers or annyone like tha'—annyone tha' behaves themselves an' likes their pint should be allowed in.

They could tell by the way he spoke and looked at them that he wanted them to agree with him; he was nearly begging them.

—No way, said Jimmy Sr. —No fuckin' way.

Bertie agreed.

—Si, he said.

—Ah; why not?

—Look it, Jimmy Sr started, although he hadn't a breeze what he was going to say.

—Compadre, Bertie took over.

He sat up straight.

—Say we go into town, righ'; we go into town an' we try an' get into one o' those disco bars, righ'?

—Yeah, said Jimmy Sr.

—Would we be let in, would yeh say? Bertie asked Bimbo.

—I wouldn't want to go into one o' them, said Bimbo.

—Answer me question, said Bertie.

Bimbo thought about it.

It wasn't the pints Jimmy Sr loved; that wasn't it. He liked his pint—he fuckin' loved his pint—but that wasn't why he was here. He could do without it. He WAS doing without it. He only came up about two times a week these days, since he'd been laid off, and he never missed the drink, not really. Every night at about nine o'clock—when he heard the News music—he started getting itchy and he had to concentrate on staying sitting there and watching the News and being interested in it, but it wasn't the gargle he was dying for: it was this (he sat back and smiled at Bimbo); the lads here, the crack, the laughing. This was what he loved.

—Well? Bertie said to Bimbo.

Being on the labour wouldn't have been that bad if you could've come up here every night, or even every second night, and have got your batteries charged. But there you were; he'd a family to feed and that. He was only here now because one of his young fellas had given him a fiver.

—I wouldn't say we'd get in, said Bimbo.

—I agree with yeh, said Bertic. —The hombres at the door would tell us to vamoose an' fuck off. And—

He picked up his new pint.

—they'd be right.

He disappeared behind his pint. Jimmy Sr and Bimbo waited for him.

—Now, said Bertie, and he was looking at Bimbo, —why would they be righ'?

Jimmy Sr loved this.

Bimbo took up his pint, and put it down on the mat again.

—I give up, he said. —I don't know.

—Yeh do know, said Bertie. —It's because we've no righ' to be there. Amn't I righ'?

—Yeah, said Jimmy Sr.

—Disco bars aren't there for the likes of us, Bertie told Bimbo. —They're for young fellas an' signoritas. To go for a drink an' a dance an' wha'ever happens after, if yeh get me drift.

They laughed.

—It's not our scene, said Bertie.

He swept his open hand up and across from left to right, and showed them the room.

—This is our scene, compadre, he said.

—Fuckin' sure, said Jimmy Sr.

Bertie was really enjoying himself. He pointed the things out to them.

—Our pints. Our table here with the beermat under it stoppin' it from wobblin'. Our dart board an' our hoops, over there, look it.

He stamped his foot.

—Our floor with no carpet on it. Our chairs here with the springs all stickin' up into our holes. We fit here, Bimbo, said Bertie. —An' those fuckers over there should go upstairs to the Lounge where they fuckin' belong.

—Ah well, said Bimbo after he'd stopped laughing. —I suppose you're righ'.

—Oh, I am, said Bertie. —I am.

—Yeh are, o' course, said Jimmy Sr. —Come here but, Bertie. You were in one o' them before, weren't yeh? In a disco bar.

—I was indeed, compadre, said Bertie.

—Were yeh? said Bimbo. —Wha' were yeh doin' in one them places?

—Watchin' the greyhound racin', said Jimmy Sr.

—Yeh know wha' I mean, said Bimbo. —Don't start now.

—What d'yeh think he was doin' there, for fuck sake?

Bimbo ignored him.

—Excuse me, Bertie, he said. —Why were yeh in the disco bar?

—There was nowhere else, Bertie told him.

He waited.

—Wha' d'yeh mean?

—There was nowhere else to go cos all the other canteenas were shut; comprende?

—No. Not really.

—I got into Limerick after—

—Limerick!?

—Si.

—Wha' were yeh doin' there?

—Ah now, said Bertie. —It's a long story, an' it doesn't matter cos it's got nothin' to do with the disco bar.

—Yeah, but why were yeh in Limerick? Jimmy Sr asked him.

—You're beginnin' to annoy me, compadre, said Bertie.

—I was only askin', said Jimmy Sr. —My round, lads.
—No, hang on, Jim, said Bimbo. —I'll get this one.
—It's my round but.
—You're alrigh', said Bimbo. —Don't worry 'bout it.
Bimbo stood up so that Leo could see him.
—No, hang on, said Jimmy Sr. —Sit down.
—Not at all, said Bimbo. —You're alrigh'.
—Sit down!
Bimbo didn't know what to do.
—I'll buy me own round, said Jimmy Sr. —Righ'?
People were looking over at them, and wanting something to happen. Leo was at the end of the bar, ready to jump in and save the glass.
Bimbo sat down.
—O' course, Jim, he said. —No problem. I just—Sorry.
—You're alrigh', said Jimmy Sr.
He patted Bimbo's leg.
—Sorry for shoutin' at yeh, he said. —But I'll pay my own way, alrigh'.
—Yeh'd better, said Bertie.
Jimmy Sr smiled.
—Sorry, Jimmy, said Bimbo. —I didn't mean—
—No, Jimmy Sr stopped him.
He stood up.
—Three nice pints here, Leo!
He had a look at his watch on his way back down: he was safe; there wouldn't be time for another full round.
—Wha' were yeh doin' in a shaggin' disco bar? Bimbo asked Bertie. —Of all places.
—He told yeh, said Jimmy Sr.
—No, said Bimbo. —He didn't; not really. He only said he was in Limerick.
—Correction, said Bertie. —I told yeh, there was nowhere else to go to.
—Why was tha'?
—Jesus, he's thick, Jimmy Sr told Bertie.
—Everywhere else was shut, Bertie told Bimbo. —By the time I got my burro corralled an' I'd thrown a bit of water on me face an' dusted me poncho it was past closin' time; comprende?
—Yeah, said Bimbo.

—So, said Bertie. —There was this disco bar in the hotel—

—Did yeh stay in a hotel? Jimmy Sr asked him.

—Si.

—Jaysis, wha'.

—Nothin' but the best, said Bertie.

—Was it dear?

—Twenty-six quid.

—Are yeh serious? said Bimbo. —For the one night only?

—Oh, si.

—My God, said Bimbo. —Breakfast?

—Ah, yeah, said Bertie. —'Course.

—Was it one o' them continental ones, Bertie? Jimmy Sr asked him.

—Fuck, no, said Bertie. —I speet on your continental breakfast. A fry.

—Lovely, said Bimbo. —Was it nice?

—Alrigh', said Bertie.

—That's gas, said Bimbo. —Isn't it?

—Wha'? said Jimmy Sr.

—Bertie bein' in a hotel.

—I still want to know wha' he was doin' in fuckin' Limerick, said Jimmy Sr.

—Now, Leo shouted from the bar.

—That's me, said Jimmy Sr.

He was up and over to the bar in a second.

—Wha' was it like, an'annyway? Bimbo asked Bertie.

—What's tha'?

—The disco bar.

—Oh, tha'. Grand. It wasn't too bad at all.

Jimmy Sr was back.

—Get rid o' some o' them glasses there, Bimbo, will yeh. Good man.

He lowered the pints onto the table.

—Look at them now, wha'.

—Tha' man's a genius, said Bimbo.

—Si, said Bertie.

—How come they let yeh in? Bimbo asked Bertie.

—What's this? said Jimmy Sr.

—The disco bar.

—Oh, yeah.

—I was a guest, compadre, Bertie told Bimbo. —I was entitled
to get in.

—Is tha' righ'?

—Si. I made a bit of an effort.

He held the collar of his shirt for a second.

—Know wha' I mean?

—Yeh brasser, yeh, said Jimmy Sr.

—Fuck off, you, said Bertie. —I'll tell yeh one thing. It works.

—Wha?'

—Makin' the effort. Dressin' up.

Jimmy Sr made his face go sceptical.

—I'd say it does alrigh', he said.

—I'm tellin' yeh, said Bertie.

—Maybe, said Jimmy Sr.

Bimbo was a bit lost.

—He's tryin' to tell us he got off with somethin', Jimmy Sr told
him.

—Ah no, said Bimbo. —You're jokin'.

—He is, o' course, said Jimmy Sr.

—I'm sayin' nothin', said Bertie.

Bimbo was looking carefully at Bertie, making sure that he was
only messing. Bimbo didn't like that sort of thing; Bertie was
married. But he thought he was having them on; he could tell
from Bertie's face, looking around him like he'd said nothing. He
was definitely codding them.

Bertie caught Bimbo looking at him.

—A big girl, she was, he told him.

—Ah, get ou' of it, said Bimbo.

Jimmy Sr was looking at Bertie as well. He was the same age
as Bertie, a few years older only. Bertie hadn't got off with any
young one in Limerick; he could tell. But he kept looking.

*

Jimmy Sr was having problems with one of his laces. The knot
was tiny and his fingernails weren't long enough to get at it properly. He'd have to turn the light on; he could hardly feel the knot
now it was so small. He'd no nails left either, all bitten to fuck.

—Christ!

He didn't roar it or anything, but it exploded out. And he threw
his head up because his neck felt like it was going to burst. He
was sitting on the bed, bent over.

His nails usen't to be like this.

He tried to pull the fuckin' shoe off. His neck was getting sorer. He shut his eyes.

—Is that you?

Now he'd woken Veronica.

—Can't get me fuckin' poxy shoe off.

But it was good that she'd woken up. He slumped, then stretched and rubbed his neck.

—Sorry, he said.

—How was it?

—Grand.

—How are all the lads?

She always said Lads like they were kids, like he went out to play with them.

—Grand, he said. —Bimbo was askin' for yeh.

—And what did you tell him?

—Eh—

That was a hard one.

—I said yeh were fine, said Jimmy Sr.

—Did you cross your fingers when you said it?

—Ah, Veronica.

—Ah, Jimmy.

It was alright; she wasn't getting at him.

—I'll have to get into bed with the fuckin' shoe on; look.

Veronica sat up and turned on the lamp beside her.

—What's wrong? she said.

—Me shoe; look it.

She looked.

—Can you not tie your laces properly yet?

And she put his foot in her lap and got going on the knot. He nearly fell off the bed turning for her.

—You're useless, she said. —You really are.

For a split second he was going to straighten his leg quick and put his foot in her stomach, the way she spoke to him like that; for a split second only. Not really.

—There.

She had it done already.

It was nice as well sometimes, being mothered by Veronica.

—Thanks very much, he said.

THE KERUKOPAEDIA

A Fragment in the manner of Rabelais

Laurence Sterne

Roddy Doyle's great Irish forerunner in ribald humour was Laurence Sterne (1713–1768), whose work The Life and Opinions of Tristram Shandy *(1759–1767) is one of the jewels of literature as well as standing high among the world's great comic novels. Of Sterne,* Chambers' Biographical Dictionary *(1991) says, 'Few writers of any age or country have displayed such mastery over every form of humour both in situation and in character, a humour at times coming near to that of his acknowledged master, Cervantes.' Other critical works have also drawn comparisons between Sterne's wildly eccentric style, which is unashamedly dedicated to making the reader laugh aloud, and the works of Swift and Rabelais.*

Laurence Sterne was born in Clonmel, the son of an infantryman, and led a precarious childhood in Ireland before being sent to England to study at Jesus College, Cambridge. In 1738 he was ordained and appointed to the living at Sutton on the Forest, near York. The success of the first two books describing the riotous adventures of Tristram Shandy made their author enormously popular with the public, and volumes three and four followed in 1761. The remainder of this comic masterpiece appeared between 1761 and 1767 when Sterne's health was already beginning to fail. Apart from his contribution to the development of the novel—widening its scope and giving more freedom to its structure—Sterne also wrote a burlesque satire, The History of a Good Warm Watch-Coat *(1759), about a squabble between a grasping lawyer, Francis Topham, and the Dean of York, John Fontayne. (Topham later appeared as Didius, the church-lawyer, in* Tristram Shandy.)

The following humorous piece, written in the style of Rabelais, was left unpublished at the time of the author's death and did not appear in print until 1775 in a collection of Sterne's letters. It is sad that the master of humour did not live to complete his comic yarn . . .

*   *   *

Chapter I

Shewing two things; first, what a Rabelaic Fellow Longinus Rabelaicus is; and secondly, how cavalierly he begins his Book.

My dear and thrice-reverend brethren, as well archbishops and bishops, as the rest of the inferior clergy! Would it not be a glorious thing, if any man of genius and capacity amongst us for such a work, was fully bent within himself to sit down immediately and compose a thorough-stitched system of the Kerukopaedia; fairly setting forth, to the best of his wit and memory, and collecting for that purpose, all that is needful to be known and understood of that art?—Of what art? cried Panurge. Good God! answered Longinus (making an exclamation, but taking care at the same time to moderate his voice), why, of the art of making all kinds of your theological, hebdodomical, rostrummical, humdrummical what d'ye call 'ems.—I will be shot, quoth Epistemon, if all this story of thine of a roasted horse, is simply no more than S—— Sausages! quoth Panurge. Thou hast fallen twelve feet and about five inches below the mark, answered Epistemon; for I hold them to be Sermons,—which said word (as I take the matter) being but a word of low degree for a book of high rhetoric,—Longinus Rabelaicus was fore-minded to usher and lead in his dissertation with as much pomp and parade as he could afford;—and for my own part, either I know no more of Latin than my horse, or the Kerukopaedia is nothing but the art of making 'em.—And why not, quoth Gymnast, of preaching them when we have done?—Believe me, dear souls, this is half in half;—and if some skilful body would but put us in a way to do this to some tune—Thou wouldst not have them chanted, surely? quoth Triboulet, laughing.—No; nor canted neither ! quoth Gymnast, crying;—but what I mean, my friends, says Longinus Rabelaicus (who is certainly one of the greatest critics in the western world, and as Rabelaic a fellow as ever existed), what I mean, says he, interrupting them both, and resuming his discourse, is this, that if all the scattered rules of the Kerukopaedia could be but once carefully collected into one code, as thick as Panurge's head, and the whole cleanly digested—(Pooh! says Panurge, who felt himself aggrieved)—and bound up, continued Longinus, by way of a regular institute, and then put into the hands of every licensed preacher in Great Britain and Ireland, just before he began to compose, I maintain it.—I deny it flatly, quoth Panurge.—What? answered Longinus Rabelaicus with all the temper in the world.

Chapter II

In which the Reader will begin to form a Judgment of what an Historical, Dramatical, Anecdotical, Allegorical, and Comical kind of a Work he has got hold of.

Homenas, who had to preach next Sunday (before God knows whom), knowing nothing at all of the matter,—was all this while at it as hard as he could drive, in the very next room:—for having fouled two clean sheets of his own, and being quite stuck fast in the entrance upon his third general division, and finding himself unable to get either forwards or backwards with any grace—'Curse it!' says he (thereby excommunicating every mother's son who should think differently), 'why may not a man lawfully call in for help in this, as well as any other human emergency?'—So without any more argumentation, except starting up and nimming down from the top shelf but one, the second volume of Clark,—though without any felonious intentions in so doing, he had begun to clap me in (making a joint first) five whole pages, nine round paragraphs, and a dozen and a half of good thoughts all of a row, and because there was a confounded high gallery,—was transcribing it away like a little devil.—Now,—quoth Homenas to himself, 'though I hold all this to be fair and square, yet, if I am found out, there will be the deuce and all to pay.—Why are the bells ringing backwards, you lad? What is all that crowd about, honest man? Homenas was got upon Doctor Clark's back, sir.—And what of that, my lad? Why, an' please you, he has broke his neck and fractured his skull, and befouled himself into the bargain, by a fall from the pulpit two stories high. Alas! poor Homenas! Homenas has done his business!—Homenas will never preach more, while breath is in his body.—No, faith, I shall never again be able to tickle it off as I have done. I may sit up whole winter nights, baking my blood with hectic watchings, and write as solid as a Father of the Church;—or I may sit down whole summer days, evaporating my spirits into the finest thoughts, and write as florid as a Mother of it.—In a word, I may compose myself off my legs, and preach till I burst;—and when I have done, it will be worse than if not done at all.—Pray Mr Such-a-one, who held forth last Sunday?—Doctor Clark, I trow, says one.—Pray what Doctor Clark? says a second.—Why Homenas's Doctor Clark, quoth a third. O rare Homenas! cries a fourth. Your servant, Mr Homenas, quoth a fifth.—'Twill be all over with me, by Heaven!—I may as well put the book from whence I took it.'—Here Homenas burst into a flood of tears, which, falling down, helter-skelter, ding-dong, without any kind of intermission for six minutes and almost twenty-five seconds, had a marvellous effect upon his discourse; for the aforesaid tears, do you mind, did so temper the wind that was rising upon the aforesaid discourse, but falling for the most part perpendicularly, and hitting the spirits at right angles, which were mounting horizontally all over the surface of his harangue, they not only played the devil and all with the sublimity,—but moreover the said tears, by their nitrous quality, did so refrigerate, precipitate, and hurry down to the bottom of his soul, all unsavoury particles which lay fermenting (as you saw) in the middle of his conception, that he went on in the coolest and chastest style (for a soliloquy, I think) that ever mortal man uttered.

'This is really and truly a very hard case,' continued Homenas to himself.—Panurge, by the bye, and all the company in the next room, hearing all along every syllable he spoke! for you must know, that, notwithstanding Panurge had opened his mouth as wide as he could for his blood, in order to give a round answer to Longinus Rabelaicus's interrogation, which concluded the last chapter,—yet Homenas's rhetoric had poured in so like a torrent, slap-dash through the wainscot, amongst them, and happening at the uncritical crisis when Panurge had just put his ugly face into the above said posture of defence,—that he stopped short!—he did indeed, and though his head was full of matter, and he had screwed up every nerve and muscle belonging to it, till all cried crack again, in order to give a due projectile force to what he was going to let fly full in Longinus Rabelaicus's teeth, who sat over against him,—yet, for all that, he had the continence to contain himself; for he stopped short, I say, without uttering one word, except Z——ds! Many reasons may be assigned for this; but the most true, the most strong, the most hydrostatical, and the most philosophical reason, why Panurge did not go on, was—that the fore-mentioned torrent did not so drown his voice that he had none left to go on with.—God help him, poor fellow! so he stopped short (as I have told you before); and all the time Homenas was speaking he said not another word, good or bad, but stood gaping and staring, like what you please:—so that the break marked thus——, which Homenas's grief had made in the middle of his discourse, which he could no more help than he could fly,—produced no other change in the room where Longinus Rabelaicus, Epistemon, Gymnast, Triboulet, and nine or ten more honest blades had got Kerukopaedising together, but that it gave time to Gymnast to give Panurge a good squashing chuck under his double chin; which Panurge taking in good part, and just as it was meant by Gymnast, he forthwith shut his mouth; eccentrically, and out of neighbour's row, but listening, as all the rest did, with might and main, they plainly and distinctly heard every syllable of what you will find recorded in the next chapter.

THE INVISIBLE MAN

Charles Lever

*Another Irish writer responsible for an important landmark in the
history of humorous fiction was Charles James Lever (1806–1872),
who popularised the concept of the slick-talking, rollicking Irish
blade. In his introduction to* The Masterpiece Library of Short
Stories *(1936) Sir J. A. Hammerton argues that Lever deserves even
higher acclaim as the man whose books 'did in many ways for
Ireland what Sir Walter Scott's Waverley Novels did for Scotland'.
His comic tales of Irish life certainly made him very popular with
readers in England, where he was known as 'Harry Rollicker' and
'The Lord of Romantic Misrule' and became a friend of Dickens,
Thackeray and Trollope.*

*Born in Dublin, Lever graduated at Trinity College and went to
study medicine at Göttingen. On his return to Ireland he took the
first of several practices in country towns and also began to contribute to journals such as the* Dublin University Magazine. *He wrote
his first novel,* The Confessions of Harry Lorrequer, *in 1839, and
its reception encouraged him to produce* Charles O'Malley *(1841),
a humorous tale based on his own college life in Dublin which
proved to be his best-known book. Another of Lever's admirers,
Professor James M. Cahalan, has said of this work in* The Irish
Novel: A Critical History *(1988) that 'The opening Trinity College
chapters look ahead to Flann O'Brien's* At Swim-Two Birds *and
J. P. Donleavy's* The Ginger Man.' *Lever continued to write with
unfailing vigour, basing a number of his books on travels he undertook in North America and Europe. According to one story, while
exploring in Canada, Lever was captured by some Indians, rescued
by a squaw with whom he fell in love, and when he returned to
Dublin brought as a souvenir a canoe which he was thereafter often
seen rowing up and down the Grand Canal!*

Lever's success as a novelist was resented in certain quarters in Ireland where he was accused of making fun of his fellow countrymen and having created 'the stage Irishman'. Perhaps as a result of these attacks, his later books became generally more serious in tone and dealt with nationalist subjects as well as the plight of the poor in the same sort of country districts where he had worked as a doctor. In hindsight, Lever was at his best when giving free reign to his wild sense of humour in tales such as 'The Invisible Man', which Cahalan has described as 'the funniest scene in any nineteenth-century Irish novel, an episode of sheer absurdity as well as a bizarre commentary on the power of Irish patriotism'. I too commend this hilarious story by a now sadly neglected and often maligned writer deserving of rediscovery.

*   *   *

Among the many peculiar tastes which distinguished Mr Francis Webber, was an extraordinary fancy for street-begging; he had, over and over, won large sums upon his success in that difficult walk; and so perfect were his disguises, both of dress, voice, and manner, that he actually, at one time, succeeded in obtaining charity from his very opponent in the wager. He wrote ballads with the greatest facility, and sung them with infinite pathos and humour; and the old woman at the corner of College Green was certain of an audience when the severity of the night would leave all other minstrelsy deserted. As these feats of *jonglerie* usually terminated in a row, it was a most amusing part of the transaction to see the singer's part taken by the mob against the college men, who, growing impatient to carry him off to supper somewhere, would invariably be obliged to have a fight for the booty.

Now, it chanced that a few evenings before, Mr Webber was returning with a pocket well lined with copper, from a musical *réunion* he had held at the corner of York Street, when the idea struck him to stop at the end of Grafton Street, where a huge stone grating at that time exhibited, perhaps it exhibits still, the descent to one of the great main sewers of the city.

The light was shining brightly from a pastry-cook's shop, and showed the large bars of stone, between which the muddy water was rushing rapidly down, and splashing in the torrent that ran boisterously several feet beneath.

To stop in the street of any crowded city is, under any circumstances, an invitation to others to do likewise, which is rarely unaccepted; but when in addition to this, you stand fixedly in one spot, and regard with stern intensity any object near you, the chances are ten to one that you have several companions in your curiosity before a minute expires.

Now, Webber, who had at first stood still, without any peculiar thought in view, no sooner perceived that he was joined by others, than the idea of making something out of it immediately occurred to him.

'What is it, agra?' inquired an old woman, very much in his own style of dress, pulling at the hood of his cloak.

'And can't you see for yourself, darling?' replied he sharply, as he knelt down, and looked most intensely at the sewer.

'Are ye long there, avick?' inquired he of an imaginary individual below, and then waiting as if for a reply, said, 'Two hours! Blessed virgin! He's two hours in the drain!'

By this time the crowd had reached entirely across the street, and the crushing and squeezing to get near the important spot was awful.

'Where did he come from? Who is he? How did he get there?' were questions on every side, and various surmises were afloat, till Webber, rising from his knees, said, in a mysterious whisper to those nearest him, 'He's made his escape tonight out o' Newgate by the big drain, and lost his way; he was looking for the Liffey, and took the wrong turn.'

To an Irish mob, what appeal could equal this? A culprit, at any time, has his claim upon their sympathy; but let him be caught in the very act of cheating the authorities and evading the law, and his popularity knows no bounds. Webber knew this well, and, as the mob thickened around him, sustained an imaginary conversation that Savage Landor might have envied, imparting now and then such hints concerning the runaway as raised their interest to the highest pitch, and fifty different versions were related on all sides—of the crime he was guilty—the sentence that was passed on him—and the day he was to suffer.

'Do ye see the light, dear?' said Webber, as some ingeniously benevolent individual had lowered down a candle with a string;

'Do ye see the light? Oh! he's fainted, the creature.' A cry of horror from the crowd burst forth at these words, followed by an universal shout of 'Break open the street.'

Pickaxes, shovels, spades, and crowbars, seemed absolutely the walking accompaniments of the crowd, so suddenly did they appear upon the field of action, and the work of exhumation was begun with a vigour that speedily covered nearly half of the street with mud and paving stones; parties relieved each other at the task, and, ere half an hour, a hole capable of containing a mail coach was yawning in one of the most frequented thoroughfares of Dublin. Meanwhile, as no appearance of the culprit could be had, dreadful conjectures as to his fate began to gain ground. By this time the authorities had received intimation of what was going forward, and attempted to disperse the crowd; but Webber, who still continued to conduct the prosecution, called on them to resist the police, and save the poor creature; and now began a most terrific fray, the stones forming a ready weapon, were hurled at the unprepared constables, who, on their side, fought manfully, but against superior numbers; so that, at last, it was only by the aid of a military force the mob could be dispersed, and a riot, which had assumed a very serious character, got under. Meanwhile, Webber had reached his chambers and changed his costume, and was relating over a supper-table the narrative of his philanthropy to a very admiring circle of his friends.

A RHINOCEROS, SOME LADIES, AND A HORSE

James Stephens

James Stephens (1880–1950) was the man who had the idea of reintroducing the ancient supermen of Irish mythology into contemporary Ireland, where they were invariably tempted to interfere in the lives of men and women—especially pretty young women who could not resist the beauty and blandishments of these gods in disguise. Stephens himself was quite the reverse of the Dionysian characters he created: a diminutive figure who apparently looked almost exactly like the traditional idea of a leprechaun. Indeed, Professor Cahalan has written that for years he was 'a victim of the image he himself helped to create in The Crock of Gold *(1912)— that of the comic leprechaun'.*

Perhaps it was understandable that James Stephens's writing escaped into humour and fantasy, for as a child he had been abandoned by his parents and grew up hungry and poor. He graduated from being a typist in a lawyer's office to becoming a contributor to the magazine Sinn Féin, *where his talent as a storyteller was discovered by George Russell. Today there are those who believe him to be one of Ireland's most original writers of the first half of this century and point to books like* The Crock of Gold, The Charwoman's Daughter *(1912),* In The Land of Youth *(1924) and* Etched In Moonlight *(1928), all of which earned him an international reputation. He was also a master of the humorous short story in which outlandish characters abounded. 'A Rhinoceros, Some Ladies, and a Horse' is rather less well known than some of these tales, but nonetheless represents the comic genius of James Stephens at its best . . .*

* * *

One day, in my first job, a lady fell in love with me. It was quite unreasonable, of course, for I wasn't wonderful: I was small and thin, and I weighed much the same as a largish duck-egg. I didn't fall in love with her, or anything like that. I got under the table, and stayed there until she had to go wherever she had to go to.

I had seen an advertisement—'Smart boy wanted', it said. My legs were the smartest things about me, so I went there on the run. I got the job.

At that time there was nothing on God's earth that I could do, except run. I had no brains, and I had no memory. When I was told to do anything I got into such an enthusiasm about it that I couldn't remember anything else about it. I just ran as hard as I could, and then I ran back, proud and panting. And when they asked me for the whatever-it-was that I had run for, I started, right on the instant, and ran some more.

The place I was working at was, amongst other things, a theatrical agency. I used to be sitting in a corner of the office floor, waiting to be told to run somewhere and back. A lady would come in—a music-hall lady that is—and, in about five minutes, howls of joy would start coming from the inner office. Then, peacefully enough, the lady and my two bosses would come out, and the lady always said, 'Splits! I can do splits like no one.' And one of my bosses would say, 'I'm keeping your splits in mind.' And the other would add, gallantly—'No one who ever saw your splits could ever forget 'em.'

One of my bosses was thin, and the other one was fat. My fat boss was composed entirely of stomachs. He had three baby-stomachs under his chin: then he had three more descending in even larger englobings nearly to the ground: but, just before reaching the ground, the final stomach bifurcated into a pair of boots. He was very light on these and could bounce about in the neatest way.

He was the fattest thing I had ever seen, except a rhinoceros that I had met in the Zoo the Sunday before I got the job. That rhino was *very* fat, and it had a smell like twenty-five pigs. I was standing outside its palisade, wondering what it could possibly feel like to be a rhinoceros, when two larger boys passed by. Suddenly they caught hold of me, and pushed me through the bars of the palisade. I was very skinny, and in about two seconds I was right inside, and the rhinoceros was looking at me.

It was very fat, but it wasn't fat like stomachs, it was fat like barrels of cement, and when it moved it creaked a lot, like a woman I used to know who creaked like an old bedstead. The rhinoceros swaggled over to me with a bunch of cabbage sticking out of its mouth. It wasn't angry, or anything like that, it just wanted to see who I was. Rhinos are blindish: they mainly see by smelling, and they smell in snorts. This one started at my left shoe, and snorted right up that side of me to my ear. He smelt that very carefully: then he switched over to my right ear, and snorted right down that side of me to my right shoe: then he fell in love with my shoes and began to lick them. I, naturally, wriggled my feet at that, and the big chap was so astonished that he did the strangest step-dance backwards to his pile of cabbages, and began to eat them.

I squeezed myself out of his cage and walked away. In a couple of minutes I saw the two boys. They were very frightened, and they asked me what I had done to the rhinoceros. I answered, a bit grandly, perhaps, that I had seized it in both hands, ripped it limb from limb, and tossed its carcass to the crows. But when they began shouting to people that I had just murdered a rhinoceros I took to my heels, for I didn't want to be arrested and hanged for a murder that I hadn't committed.

Still, a man can't be as fat as a rhinoceros, but my boss was as fat as a man can be. One day a great lady of the halls came in, and was received on the knee. She was very great. Her name was Maudie Darling, or thereabouts. My bosses called her nothing but 'Darling', and she called them the same. When the time came for her to arrive the whole building got palpitations of the heart. After waiting a while my thin boss got angry, and said—'What does the woman think she is? If she isn't here in two twos I'll go down to the entry, and when she does come I'll boot her out.' The fat boss said—'She's only two hours late, she'll be here before the week's out.'

Within a few minutes there came great clamours from the courtyard. Patriotic cheers, such as Parnell himself never got, were thundering. My bosses ran instantly to the inner office. Then the door opened, and the lady appeared.

She was very wide, and deep, and magnificent. She was dressed in camels and zebras and goats: she had two peacocks in her hat and a rabbit muff in her hand, and she strode among these with prancings.

But when she got right into the room and saw herself being looked at by three men and a boy she became adorably shy: one could see that she had never been looked at before.

'O,' said she, with a smile that made three and a half hearts beat like one, 'O,' said she, very modestly, 'is Mr Which-of-'em-is-it really in? Please tell him that Little-Miss-Me would be so glad to see and to be—'

Then the inner door opened, and the large lady was surrounded by my fat boss and my thin boss. She crooned to them—'O, you dear boys, you'll never know how much I've thought of you and longed to see you.'

That remark left me stupefied. The first day I got to the office I heard that it was the fat boss's birthday, and that he was thirty years of age: and the thin boss didn't look a day younger than the fat one. How the lady could mistake these old men for boys seemed to me the strangest fact that had ever come my way. My own bet was that they'd both die of old age in about a month.

After a while they all came out again. The lady was helpless with laughter: she had to be supported by my two bosses—'O,' she cried, 'you boys will kill me.' And the bosses laughed and laughed, and the fat one said—'Darling, you're a scream,' and the thin one said—'Darling, you're a riot.'

And then . . . she saw me! I saw her seeing me the very way I had seen the rhinoceros seeing me: I wondered for an instant would she smell me down one leg and up the other. She swept my two bosses right away from her, and she became a kind of queen, very glorious to behold: but sad, startled. She stretched a long, slow arm out and out and out and then she unfolded a long, slow finger, and pointed it at me—'Who is THAT??' she whispered in a strange whisper that could be heard two miles off.

My fat boss was an awful liar—'The cat brought that in,' said he.

But the thin boss rebuked him: 'No,' he said, 'it was not the cat. Let me introduce you; darling, this is James. James, this is the darling of the gods.'

'And of the pit,' said she, sternly.

She looked at me again. Then she sank to her knees and spread out both arms to me—

'Come to my Boozalum, angel,' said she in a tender kind of way.

I knew what she meant, and I knew that she didn't know how
to pronounce that word. I took a rapid glance at the area indicated.
The lady had a boozalum you could graze a cow on. I didn't wait
one second, but slid, in one swift, silent slide, under the table.
Then she came forward and said a whole lot of poems to me under
the table, imploring me, among a lot of odd things, to 'come forth,
and gild the morning with my eyes', but at last she was reduced
to whistling at me with two fingers in her mouth, the way you
whistle for a cab.

I learned after she had gone that most of the things she said to
me were written by a poet fellow named Spokeshave. They were
very complimentary, but I couldn't love a woman who mistook
my old bosses for boys, and had a boozalum that it would take an
Arab chieftain a week to trot across on a camel.

The thin boss pulled me from under the table by my leg, and
said that my way was the proper way to treat a rip, but my fat
boss said, very gravely—'James, when a lady invites a gentleman
to her boozalum a real gentlemen hops there as pronto as possible,
and I'll have none but real gentlemen in this office.'

'Tell me,' he went on, 'what made that wad of Turkish Delight
fall in love with you?'

'She didn't love me at all, sir,' I answered.

'No?' he inquired.

'She was making fun of me,' I explained.

'There's something in that,' said he seriously, and went back to
his office.

I had been expecting to be sacked that day. I was sacked the
next day, but that was about a horse.

I had been given three letters to post, and told to run or they'd
be too late. So I ran to the post office and round it and back, with,
naturally, the three letters in my pocket. As I came to our door
a nice, solid, red-faced man rode up on a horse. He thrust the
reins into my hand—

'Hold the horse for a minute,' said he.

'I can't,' I replied, 'my boss is waiting for me.'

'I'll only be a minute,' said he angrily, and he walked off.

Well, there was I, saddled, as it were, with a horse. I looked at
it, and it looked at me. Then it blew a pint of soap-suds out of its
nose and took another look at me, and then the horse fell in love

with me as if he had just found his long-lost foal. He started to
lean against me and to woo me with small whinnies, and I
responded and replied as best I could—

'Don't move a toe,' said I to the horse, 'I'll be back in a minute.'

He understood exactly what I said, and the only move he made
was to swing his head and watch me as I darted up the street. I
was less than half a minute away anyhow, and never out of his
sight.

Up the street there was a man, and sometimes a woman, with
a barrow, thick-piled with cabbages and oranges and apples. As I
raced round the barrow I pinched an apple off it at full speed, and
in ten seconds I was back at the horse. The good nag had watched
every move I made, and when I got back his eyes were wide open,
his mouth was wide open, and he had his legs all splayed out so
that he couldn't possibly slip. I broke the apple in halves and
popped one half into his mouth. He ate it in slow crunches, and
then he looked diligently at the other half. I gave him the other
half, and, as he ate it, he gurgled with cidery gargles of pure joy.
He then swung his head round from me and pointed his nose up
the street, right at the apple-barrow.

I raced up the street again, and was back within the half-minute
with another apple. The horse had nigh finished the first half of it
when a man who had come up said, thoughtfully—

'He seems to like apples, bedad!'

'He loves them,' said I.

And then, exactly at the speed of lightning, the man became
angry, and invented bristles all over himself like a porcupine—

'What the hell do you mean,' he hissed, and then he bawled,
'by stealing my apples?'

I retreated a bit into the horse—

'I didn't steal your apples,' I said.

'You didn't!' he roared, and then he hissed, 'I saw you,' he
hissed.

'I didn't steal them,' I explained, 'I pinched them.'

'Tell me that one again,' said he.

'If,' said I patiently, 'if I took the apples for myself that would
be stealing.'

'So it would,' he agreed.

'But as I took them for the horse that's pinching.'

'Be dam, but!' said he. ''Tis a real argument,' he went on,

staring at the sky. 'Answer me that one,' he demanded of himself, and he in a very stupor of intellection. 'I give it up,' he roared, 'you give me back my apples.'

I placed the half apple that was left into his hand, and he looked at it as if it was a dead frog—

'What'll I do with that?' he asked earnestly.

'Give it to the horse,' said I.

The horse was now prancing at him, and mincing at him, and making love at him. He pushed the half apple into the horse's mouth, and the horse mumbled it and watched him, and chewed it and watched him, and gurgled it and watched him—

'He does like his bit of apple,' said the man.

'He likes you too,' said I. 'I think he loves you.'

'It looks like it,' he agreed, for the horse was yearning at him, and its eyes were soulful.

'Let's get him another apple,' said I, and, without another word, we both pounded back to his barrow and each of us pinched an apple off it. We got one apple into the horse, and were breaking the second one when a woman said gently—

'Nice, kind, Christian gentlemen, feeding dumb animals—with my apples,' she yelled suddenly.

The man with me jumped as if he had been hit by a train—

'Mary,' said he humbly.

'Joseph,' said she in a completely unloving voice.

But the woman transformed herself into nothing else but woman—

'What about my apples?' said she. 'How many have we lost?'

'Three,' said Joseph.

'Four,' said I, 'I pinched three and you pinched one.'

'That's true,' said he. 'That's exact, Mary. I only pinched one of our apples.'

'You only,' she squealed—

And I, hoping to be useful, broke in—

'Joseph,' said I, 'is the nice lady your boss?'

He halted for a dreadful second, and made up his mind—

'You bet she's my boss,' said he, 'and she's better than that, for she's the very wife of my bosum.'

She turned to me—

'Child of Grace—' said she—

Now, when I was a child, and did something that a woman didn't like she always expostulated in the same way. If I tramped on her foot, or jabbed her in the stomach—the way women have multitudes of feet and stomachs is always astonishing to a child—the remark such a woman made was always the same. She would grab her toe or her stomach, and say—'Childagrace, what the hell are you doing?' After a while I worked it out that Childagrace was one word, and was my name. When any woman in agony yelled Childagrace I ran right up prepared to be punished, and the woman always said tenderly, 'What are you yowling about, Childagrace.'

'Childagrace,' said Mary earnestly, 'how's my family to live if you steal our apples? You take my livelihood away from me! Very good, but will you feed and clothe and educate my children in,' she continued proudly, 'the condition to which they are accustomed?'

I answered that question cautiously—

'How many kids have you, ma'am?' said I.

'We'll leave that alone for a while,' she went on. 'You owe me two and six for the apples.'

'Mary!' said Joseph, in a pained voice.

'And you,' she snarled at him, 'owe me three shillings. I'll take it out of you in pints.' She turned to me—

'What do you do with all the money you get from the office here?'

'I give it to my landlady.'

'Does she stick to the lot of it?'

'Oh, no,' I answered, 'she always gives me back threepence.'

'Well, you come and live with me and I'll give you back fourpence.'

'All right,' said I.

'By gum,' said Joseph, enthusiastically, 'that'll be fine. We'll go out every night and we won't steal a thing. We'll just pinch legs of beef, and pig's feet, and barrels of beer—'

'Wait now,' said Mary. 'You stick to your own landlady. I've trouble enough of my own. You needn't pay me the two and six.'

'Good for you,' said Joseph heartily, and then, to me—

'You just get a wife of your bosum half as kind as the wife of my bosum and you'll be set up for life. Mary,' he cried joyfully, 'let's go and have a pint on the strength of it.'

'You shut up,' said she.

'Joseph,' I interrupted, 'knows how to pronounce that word properly.'

'What word?'

'The one he used when he said you were the wife of his what-you-may-call-it.'

'I'm not the wife of any man's what-you-may-call-it,' said she, indignantly—'Oh, I see what you mean! So he pronounced it well, did he?'

'Yes, ma'am.'

She looked at me very sternly—

'How does it come you know about all these kinds of words?'

'Yes,' said Joseph, and he was even sterner than she was, 'when I was your age I didn't know any bad words.'

'You shut up,' said she, and continued, 'what made you say that to me?'

'A woman came into our office yesterday, and she mispronounced it.'

'What did she say now?'

'Oh, she said it all wrong.'

'Do you tell me so? We're all friends here: what way did she say it, son?'

'Well, ma'am, she called it boozalum.'

'She said it wrong all right,' said Joseph, 'but 'tis a good, round, fat kind of a word all the same.'

'You shut up,' said Mary. 'Who did she say the word to?'

'She said it to me, ma'am.'

'She must have been a rip,' said Joseph.

'Was she a rip, now?'

'I don't know, ma'am. I never met a rip.'

'You're too young yet,' said Joseph, 'but you'll meet them later on. I never met a rip myself until I got married—I mean,' he added hastily, 'that they were all rips except the wife of my what-do-you-call-ems, and that's why I married her.'

'I expect you've got a barrel-full of rips in your past,' said she bleakly, 'you must tell me about some of them tonight.' And then, to me, 'Tell us about the woman,' said she.

So I told them all about her, and how she held out her arms to me, and said, 'Come to my boozalum, angel.'

'What did you do when she shoved out the old arms at you?' said Joseph.

'I got under the table,' I answered.

'That's not a bad place at all, but,' he continued earnestly, 'never get under the bed when there's an old girl chasing you, for that's the worst spot you could pick on. What was the strap's name?'

'Maudie Darling, she called herself.'

'You're a blooming lunatic,' said Joseph, 'she's the loveliest thing in the world, barring,' he added hastily, 'the wife of my blast-the-bloody-word.'

'We saw her last night,' said Mary, 'at Dan Lowrey's Theatre, and she's just lovely.'

'She isn't as nice as you, ma'am,' I asserted.

'Do you tell me that now?' said she.

'You are twice as nice as she is, and twenty times nicer.'

'There you are,' said Joseph, 'the very words I said to you last night.'

'You shut up,' said Mary scornfully, 'you were trying to knock a pint out of me! Listen, son,' she went on, 'we'll take all that back about your landlady. You come and live with me, and I'll give you back sixpence a week out of your wages.'

'All right, ma'am,' I crowed in a perfectly monstrous joy.

'Mary,' said Joseph, in a reluctant voice—

'You shut up,' said she.

'He can't come to live with us,' said Joseph. 'He's a bloody Prodestan,' he added sadly.

'Why–' she began—

'He'd keep me and the childer up all night, pinching apples for horses and asses, and reading the Bible, and up to every kind of devilment.'

Mary made up her mind quickly—

'You stick to your own landlady,' said she, 'tell her that I said she was to give you sixpence.' She whirled about, 'There won't be a thing left on that barrow,' said she to Joseph.

'Damn the scrap,' said Joseph violently.

'Listen,' said Mary to me very earnestly, 'am I nicer than Maudie Darling?'

'You are, ma'am,' said I.

Mary went down on the road on her knees: she stretched out both arms to me, and said—

'Come to my boozalum, angel.'

I looked at her, and I looked at Joseph, and I looked at the horse. Then I turned from them all and ran into the building and into the office. My fat boss met me—

'Here's your five bob,' said he. 'Get to hell out of here,' said he.

And I ran out.

I went to the horse, and leaned my head against the thick end of his neck, and the horse leaned as much of himself against me as he could manage. Then the man who owned the horse came up and climbed into his saddle. He fumbled in his pocket—

'You were too long,' said I. 'I've been sacked for minding your horse.'

'That's too bad,' said he: 'that's too damn bad,' and he tossed me a penny.

I caught it, and lobbed it back into his lap, and I strode down the street the most outraged human being then living in the world.

LOVE AND LETHE

Samuel Beckett

Vivian Mercier in The Irish Comic Tradition *(1962) has written that Samuel Beckett (1906–1989) deserves to be regarded as a master humorist—although he qualified this by admitting that the claim 'has to rest almost exclusively on Beckett's treatment of the grotesque and the macabre'. Beckett, the quantity surveyor's son from Foxrock in Dublin who received a classical education and was for a time a teacher, later became the idol of the avant-garde public with his grotesque novels,* Murphy *(1938) and* Watt *(1953), as well as for his equally famous plays,* Waiting For Godot *(1953) and* End Game *(1957). Earlier, however, he had begun his career as a writer with a series of short stories about a lascivious Dubliner named Belacqua who mixes a sense of gloom with humorous observation during his exploits in the city. It is gloom, however, that makes Belacqua happiest, as Beckett demonstrates through his unmistakable style of humour. 'Love and Lethe' is arguably among the best of these black comedies: an episode in which Belacqua careers around the city in a car he cannot drive and then pursues the latest object of his desires on an absolutely hilarious hill climb . . .*

*   *   *

The Toughs, consisting of Mr and Mrs and their one and only Ruby, lived in a small house in Irishtown. When dinner, which they took in the middle of the day, was ended, Mr Tough went to his room to lie down and Mrs Tough and Ruby to the kitchen for a cup of coffee and a chat. The mother was low-sized, pale and plump, admirably preserved though well past the change. She poured the right amount of water into the saucepan and set it to boil.

'What time is he coming?' she said.

'He said about three' said Ruby.

'With car?' said Mrs Tough.

'He hoped with car' answered Ruby.

Mrs Tough hoped so most devoutly, for she had an idea that she might be invited to join the party. Though she would rather have died than stand in the way of her daughter, yet she saw no reason why, if she kept herself in the dicky, there should be any objection to her joining in the fun. She shook the beans into the little mill and ground them violently into powder. Ruby, who was neurasthenic on top of everything else, plugged her ears. Mrs Tough, taking a seat at the deal table against the water would be boiling, looked out of the window at the perfect weather.

'Where are you going?' she said. She had the natural curiosity of a mother in what concerns her child.

'Don't ask me' answered Ruby, who was inclined to resent all these questions.

He to whom they referred, who had hopes of calling at three with a car, was the doomed Belacqua and no other.

The water boiling, Mrs Tough rose and added the coffee, reduced the flame, stirred thoroughly and left to simmer. Though it seems a strange way to prepare coffee, yet it was justified by the event.

'Let me put you up some tea' implored Mrs Tough. She could not bear to be idle.

'Ah no' said Ruby 'no thanks really.'

It struck the half-hour in the hall. It was half-past two, that zero hour, in Irishtown.

'Half-two!' ejaculated Mrs Tough, who had no idea it was so late.

Ruby was glad that it was not earlier. The aroma of coffee pervaded the kitchen. She would have just nice time to dream over her coffee. But she knew that this was quite out of the question with her mother wanting to talk, bursting with questions and suggestions. So when the coffee was dispensed and her mother had settled down for the comfortable chat that went with it she unexpectedly said:

'I think, mother, if you don't mind, I'll take mine with me to the lav, I don't feel very well.'

Mrs Tough was used to the whims of Ruby and took them

philosophically usually. But this latest fancy was really a little bit too unheard of. Coffee in the lav! What would father say when he heard? However.

'And the rosiner' said Mrs Tough, 'will you have that in the lav too?'

Reader, a rosiner is a drop of the hard.

Ruby rose and took a gulp of coffee to make room.

'I'll have a gloria' she said.

Reader, a gloria is coffee laced with brandy.

Mrs Tough poured into the proffered cup a smaller portion of brandy than in the ordinary way she would have allowed, and Ruby left the room.

We know something of Belacqua, but Ruby Tough is a stranger to these pages. Anxious that those who read this incredible adventure shall not pooh-pooh it as unintelligible we avail ourselves now of this lull, what time Belacqua is on his way, Mrs Tough broods in the kitchen and Ruby dreams over her gloria, to enlarge a little on the latter lady.

For a long period, on account of the beauty of her person and perhaps also, though in lesser degree, the distinction of her mind, Ruby had been the occasion of much wine-shed; but now, in the thirty-third or fourth year of her age, she was so no longer. Those who are in the least curious to know what she looked like at the time in which we have chosen to cull her we venture to refer to the Magdalene* in the Perugino Pietà in the National Gallery of Dublin, always bearing in mind that the hair of our heroine is black and not ginger. Further than this hint we need not allow her outside to detain us, seeing that Belacqua was scarcely ever aware of it.

The facts of life had reduced her temper, naturally romantic and idealistic in the highest degree, to an almost atomic despair. Her sentimental experience had indeed been unfortunate. Requiring of love, as a younger and more appetising woman, that it should unite or fix her as firmly and as finally as the sun of a binary in respect of its partner, she had come to avoid it more and more

---

* This figure, owing to the glittering vitrine behind which the canvas cowers, can only be apprehended in sections. Patience, however, and a retentive memory have been known to elicit a total statement approximating to the intention of the painter.

as she found, with increasing disappointment and disgust, its effect at each successive manifestation, for she had been in great demand, to be of quite a different order. The result of this erotic frustration was, firstly, to make her eschew the experience entirely; secondly, to recommend her itch for syzygy to more ideal measures, among which she found music and malt the most efficacious; and finally, to send her caterwauling to the alcove for whatever shabby joys it could afford. These however, embarras de richesse as long as she remained the scornful maiden, were naturally less at pains to solicit one whose sense of proportion had been acquired to the great detriment of her allurements. The grapes of love, set aside as abject in the days of hot blood, turned sour as soon as she discovered a zest for them. As formerly she had recoiled into herself because she would not, so now she did because she could not, except that in her retreat the hope that used to solace her was dead. She saw her life as a series of staircase jests.

Belacqua, paying pious suit to the hem of her garment and gutting his raptures with great complacency at a safe remove, represented precisely the ineffable long-distance paramour to whom as a home-sick meteorite abounding in IT she had sacrificed her innumerable gallants. And now, the metal of stars smothered in earth, the IT run dry and the gallants departed, he appeared, like the agent of an ironical Fortune, to put her in mind of what she had missed and rowel her sorrow for what she was missing. Yet she tolerated him in the hope that sooner or later, in a fit of ebriety or of common or garden incontinence, he would so far forget himself as to take her in his arms.

Join to all this the fact that she had long been suffering from an incurable disorder and been assured positively by no fewer than fifteen doctors, ten of whom were atheists, acting independently, that she need not look forward to her life being much further prolonged, and we feel confident that even the most captious reader must acknowledge, not merely the extreme wretchedness of Ruby's situation, but also the verisimilitude of what we hope to relate in the not too distant future. For we assume the irresponsibility of Belacqua, his faculty for acting with insufficient motivation, to have been so far evinced in previous misadventures as to be no longer a matter for surprise. In respect of this apparent gratuity of conduct he may perhaps with some colour of justice be

likened to the laws of nature. A mental home was the place for
him.

He cultivated Ruby, for whom at no time did he much care,
and made careful love in the terms he thought best calculated to
prime her for the part she was to play on his behalf, the gist of
which, as he revealed when he deemed her ripe, provided that she
should connive at his felo de se, which he much regretted he could
not commit on his own bottom. How he had formed this resolution
to destroy himself we are quite unable to discover. The simplest
course, when the motives of any deed are found subliminal to the
point of defying expression, is to call that deed ex nihilo and have
done. Which we beg leave to follow in the present instance.

The normal woman of sense asks 'what?' in preference to 'why?'
(this is very deep), but poor Ruby had always been deficient in
that exquisite quality, so that no sooner had Belacqua opened his
project than she applied for his reasons. Now though he had none,
as we have seen, that he could offer, yet he had armed himself so
well at this point, forewarned by the study he had made of his
catspaw's mind, that he was able to pelt her there and then with
the best that diligent enquiry could provide: Greek and Roman
reasons, Sturm und Drang reasons, reasons metaphysical, aesthetic, erotic, anterotic and chemical, Empedocles of Agrigentum
and John of the Cross reasons, in short all but the true reasons,
which did not exist, at least not for the purposes of conversation.
Ruby, flattened by this torrent of incentive, was obliged to admit
that this was not, as she had inclined to suspect, a greenhorn
yielding to the spur of a momentary pique, but an adult desperado
of fixed and even noble purpose, and from this concession passed
to a state almost of joy. She was done in any case, and here was
a chance to end with a fairly beautiful bang. So the thing was
arranged, the needful measures taken, the date fixed in the spring
of the year and a site near by selected, Venice in October having been
rejected as alas impracticable. Now the fateful day had come and
Ruby, in the posture of Philosopher Square behind Molly Sea-
grim's arras, sat winding herself up, while Belacqua, in a swagger
sports roadster chartered at untold gold by the hour, trod on the
gas for Irishtown.

So fiercely indeed did he do this, though so far from being
insured against third-party risks he was not even the holder of a
driving-licence, that he scored a wake of objurgation as he sped

through the traffic. The better-class pedestrians and cyclists turned and stared after him. 'These stream-lined Juggernauts' they said, shaking their heads, 'are a positive menace.' Civic Guards at various points of the city and suburbs took his number. In Pearse Street he smote off the wheel of a growler as cleanly as Peter Malchus's ear after the agony, but did not stop. Further on, in some lowly street or other, the little children playing beds and ball and other games were scattered like chaff. But before the terrible humped Victoria Bridge, its implacable bisection, in a sudden panic at his own temerity he stopped the car, got out and pushed her across with the help of a bystander. Then he drove quietly on through the afternoon and came in due course without further mishap to the house of his accomplice.

Mrs Tough flung open wide the door. She was all over Belacqua, with his big pallid gob much abused with imagined debauches.

'Ruby' she sang, in a third, like a cuckoo, 'Ru-bee! Ru-bee!'

But would she ever change her tune, that was the question.

Ruby dangled down the stairs, with the marks of her teeth in her nether lip where she could persuade no bee to sting her any more.

'Get on your bonnet and shawl' said Belacqua roughly 'and we'll be going.'

Mrs Tough recoiled aghast. This was the first time she had ever heard such a tone turned on her Ruby. But Ruby got into a coat like a lamb and seemed not to mind. It became only too clear to Mrs Tough that she was not going to be invited.

'May I offer you a little refreshment' she said in an icy voice to Belacqua 'before you go?' She could not bear to be idle.

Ruby thought she had never heard anything quite so absurd. Refreshment before they went! It was if and when they returned that they would be in need of refreshment.

'Really mother' she said, 'can't you see we must be off.'

Belacqua chimed in with a heavy lunch at the Bailey. The truth was not in him.

'Off where?' said Mrs Tough.

'Off' cried Ruby, 'just off.'

What a strange mood she is in to be sure, thought Mrs Tough. However. At least they could not prevent her from going as far as the gate.

'Where did you raise the car?' she said.

If you had seen the car you would agree that this was the most natural question.

Belacqua mentioned a firm of motor engineers.

'Oh indeed' said Mrs Tough.

Mr Tough crept to the window and peeped out from behind the curtain. He had worked himself to the bone for his family and he could only afford a safety-bicycle. A bitter look stole over his cyanosis.

Belacqua got in a gear at last, he had no very clear idea himself which, after much clutch-burning, and they shot forward in Hollywood style. Mrs Tough might have been waving to Lot for all the response she received. Was the cut-out by way of being their spokesman? Ruby's parting gird, 'Expect us when you see us', echoed in her ears. On the stairs she met Mr Tough descending. They passed.

'There is something about that young man' called down Mrs Tough 'that I can't relish.'

'Pup' called up Mr Tough.

They increased the gap between them.

'Ruby is very strange' cried down Mrs Tough.

'Slut' cried up Mr Tough.

Though he might be only able to afford a safety-bicycle he was nevertheless a man of few words. There are better things, he thought, going to the bottle, there are better things in this stenching world than Blue Birds.

The pup and slut drove on and on and there was dead silence between them. Not a syllable did they exchange until the car was safely stowed at the foot of a mountain. But when Ruby saw Belacqua open the dicky and produce a bag she thought well to break a silence that was becoming a little awkward.

'What have you got' she said 'in the maternity-bag?'

'Socrates' replied Belacqua 'the son of his mother, and the hemlocks.'

'No' she said, 'codding aside, what?'

Belacqua let fly a finger for each item.

'The revolver and balls, the veronal, the bottle and glasses, and the notice.'

Ruby could not repress a shiver.

'In the name of God' she said 'what notice?'

'The one that we are fled' replied Belacqua, and not another word would he say though she begged him to tell her. The notice was his own idea and he was proud of it. When the time came she would have to subscribe to it whether she liked it or not. He would keep it as a little surprise for her.

They ascended the mountain in silence. Wisps of snipe and whatever it is of grouse squirted out of the heather on all sides, while the number of hares, brooding in their forms, that they started and sent bounding away, was a credit to the gamekeeper. They plunged on and up through the deep ling and whortleberry. Ruby was sweating. A high mesh wire fence, flung like a shingles round the mountain, obstructed their passage.

'What are all the trusses for?' panted Ruby.

Right along on either hand as far as they could see there were fasces of bracken attached to the wire. Belacqua racked his brains for an explanation. In the end he had to give it up.

'God I don't know at all' he exclaimed.

It certainly was the most astounding thing.

Ladies first. Ruby scaled the fence. Belacqua, holding gallantly back with the bag in his hand, enjoyed a glimpse of her legs' sincerity. It was the first time he had had occasion to take stock of those parts of her and certainly he had seen worse. They pushed on and soon the summit, complete with fairy rath, came into view, howbeit still at a considerable distance.

Ruby tripped and fell, but on her face. Belacqua's strong arms were at hand to raise her up.

'Not hurt' he kindly enquired.

'This foul old skirt gets in my way' she said angrily.

'It is an encumbrance' agreed Belacqua, 'off with it.'

This struck Ruby as being such a good suggestion that she acted upon it without further ado and stood revealed as one of those ladies who have no use for a petticoat. Belacqua folded the skirt over his arm, there being no room for it in the bag, and Ruby, greatly eased, stormed the summit in her knickers.

Belacqua, who was in the lead, halted all of a sudden, clapped his hands, spun round and told Ruby he had got it. He was keenly conscious of her standing knee-deep in the ling before him, grateful for a breather and not bothering to ask what.

'They tie those bundles to the wire' he said 'so that the grouse will see them.'

Still she did not understand.

'And not fly against the fence and hurt themselves.'

Now she understood. The calm way she took it distressed Belacqua. It was to be hoped that the notice would have better success than this splendid divulgation. Now the ling was up to her garters, she seemed to be sinking in the heath as in a quicksand. Could it be that she was giving at the knees?

'Spirits of this mountain' murmured the heart of Belacqua 'keep me steadfast.'

Now since parking the car they had not seen a living soul.

The first thing they had to do of course when they got to the top was admire the view, with special reference to Dun Laoghaire framed to perfection in the shoulders of Three Rock and Kilmashogue, the long arms of the harbour like an entreaty in the blue sea. Young priests were singing in a wood on the hillside. They heard them and they saw the smoke of their fire. To the west in the valley a plantation of larches nearly brought tears to the eyes of Belacqua, till raising those unruly members to the slopes of Glendoo, mottled like a leopard, that lay beyond, he thought of Synge and recovered his spirits. Wicklow, full of breasts with pimples, he refused to consider. Ruby agreed. The city and the plains to the north meant nothing to either of them in the mood they were in. A human turd lay within the rath.

Like fantoccini controlled by a single wire they flung themselves down on the western slope of heath. From now on till the end there is something very secco and Punch and Judy about their proceedings, Ruby looking more bawdy Magdalene than ever, Belacqua like a super out of the Harlot's Progress. He kept putting off opening the bag.

'I thought of bringing the gramophone' he said 'and Ravel's Pavane. Then—'

'Then you thought again' said Ruby. She had a most irritating habit of interrupting.

'Oh yes' said Belacqua, 'the usual pale cast.'

Notice the literary man.

'S'pity' said Ruby, 'it might have made things easier.'

Happy Infanta! Painted by Velasquez and then no more pensums!

'If you would put back your skirt' said Belacqua violently, 'now that you have done walking, you would make things easier for me.'

How difficult things were becoming, to be sure. The least thing might upset the apple-cart at this juncture.

Ruby pricked up her ears. Was this a declaration at last? In case it might be she would not oblige him.

'I prefer it off' she said.

Belacqua, staring fiercely at the larches, sulked for a space.

'Well' he grumbled at last, 'shall we have a little drink to start off?'

Ruby was agreeable. He opened the bag as little as possible, put in his hand, snatched out the bottle, then the glasses and shut it quick.

'Fifteen year old' he said complacently, 'on tick.'

All the money he owed for one thing or another. If he did not pull it off now once and for all he would be broke.

'God' he exclaimed, executing a kind of passionate tick-tack through his pockets, 'I forgot the screw.'

'Pah' said Ruby. 'What odds. Knock its head off, shoot its neck off.'

But the screw turned up as it always does and they had a long drink.

'Length without breath' gasped Belacqua, 'that's the idea, Hiawatha at Dublin bar.'

They had another.

'That makes four doubles' said Ruby 'and they say there's eight in a bottle.'

Belacqua held up the bottle. In that case there was something wrong with her statement.

'Never two without three' he said.

They had another.

'O Death in Life' vociferated Belacqua, 'the days that are no more.'

He fell on the bag and ripped out the notice for her inspection. Painted roughly in white on an old number-plate she beheld:

TEMPORARILY SANE

IK-6996 had been erased to make room for this inscription. It was a palimpsest.

Ruby, pot-valiant, let a loud scoff.

'It won't do' she said, 'it won't do at all.'

It was a disappointment to hear her say this. Poor Belacqua. Sadly he held the plate out at arm's length.

'You don't like it' he said.

'Bad' said Ruby, 'very bad.'

'I don't mean the way it's presented' said Belacqua, 'I mean the idea.'

It was all the same what he meant.

'If I had a paddle' she said 'I'd bury it, idea and all.'

Belacqua laid the offensive object face downward in the heather. Now there was nothing left in the bag but the firearm, the ammunition and the veronal.

The light began to die, there was no time to be lost.

'Will you be shot' said Belacqua 'or poisoned? If the former, have you any preference? The heart? The temple? If the latter' passing over the bag, 'help yourself.'

Ruby passed it back.

'Load' she ordained.

'Chevaliers d'industrie' said Belacqua, inserting the ball, 'nearly all blow their brains out. Kreuger proved the rule.'

'We don't exactly die together darling' drawled Ruby 'or do we?'

'Alas' sighed Belacqua 'what can you expect? But a couple of minutes' with a bounteous brandish of the revolver, 'the time it takes to boil an egg, what is that to eternity?'

'Still' said Ruby 'it would have been rather nice to pass out together.'

'The problem of precedence' said Belacqua, as from a rostrum, 'always arises, even as between the Pope and Napoleon.'

'"The Pope the puke"' quoted Ruby '"he bleached her soul . . ."'

'But perhaps you don't know that story' said Belacqua, ignoring the irrelevance.

'I do not' said Ruby 'and I have no wish to.'

'Well' said Belacqua 'in that case I will merely say that they solved it in a strictly spatial manner.'

'Then why not we?' said Ruby.

The gas seems to be escaping somewhere.

'We; said Belacqua 'like twins—'

'Are gone astray' sneered Ruby.

'Are slaves of the sand-glass. There is not room for us to run out arm in arm.'

'As though there were only the one in the world' said Ruby. 'Pah!'

'We happen to pine in the same one' said Belacqua, 'that is the difficulty.'

'Well, it's a minor point' said Ruby 'and by all means ladies first.'

'Please yourself' said Belacqua, 'I'm the better shot.'

But Ruby, instead of expanding her bosom or holding up her head to be blown off, helped herself to a drink. Belacqua fell into a passion.

'Damn it' he cried 'didn't we settle all these things weeks ago? Did we or did we not?'

'A settlement was reached' said Ruby, 'certainly.'

'Then why all this bloody talk?'

Ruby drank her drink.

'And leave us a drop in the bottle' he snarled, 'I'll need it when you're gone.'

That indescribable sensation, compound of exasperation and relief, relaxing, the better to grieve, the coenaesthesis of the consultant when he finds the surgeon out, now burst inside Belacqua. He felt suddenly hot within. The bitch was backing out.

Though whiskey as a rule helped Ruby to feel starry, yet somehow on this occasion it failed to effect her in that way, which is scarcely surprising if we reflect what a very special occasion it was. Now to her amazement the revolver went off, harmlessly luckily, and the bullet fell in terram nobody knows where. But for fully a minute she thought she was shot. An appalling silence, in the core of which their eyes met, succeeded the detonation.

'The finger of God' whispered Belacqua.

Who shall judge of his conduct at this crux? Is it to be condemned as wholly despicable? Is it not possible that he was gallantly trying to spare the young woman embarrassment? Was it tact or concupiscence or the white feather or an accident or what? We state the facts. We do not presume to determine their significance.

'Digitus Dei' he said 'for once.'

The remark rather gives him away, does it not?

When the first shock of surprise had passed and the silence spent its fury a great turmoil of life-blood sprang up in the breasts of our two young felons, so that they came together in inevitable nuptial. With the utmost reverence at our command, moving away on tiptoe from where they lie in the ling, we mention this in a low voice.

It will quite possibly be his boast in years to come, when Ruby is dead and he an old optimist, that at least on this occasion, if never before nor since, he achieved what he set out to do; car, in the words of one competent to sing of the matter, l'Amour et la Mort—caesura—n'est qu'une mesme chose.

May their night be full of music at all events.

THE WOMAN WHO MARRIED CLARK GABLE

Sean O'Faolain

Although Sean O'Faolain (1900–1991), the novelist, biographer and short story writer, is perhaps best known for his stories of love and patriotism, there is a broad streak of typically Irish humour often lurking just beneath the surface of events. In the early days of his literary career, O'Faolain, who grew up in Cork, was regularly in trouble with the Censorship Board for his descriptions of sexual relations, which were considered dangerous to morals, and his first collection of stories, Midsummer Night Madness *(1932), was actually banned. By the middle of the century, however, he had become recognised as one of the most influential social commentators on Ireland thanks to several collections of his work in which he ingeniously used humour to take on entrenched views—as in 'The Man Who Invented Sin', about a curate who objects to the quite innocent fun of a group of monks and nuns studying Irish in the Gaeltacht. Other humorous tales in later volumes such as 'The Bosom of the Country' (*Heat of the Sun, *1966), about a retired major and his mistress who finally decide to marry with an unexpected effect on their sexual relationship, and 'The Time of their Lives' (*The Talking Trees, *1970), in which an Italian count courts a frumpy Irish woman apparently for her money, both contain strong comic elements to make the author's points about Irish attitudes. 'The Woman Who Married Clark Gable' is, however, perhaps the most deliberately ribald of all O'Faolain's stories and re-emphasises—if such were required—what a truly versatile writer he was . . .*

*　　*　　*

She should have lived in Moscow. If she had been a Russian she would have said: 'O God, life is passing and I have yet to live.

All last Easter when the baby clouds were passing over the birch-woods, and the streams were whispering of the coming of summer, and the bells were dancing and singing in the monastery towers, I sat at home and drank vodka and longed for love. I do not know whether life is angry with me because I do not live it, or whether I am angry with life because it will not let me live. Ivan Ivanovitch, for God's sake, meet me tonight by the frog-pond and tell me what is this pain in my heart.' And Ivan would have met her and told her in very simple terms. Instead of that she lived in Dublin (South Circular Road, small red house, red terrace, small garden, near the Old Woman's Hostel—full—and Kilmainham Jail—disused). She nagged her husband virtuously when she should have got drunk with him and poured her virtue down the drains. She went twice a week to the movies, hoovered the house until she had all the pile sucked off the carpets, bought a new knick-knack for the mantelpiece every week, washed the dog, polished the windows, slept after lunch, read *Chit Chat* and *Winifred's Weekly*, went for a walk, and then sat around waiting for her husband to come back from the job.

Every night the conversation was the same.

'Had a hard day, darling?'—from her.

'Not so bad, dearie'—from him.

'What did you have for lunch?'

'A very nice lunch. Pork chop, spinach, chips, rhubarb pie, coffee. Very tasty.'

'I washed Herbie. Look at him. It was an awful job. But he is a pet. Aren't you, Herbie?'

'Nice old 'Erbie. Like your bathie. Soapy-soapy? Not tired, dearie?'

And she would always say she was, very tired, or that she had a stitch in her side, or a pain in her head, and she would put on a miserable face, and he would tell her she ought not to do it, not really, and she would tilt her eyebrows and ask sadly for the evening paper. He would suggest a stroll, or a movie, or have a pipe, or tell her a dirty story, and so to bed, and *da capo* the next day and the next. Before she got into bed she would always say the Rosary, and then she would curl up next to him and wait for him to snore. She liked him; he was an honourable, hardworking, straightforward, generous man; but she did not love him. It must be added that they had no children and she worried about that.

It must also be understood that he was a Methodist and went regularly to the tin chapel along the road, and she worried about that too. She was always praying that he might be converted: that was why she said the Rosary every night, though she never told him that. He was English and was rather stubborn about religious matters.

One morning as she kissed him goodbye at the gate of her little garden she drew back hastily and peered at him.

'Darling, you haven't shaved?'

He grinned fatuously, lifted his bowler-hat, said: 'I'm growing a moustache,' and ran. For weeks after that their nightly conversation had an extra five lines:

'I don't like that moustache, darling.'

'It's coming on. Chaps at the works rag me a lot about it. But I don't mind. Jealous, I say.'

'But it tickles, darling.'

'Aain't that nice, dearie?'

One night they went to the movies to see *San Francisco*, with Jeanette MacDonald and Clark Gable. This picture dealt with a rake and a good man and a singing heroine, friends in spite of everything, even the singing and the fact that the good man (Spencer Tracy) was a priest. The rake had a squabble with the priest, and although the priest—he was a Boxing Padre—could have knocked him on the canvas for twenty he merely wiped the blood off the corner of his mouth and looked sadly at the rake. In the end there is an earthquake and the earth opens and all sorts of things fall down into holes and the rake kneels down and is converted. They show Mr Gable's boot soles because nobody looking at his face would believe it. Then they all join hands and march down the hill into the camera and the closing, gauzy iridescent curtains of the cinema, singing the theme-song, 'Sa-a-n Francisco, Open your pearly gates . . .' (etc.), and everybody goes home happy.

She walked home that night in a dreamy silence. She heard none of his remarks about the picture, and when they were back home she kept looking at him in a strange, distant way. She went restlessly in and out of the parlour, threw guilty sidelong glances at him, did not seem to want to go to bed, hardly said a word in answer to his chatter, forgot to pray for his conversion, and lay awake for hours looking out at the tops of the London plane waving faintly against the dull upthrown glow of the city.

She went to the same cinema, alone, the next day; and that night she made him take her to it again; which he was pleased to do because he wanted to know how they got all those things to fall into holes in the ground. All through the picture she held his hand and stole sideward glances at the black line of his Gablesque moustache. That night she put on her pink chiffon nightgown— the one she bought the time she thought she was going to have a baby and only had a miss; and she had worn it again the time she had her gallstones out; and the time she had the appendix; and the time she went to the nursing home when she tumbled down stairs. She put scent behind her ears and looking at herself in the mirror said,

'Darling, did I ever tell you I had rather a good voice when I was . . . I mean before I married you?' And she swayed and began to hum, 'San Francisco, Open your pearly gates!'

'It sounds like hydraulic pressure,' he ruminated. 'You know, like a lift going down.'

When she lay beside him she looked at his profile and whispered.

'Darling, supposing this was San Francisco. You and me? And the earth begins to shake?'

'Lummy,' he cried. 'Like this?' And he began to bounce up and down on the springs.

She gave a frightened scream.

'Why, dearie, what's wrong?'

'You're so rough,' she said adoringly.

'My poor little upsydaisy, isum frightened?'

She put out the light.

For about two weeks they were happier than at any time since their honeymoon, in that little redbrick house on the South Circular Road. She bought a record of *Open your pearly gates*. She asked him questions about earthquakes and he began to read them up. One Saturday she heard the film was at Bray and, under pretence of a day's outing by the sea, made him take her to it again. This he found a bit boring, but being a kind-hearted chap he humoured her. When it moved on up to Malahide and she wanted to follow it he demurred. To his surprise she crumbled at once and said that if he hit her she wouldn't blame him, and that she probably deserved it. He did no more than tease her when he found a picture of Mr Gable garbed for the boxing-ring pinned up in their parlour the next day. But he did begin to get a bit worried when she bought him a cravat, an old-time three-cornered collar, asked him to take up boxing-lessons, and wanted him to meet her priest and become great friends with him. He drew the line at the priest and the boxing but he did wear the cravat and the collar in which he looked like a horse in demi-harness.

She noticed the worried look on his face the first morning he wore this contraption and decided that he was unhappy because he guessed that she was deceiving him with Mr Gable. She went off to consult her priest.

He heard her problem in complete silence and then said, 'It's a very fine point, I think you'd better give me a week to think it over.' So at the end of the week she went again, this time in a black veil, and he explained to her that the chief end of marriage is, of course, the bearing of children and that what we call Love is, naturally, secondary to this great end. And after all, he said, what *is* Love? Indeed, what are all those curious human manifestations which lead to the great end (which he had already defined)? To a mere celibate these things were all very strange. But then, he added quickly, who are we, anyway, to question the devices of Providence which, indeed, as we may see, are frequently not merely puzzling but baffling? At all events, he hurried on, be that as it might, it appeared to him that, theologically speaking, and always provided that she kept that great end in view, and had no other end in view at any time—he stressed the words *at any time*—there could be no objection to her deciding that she was living with this Mr Mark Cable. Indeed, he added testily, for the matter had caused him a great deal of worry, and caused him to read a great many dull Latin volumes, she could (always provided she kept that great end in view) go on believing that she was living with her grandfather; and he dismissed her abruptly. She left him, a little hurt by the reference to her grandfather, but more content with the propriety of her behaviour than she had ever been since her wedding night.

Her joy was brief. It was on her way home that she purchased the film-magazine which reported, with a large portrait of Mr Clark Gable, that there were rumours flying about New York to the effect that 'our Clark' had lately been seen in gay places in the company of a well-known oil millionairess.

That night she saw at once that her George was giving her worried looks; as well he might since she kept looking at him in a very peculiar fashion.

'Tired, dearie?' he asked.

'A fat lot you care,' she cried tragically.

'But I do care, dearie!'

'You,' she charged with passion, 'care nothing whatsoever for me. What did you have for lunch today?'

'Why,' he mumbled, a bit taken aback by this divergence, 'I 'ad a spot of steak-and-kidney, rhubarb and cuss, black coffee, all very tasty too.'

At this she laughed scornfully.

'Alone?' she challenged.

'Wotcher mean, alone?'

'Were—you—alone?'

'Well, not quite alone. A couple of the chaps as usual.'

'Chaps!'

She uttered what she considered to be a strangled cry, gave a broken sob, ended up with a groan of despair and made a fair shot at hurling herself from the room. He, staring at the dog wagging its tail hopefully, began to examine his conscience; and as any man can always find some little thing somewhere in his conscience, even if it is only a pinched bottom, he played a good deal at finger-under-the-collar before he went up to bed. She did not speak one word to him. Once he asked her if she had a cold, because she was sobbing into her pillow; at which she moaned as if her poor little heart would break, causing him to beg her to tell him if she had a tooth-ache. His patience gave out when she refused to get up and cook his breakfast, for an Englishman will stand much but he will not stand for a breakfast of cold milk and dog-biscuits. He drank neat whiskey at lunch and he drank neat whiskey (several times) on his way home in the evening, and he tore off his horse-collar and dropped it into the canal, and he had a haircut and shave, and he even had the barber shave off his moustache, and when he squeaked open the garden gate he was full of fight.

She was not. She had bought another film-magazine that afternoon which scornfully denied the story about Mr Clark Gable and the millionairess; said that Mr Gable was very cross about it, in fact. In a high state of nerves she awaited his return and she was trembling when she opened the hall-door. She gave one look at the bald face and collarless neck before her, realised simultaneously that she was being confronted by her husband and had been abandoned by Mr Gable, and the next thing she did was to sink in a faint on the mat and give her poll a terrific wallop off the lino.

It took poor George an hour to bring her around and calm her down, and by that time all the fight had gone out of him. Besides he was too relieved to find that she was her old self again—moaning and groaning at him to his heart's content. When she wanted the evening paper she asked for it (to his great joy) quite snappishly. When, as the night was near ending, he ventured to tell her a dirty story and she laughed loudly and then put on a shocked face and said he ought to be ashamed of himself, he almost winked.

They lived unhappily ever after in complete marital satisfaction.

A BALL OF MALT AND MADAME BUTTERFLY

Benedict Kiely

Benedict Kiely (1919–   ), who was born in County Tyrone, grew up with a fascination for the tales of the traditional Irish storytellers, the Seanachie, and is now recognised as a master of the short story form. Although originally intending to be a priest, Kiely came to the conclusion that he did not have the calling for the religious life and moved instead to Dublin, where he became a journalist on The Irish Press. *Here he developed a close friendship with Flann O'Brien and, says Janet Dunlevy in* The Irish Short Story of Midcentury *(1984), discovered that O'Brien's 'irreverent humour, subtle wit, and curious ability to combine the lyric and satiric were not unlike his own'. In the company of such a man, it is hardly surprising that a rich vein of lustiness and earthy humour should run through much of Kiely's subsequent work including his novels,* Honey Seems Bitter *(1952),* The Captain With the Whiskers *(1960) and* Dogs Enjoy the Morning *(1968), plus many of the short stories to be found in* A Journey to the Seven Streams *(1963) and* The State of Ireland *(1980).*

Throughout his writing there is evidence of Kiely's interest in the Seanachie's oral narratives as well as the comical tales of William Carleton—about whom he has written a biography and whom he acknowledges as another influence. (Carleton is represented in the second section of this collection.) 'A Ball of Malt and Madame Butterfly' has been described by Anthony Burgess as one of Kiely's masterpieces, 'a genial Dublin yarn which, typically enough, turns out to be a tragicomic urban pastoral and a pubroom joke'. It is also an adventure that one can almost imagine Kiely and Flann O'Brien having shared together . . .

*   *   *

On a warm but not sunny June afternoon on a crowded Dublin street, by no means one of the city's most elegant streets, a small hotel, a sort of bed-and-breakfast place, went on fire. There was pandemonium at first, more panic than curiosity in the crowd. It was a street of decayed Georgian houses, high and narrow, with steep wooden staircases, and cluttered small shops on the ground floors: all great nourishment for flames. The first, though, didn't turn out to be serious. The brigade easily contained and controlled it. The panic passed, gave way to curiosity, then to indignation and finally, alas, to laughter about the odd thing that had happened when the alarm was at its worst.

This was it.

From a window on the top-most floor a woman, scantily clad, puts her head out and waves a patchwork bed coverlet, and screams for help. The stairway, she cries, is thick with smoke, herself and her husband are afraid to face it. On what would seem to be prompting from inside the room, she calls down that they are a honeymoon couple up from the country. That would account fairly enough for their still being abed on a warm June afternoon.

The customary ullagone and ullalu goes up from the crowd. The fire-engine ladder is aimed up to the window. A fireman begins to run up the ladder. Then suddenly the groom appears in shirt and trousers, and barefooted. For, to the horror of the beholders, he makes his bare feet visible by pushing the bride back into the room, clambering first out of the window, down the ladder like a monkey although he is a fairly corpulent man; with monkey-like agility dodging round the ascending fireman, then disappearing through the crowd. The people, indignant enough to trounce him, are still too concerned with the plight of the bride, and too astounded to seize him. The fireman ascends to the nuptial casement, helps the lady through the window and down the ladder, gallantly offering his jacket which covers some of her. Then when they are halfways down, the fireman, to the amazement of all, is seen to be laughing right merrily, the bride vituperating. But before they reach the ground she also is laughing. She is brunette, tall, but almost Japanese in appearance, and very handsome. A voice says: If she's a bride I can see no confetti in her hair.

She has fine legs which the fireman's jacket does nothing to conceal and which she takes pride, clearly, in displaying. She is a young woman of questionable virginity and well known to the firemen. She is the toast of a certain section of the town to whom she is affectionately known as Madame Butterfly, although unlike her more famous namesake she has never been married, nor cursed by an uncle bonze for violating the laws of the gods of her ancestors. She has another, registered, name: her mother's name. What she is her mother was before her, and proud of it.

The bare-footed fugitive was not, of course, a bridegroom, but a long-established married man with his wife and family and a prosperous business in Longford, the meanest town in Ireland. For the fun of it the firemen made certain that the news of his escapade in the June afternoon got back to Longford. They were fond of, even proud of, Butterfly as were many other men who had nothing at all to do with the quenching of fire.

But one man loved the pilgrim soul in her and his name was Pike Hunter.

Like Borgnefesse, the buccaneer of St Malo on the Rance, who had a buttock shot or sliced off in action on the Spanish Main, Pike Hunter had a lopsided appearance when sitting down. Standing up he was as straight and well-balanced as a man could be: a higher civil servant approaching the age of forty, a shy bachelor, reared, nourished and guarded all his life by a trinity of upper-middle-class aunts. He was pink-faced, with a little fair hair left to emphasise early baldness, mild in his ways, with a slight stutter, somewhat afraid of women. He wore always dark-brown suits with a faint red stripe, dark-brown hats, rimless spectacles, shiny square-toed brown handmade shoes with a wide welt. In summer, even on the hottest day, he carried a raincoat folded over his arm, and a rolled umbrella. When it rained he unfolded and wore the raincoat and opened and raised the umbrella. He suffered mildly from hay fever. In winter he belted himself into a heavy brown overcoat and wore galoshes. Nobody ever had such stiff white shirts. He favoured brown neckties distinguished with a pearl-headed pin. Why he sagged to one side, just a little to the left, when he sat down, I never knew. He had never been sliced or shot on the Spanish Main.

But the chance of a sunny still Sunday afternoon in Stephen's Green and Grafton Street, the select heart or soul of the city's south side, made a changed man out of him.

He had walked at his ease through the Green, taking the sun

gratefully, blushing when he walked between the rows of young ladies lying back in deck-chairs. He blushed for two reasons: they were reclining, he was walking; they were as gracefully at rest as the swans on the lake, he was awkwardly in motion, conscious that his knees rose too high, that his sparse hair—because of the warmth he had his hat in his hand—danced long and ludicrously in the little wind, that his shoes squeaked. He was fearful that his right toe might kick his left heel, or vice versa, and that he would fall down and be laughed at in laughter like the sound of silver bells. He was also alarmingly aware of the bronze knees, and more than knees, that the young ladies exposed as they leaned back and relaxed in their light summer frocks. He would honestly have liked to stop and enumerate those knees, make an inventory—he was in the Department of Statistics; perhaps pat a few here and there. But the fearful regimen of that trinity of aunts forbade him even to glance sideways, and he stumbled on like a winkered horse, demented by the flashing to right and to left of bursting globes of bronze light.

Then on the park pathway before him, walking towards the main gate and the top of Grafton Street, he saw the poet. He had seen him before, but only in the Abbey Theatre and never on the street. Indeed it seemed hardly credible to Pike Hunter that such a man would walk on the common street where all ordinary or lesser men were free to place their feet. In the Abbey Theatre the poet had all the strut and style of a man who could walk with the gods, the Greek gods that is, not the gods in the theatre's cheapest seats. His custom was to enter by a small stairway, at the front of the house and in full view of the audience, a few moments before the lights dimmed and the famous gong sounded and the curtain rose. He walked slowly, hands clasped behind his back, definitely balancing the prone brow oppressive with its mind, the eagle head aloft and crested with foaming white hair. He would stand, his back to the curtain and facing the house. The chatter would cease, the fiddlers in the orchestra would saw with diminished fury. Some of the city wits said that what the poet really did at those times was to count the empty seats in the house and make a rapid reckoning of the night's takings. But their gibe could not diminish the majesty of those entrances, the majesty of the stance of the man. And there he was now, hands behind back, noble head high, pacing slowly, beginning the course of Grafton Street. Pike Hunter walked behind him, suiting his pace to the poet's, to the easy deliberate rhythms of the early love poetry: I would that we were, my beloved, white birds on the foam of the sea. There is a queen in China or, maybe, it's in Spain.

They walked between the opulent windows of elegant glittering shops, doors closed for Sunday. The sunshine had drawn the people from the streets: to the park, to the lush green country, to the seaside. Of the few people they did meet, not all of them seemed to know who the poet was, but those who did know saluted quietly, with a modest and unaffected reverence, and one young man with a pretty girl on his arm stepped off the pavement, looked after the poet and clearly whispered to the maiden who it was that had just passed by the way. Stepping behind him at a respectful distance Pike felt like an acolyte behind a celebrant and regretted that there was no cope or cloak or cloth-of-gold of which he could humbly carry the train.

So they sailed north towards the Liffey, leaving Trinity College, with Burke standing haughty-headed and Goldsmith sipping at his honeypot of a book, to the right, and the Bank and Grattan orating Esto Perpetua, to the left, and Thomas Moore of the Melodies, brown, stooped and shabby, to the right; and came into Westmoreland Street where the wonder happened. For there approaching them came the woman Homer sung: old and grey and, perhaps, full of sleep, a face much and deeply lined and haggard, eyes sunken, yet still the face of the queen she had been when she and the poet were young and they had stood on the cliffs on Howth Head, high above the promontory that bears the Bailey Lighthouse as a warning torch and looks like the end of the world; and they had watched the soaring of the gulls and he had wished that he and she were only white birds, my beloved, buoyed out on the foam of the sea. She was very tall. She was not white, but all black in widow's weeds for the man she had married when she wouldn't marry the poet. Her black hat had a wide brim and, from the brim, an old-fashioned veil hung down before her face. The pilgrim soul in you, and loved the sorrows of your changing face.

Pike stood still, fearing that in a dream he had intruded on some holy place. The poet and the woman moved dreamlike towards each other, then stood still, not speaking, not saluting, at opposite street corners where Fleet Street comes narrowly from the east to join Westmoreland Street. Then still not speaking, not saluting, they turned into Fleet Street. When Pike tiptoed to the corner and peered around he saw that they had walked on opposite sides of the street for, perhaps, thirty paces, then turned at right angles, moved towards each other, stopped to talk in the middle of the street where a shaft of sunlight had defied the tall overshadowing buildings. Apart from themselves and Pike that portion of the town seemed to be awesomely empty; and there Pike left them and walked in a daze by the side of the Liffey to a pub called the Dark Cow. Something odd had happened to him: poetry, a vision of love?

It so happened that on that day Butterfly was in the Dark Cow, as, indeed, she often was: just Butterfly and Pike, and Jody with the red carbuncled face who owned the place and was genuinely kind to the girls of the town, and a few honest dockers who didn't count because they had money only for their own porter and were moral men, loyal to wives or sweethearts. It wasn't the sort of place Pike frequented. He had never seen Butterfly before: those odd slanting eyes, the glistening high-piled black hair, the well-defined bud of a mouth, the crossed legs, the knees that outclassed to the point of mockery all the bronze globes in Stephen's Green. Coming on top of his vision of the poet and the woman, all this was too much for him, driving him to a reckless courage that would have flabbergasted the three aunts. He leaned on the counter. She sat in an alcove that was a sort of throne for her, where on busier days she sat surrounded by her sorority. So he says to Jody whom he did not yet know as Jody: May I have the favour of buying the lady in the corner a drink?

—That you may, and more besides.

—Please ask her permission. We must do these things properly.

—Oh there's a proper way of doing everything, even screwing a goose.

But Jody, messenger of love, walks to the alcove and formally asks the lady would she drink if the gentleman at the counter sends it over. She will. She will also allow him to join her. She whispers: Has he any money?

—Loaded, says Jody.

—Send him over so. Sunday's a dull day.

Pike sits down stiffly, leaning a little away from her, which seems to her quite right for him as she has already decided that he's a shy sort of man, upper-class, but shy, not like some. He excuses himself from intruding. She says: You're not inthrudin'.

He says he hasn't the privilege of knowing her name.

Talks like a book, she decides, or a play in the Gaiety.

—Buttherfly, she says.

—Butterfly, he says, is a lovely name.

—Me mother's name was Trixie, she volunteers.

—Was she dark like you?

—Oh, a natural blonde and very busty, well developed, you know. She danced in the old Tivoli where the newspaper office is now. I'm neat, not busty.

To his confusion she indicates, with hands moving in small curves, the parts of her that she considers are neat. But he notices that she has shapely long-fingered hands and he remembers that the poet had admitted that the small hands of his beloved were not, in fact, beautiful. He is very perturbed.

—Neat, she says, and well-made. Austin McDonnell, the fire-brigade chief, says that he read in a book that the best sizes and shapes would fit into champagne glasses.

He did wonder a little that a fire-brigade chief should be a quotable authority on female sizes and shapes, and on champagne glasses. But then and there he decided to buy her champagne, the only drink fit for such a queen who seemed as if she came, if not from China, at any rate from Japan.

—Champagne, he said.

—Bubbly, she said. I love bubbly.

Jody dusted the shoulders of the bottle that on his shelves had waited a long time for a customer. He unwired the cork. The cork and the fizz shot up to the ceiling.

—This, she said, is my lucky day.

—The divine Bernhardt, said Pike, had a bath in champagne presented to her by a group of gentlemen who admired her.

—Water, she said, is better for washing.

But she told him that her mother who knew everything about actresses had told her that story, and told her that when, afterwards, the gentlemen bottled the contents of the bath and drank it, they had one bottleful too many. He was too far gone in fizz and love's frenzy to feel embarrassed. She was his discovery, his oriental queen.

He said: You're very oriental in appearance. You could be from Japan.

She said: My father was, they say. A sailor. Sailors come and go.

She giggled. She said: That's a joke. Come and go. Do you see it?

Pike saw it: He giggled with her. He was a doomed man.

She said: Austin McDonnell says that if I was in Japan I could be a geisha girl if I wasn't so tall. That's why they call me Butterfly. It's the saddest story. Poor Madame Butterfly died that her child could be happy across the sea. She married a sailor, too, an American lieutenant. They come and go. The priest, her uncle, cursed her for marrying a Yank.

—The priests are good at that, said Pike who, because of his reading allowed himself, outside office hours, a soupçon of anti-clericalism.

Touched by Puccini they were silent for a while, sipping champagne. With every sip Pike realised more clearly that he had found what the poet, another poet, an English one, had called the long-awaited long-expected spring, he knew his heart had found a time to sing, the strength to soar was in his spirit's wing, that life was full of a triumphant sound and death could only be a little thing. She was good on the nose, too. She was wise in the ways of perfume. The skin of her neck had a pearly glow. The three guardian aunts were as far away as the moon. Then one of the pub's two doors—it was a corner house—opened with a crash and a big man came in, well drunk, very jovial. He wore a wide-brimmed grey hat. He walked to the counter. He said: Jody, old bootlegger, old friend of mine, old friend of Al Capone, serve me a drink to sober me up.

—Austin, said Jody, what will it be?

—A ball of malt, the big man said, and Madame Butterfly.

—That's my friend, Austin, she said, he always says that for a joke.

Pike whose face, with love or champagne or indignation, was taut and hot all over, said that he didn't think it was much of a joke.

—Oh, for Janey's sake, Pike, be your age.

She used his first name for the first time. His eyes were moist.

—For Janey's sake, it's a joke. He's a father to me. He knew my mother.

—He's not Japanese.

—Mind your manners. He's a fireman.

—Austin, she called. Champagne. Pike Hunter's buying champagne.

Pike bought another bottle, while Austin towered above them, swept the wide-brimmed hat from his head in a cavalier half-circle, dropped it on the head of Jody whose red carbuncled face was thus half-extinguished. Butterfly giggled. She said: Austin, you're a scream. He knew Trixie, Pike. He knew Trixie when she was the queen of the boards in the old Tivoli.

Sitting down, the big man sang in a ringing tenor: For I knew Trixie when Trixie was a child.

He sipped at his ball of malt. He sipped at a glass of Pike's champagne. He said: It's a great day for the Irish. It's a great day to break a fiver. Butterfly, dear girl, we fixed the Longford lout. He'll never leave Longford again. The wife has him tethered and spancelled in the haggard. We wrote poison-pen letters to half the town, including the parish priest.

—I never doubted ye, she said.

—Leave it to the firemen, I said.

—The Dublin Fire Brigade, Austin said, has as long an arm as the Irish Republican Army.

—Austin, she told Pike, died for Ireland.

He sipped champagne. He sipped whiskey. He said: Not once, but several times. When it was neither popular nor profitable. By the living God, we was there when we was wanted. Volunteer McDonnell, at your service.

His bald head shone and showed freckles. His startlingly blue eyes were brightened and dilated by booze. He said: Did I know Trixie, light on her feet as the foam on the fountain? Come in and see the horses. That's what we used to say to the girls when I was a young fireman. Genuine horsepower the fire-engines ran on then, and the harness hung on hooks ready to drop on the horses as the firemen descended the greasy pole. And where the horses were, the hay and the straw were plentiful enough to make couches for Cleopatra. That was why we asked the girls in to see the horses. The sailors from the ships, homeless men all, had no such comforts and conveniences. They used to envy us. Butterfly, my geisha girl, you should have been alive then. We'd have shown you the jumps.

Pike was affronted. He was almost prepared to say so and take the consequences. But Butterfly stole his thunder. She stood up, kissed the jovial big man smack on the bald head and then, as light on her feet as her mother ever could have been, danced up and down the floor, tight hips bouncing, fingers clicking, singing: I'm the smartest little geisha in Japan, in Japan. And the people call me Rolee Polee Nan, Polee Nan.

Drowning in desire, Pike forgot his indignation and found that he was liking the man who could provoke such an exhibition. Breathless, she sat down again, suddenly kissed Pike on the cheek, said: I love you too. I love champagne. Let's have another bottle.

They had.

—Rolee Polee Nan, she sang as the cork and the fizz ascended.

—A great writer, a Russian, Pike said, wrote that his ideal was to be idle and to make love to a plump girl.

—The cheek of him. I'm not plump. Turkeys are plump. I love being tall, with long legs.

Displaying the agility of a trained high-kicker with hinges in her hips she, still sitting, raised her shapely right leg, up and up as if her toes would touch the ceiling, up and up until stocking-top, suspender, bare thigh and a frill of pink panties, showed. Something happened to Pike that had nothing at all to do with poetry or Jody's champagne. He held Butterfly's hand. She made a cat's cradle with their fingers and swung the locked hands pendulum-wise. She sang: Janey Mac, the child's a black, what will we do on Sunday? Put him to bed and cover his head and don't let him up until Monday.

Austin had momentarily absented himself for gentlemanly reasons. From the basement jakes his voice singing rose above the soft inland murmur of falling water: Oh my boat can lightly float in the heel of wind and weather, and outrace the smartest hooker between Galway and Kinsale.

The dockers methodically drank their pints of black porter and paid no attention. Jody said: Time's money. Why don't the two of you slip upstairs. Your heads would make a lovely pair on a pillow.

Austin was singing: Oh she's neat, oh she's sweet, she's a beauty every line, the Queen of Connemara is that bounding barque of mine.

He was so shy, Butterfly said afterwards, that he might have been a Christian Brother and a young one at that, although where or how she ever got the experience to enable her to make the comparison, or why she should think an old Christian Brother less cuthallacht than a young one, she didn't say. He told her all about the aunts and the odd way he had been reared and she, naturally, told Austin and Jody and all her sorority. But they were a kind people and no mockers, and Pike never knew, Austin told me, that Jody's clientele listened with such absorbed interest to the story of his life, and of his heart and his love-making. He was something new in their experience, and Jody's stable of girls had experienced a lot, and Austin a lot more, and Jody more than the whole shebang, and all the fire-brigade, put together.

For Jody, Austin told me, had made the price of the Dark Cow in a basement in Chicago. During the prohibition, as they called it, although what they prohibited it would be hard to say. He was one of five brothers from the bogs of Manulla in the middle of nowhere in the County of Mayo. The five of them emigrated to Chicago. When Al Capone and his merry men discovered that Jody and his brothers had the real true secret about how to make booze, and to make it good, down they went into the cellar and didn't see daylight nor breathe fresh air, except to surface to go to Mass on Sundays, until they left the USA. They made a fair fortune. At least four of them did. The fifth was murdered.

Jody was a bachelor man and he was good to the girls. He took his pleasures with them as a gentleman might, with the natural result that he was poxed to the eyebrows. But he was worth more to them than the money he quite generously paid after every turn or trick on the rumpled, always unmade bed in the two-storeyed apartment above the pub. He was a kind uncle to them. He gave them a friendly welcome, a place to sit down, free drink and smokes and loans, or advances for services yet to be rendered, when they were down on their luck. He had the ear of the civic guards and could help a girl when she was in trouble. He paid fines when they were unavoidable, and bills when they could no longer be postponed, and had an aunt who was reverend mother in a home for unmarried mothers, and who was, like her nephew, a kindly person. Now and again, like the Madame made immortal by Maupassant, he took a bevy or flock of the girls for a day at the seaside or in the country. A friend of mine and myself,

travelling into the granite mountains south of the city, to the old
stone-cutters' villages of Lackan and Ballyknockan where there
were aged people who had never seen Dublin, thirty miles away,
and never wanted to, came upon a most delightful scene in the
old country pub in Lackan. All around the bench around the walls
sat the mountainy men, the stone-cutters, drinking their pints. But
the floor was in the possession of a score of wild girls, all dancing
together, resting off and on for more drink, laughing, happy, their
gaiety inspired and directed by one man in the middle of the floor:
red-faced, carbuncled, oily black hair sleeked down and parted up
the middle in the style of Dixie Dean, the famous soccer centre-
forward, whom Jody so much admired. All the drinks were on
generous Jody.

So in Jody's friendly house Pike had, as he came close to forty
years, what he never had in the cold abode of the three aunts: a
home with a father, Austin, and a brother, Jody, and any God's
amount of sisters; and Butterfly who, to judge by the tales she
told afterwards, was a motherly sort of lover to him and, for a
while, a sympathetic listener. For a while, only: because nothing
in her birth, background, rearing or education had equipped her
to listen to so much poetry and talk about poetry.

—Poor Pike, she'd say, he'd puke you with poethry. Poethry's
all very well, but.

She had never worked out what came after that qualifying:
But.

—Give us a bar of a song, Austin. There's some sense to singing. But poethry. My heart leaps up when I behold a rainbow in
the sky. On Linden when the sun was low. The lady of Shalott
left the room to go to the pot. Janey preserve us from poethry.

He has eyes, Jody told Austin and myself, for no girl except
Butterfly. Reckon, in one way, we can't blame him for that. She
sure is the smartest filly showing in this paddock. But there must
be moderation in all things. Big Anne, now, isn't bad, nor her
sister, both well-built Sligo girls and very co-operative, nor Joany
Maher from Waterford, nor Patty Daley from Castle-island in the
County Kerry who married the Limey in Brum but left him when
she found he was as queer as a three-dollar bill. And what about
little Red Annie Byrne from Kilkenny City, very attractive if it
just wasn't for the teeth she lost when the cattleman that claimed
he caught gonorrhoea from her gave her an unmerciful hammering

in Cumberland Street. We got him before he left town. We cured more than his gonorrhoea.

—But, Austin said, when following your advice, Jody, and against my own better judgment, I tried to explain all that to Pike, what does he do but quote to me what the playboy of the Abbey Theatre, John M. Synge, wrote in a love poem about counting queens in Glenmacnass in the Wicklow mountains.

—In the Wicklow mountains, said Jody. Queens? With the smell of the bog and the peat smoke off them.

Austin, a great man, ever, to sing at the top of his tenor voice about Dark Rosaleen and the Queen of Connemara and the County of Mayo, was a literary class of a fireman. That was one reason why Pike and himself got on so well together, in spite of that initial momentary misunderstanding about the ball of malt and Madame Butterfly.

—Seven dog days, Austin said, the playboy said he let pass, he and his girl, counting queens in Glenmacnass. The queens he mentions, Jody, you never saw, even in Chicago.

—Never saw daylight in Chicago.

—The Queen of Sheba, Austin said, and Helen, and Maeve the warrior queen of Connacht, and Deirdre of the Sorrows and Gloriana that was the great Elizabeth of England and Judith out of the Bible that chopped the block of Holofernes.

—All, said Jody, in a wet glen in Wicklow. A likely bloody story.

—There was one queen in the poem that had an amber belly.

—Jaundice, said Jody. Or Butterfly herself that's as sallow as any Jap. Austin, you're a worse lunatic than Pike.

—But in the end, Jody, his own girl was the queen of all queens. They were dead and rotten. She was alive.

—Not much of a compliment to her, Jody said, to prefer her to a cartload of corpses.

—Love's love, Jody. Even the girls admit that. They've no grudge against him for seeing nobody but Butterfly.

—They give him a fool's pardon. But no doll in the hustling game, Austin, can afford to spend all her time listening to poetry. Besides, girls like a variety of pricks. Butterfly's no better or worse than the next. When Pike finds that out he'll go crazy. If he isn't crazy already.

That was the day, as I recall, that Butterfly came in wearing the fancy fur coat—just a little out of season. Jody had, for some reason or other, given her a five-pound note. Pike knew nothing about that. And Jody told her to venture the five pounds on a horse that was running at the Curragh of Kildare, that a man in Kilcullen on the edge of the Curragh had told him that the jockey's wife had already bought her ball dress for the victory celebration. The Kilcullen man knew his onions, and his jockeys, and shared his wisdom only with a select few so as to keep the odds at a good twenty to one.

—She's gone out to the bookie's, said Jody, to pick up her winnings. We'll have a party tonight.

Jody had a tenner on the beast.

—She could invest it, said Austin, if she was wise. The day will come when her looks will go.

—Pike might propose to her, said Jody. He's mad enough for anything.

—The aunts would devour him. And her.

—Here she comes, Jody said. She invested her winnings on her fancy back.

She had too, and well she carried them in the shape of pale or silver musquash, and three of her sorority walked behind her like ladies-in-waiting behind the Queen of England. There was a party in which even the dockers joined, but not Pike, for that evening and night one of his aunts was at death's door in a nursing home, and Pike and the other two aunts were by her side. He wasn't to see the musquash until he took Butterfly on an outing to the romantic hill of Howth where the poet and the woman had seen the white birds. That was the last day Pike ever took Butterfly anywhere. The aunt recovered. They were a thrawn hardy trio.

Pike had become a devotee. Every day except Sunday he lunched in Jody's, on a sandwich of stale bread and leathery ham and a glass of beer, just on the off-chance that Butterfly might be out of the doss and abroad, and in Jody's, at that, to her, unseasonable hour of the day. She seldom was, except when she was deplorably short of money. In the better eating places on Grafton Street and Stephen's Green, his colleagues absorbed the meals that enabled higher civil servants to face up to the afternoon and the responsibilities of State: statistics, land commission, local government, posts and telegraphs, internal revenue. He had never, among his own kind, been much of a mixer: so that few of his peers even noticed the speed with which, when at five in the evening the official day was done, he took himself, and his hat and coat and umbrella, and legged it off to Jody's: in the hope that Butterfly might be there, bathed and perfumed and ready for wine and love. Sometimes she was. Sometimes she wasn't. She liked Pike. She didn't deny it. She was always an honest girl, as her mother, Trixie, had been before her—so Austin said when he remembered Trixie who had died in a hurry, of peritonitis. But, Janey Mac, Butterfly couldn't have Pike Hunter for breakfast, dinner, tea and supper, and nibblers as well, all the livelong day and night. She still, as Jody said, had her first million to make, and Pike's inordinate attachment was coming between her and the real big business, as when, say, the country cattle men were in town for the market. They were the men who knew how to get rid of the money.

—There is this big cattle man, she tells Austin once, big he is in every way, who never knows or cares what he's spending. He's a gift and a godsend to the girls. He gets so drunk that all you have to do to humour him is play with him a little in the taxi going from pub to pub and see that he gets safely to his hotel. The taximen are on to the game and get their divy out of the loot.

One wet and windy night, it seems, Butterfly and this philanthropist are flying high together, he on brandy, she on champagne, for which that first encounter with Pike has given her a ferocious drouth. In the back of the taxi touring from pub to pub, the five pound notes are flowing out of your man like water out of a pressed sponge. Butterfly is picking them up and stuffing them into her handbag, but not all of them. For this is too good and too big for any taximan on a fair percentage basis. So for every one note she puts into her handbag she stuffs two or three down into the calf-length boots she is wearing against the wet weather. She knows, you see, that she is too far gone in bubbly to walk up the stairs to her own room, that the taximan, decent fellow, will help her up and then, fair enough, go through her bag and take his cut. Which, indeed, in due time he does. When she wakes up, fully clothed, in the morning on her own bed, and pulls off her boots, her ankles, what with the rain that had dribbled down into her boots, are poulticed and plastered with notes of the banks of Ireland and of England, and one moreover of the Bank of Bonnie Scotland.

—Rings on my fingers, she says, and bells on my toes.

This was the gallant life that Pike's constant attendance was cutting her off from. She also hated being owned. She hated other people thinking that she was owned. She hated like hell when Pike would enter the Dark Cow and one of the other girls or, worse still, another man, a bit of variety, would move away from her side to let Pike take the throne. They weren't married, for Janey's sake. She could have hated Pike, except that she was as tender-hearted as Trixie had been, and she liked champagne. She certainly felt at liberty to hate the three aunts who made a molly-coddle out of him. She also hated, with a hatred that grew and grew, the way that Pike puked her with poethry. And all this time poor Pike walked in a dream that he never defined for us, perhaps not even for himself, but that certainly must have looked higher than the occasional trick on Jody's rumpled bed. So dreaming, sleep-walking, he persuaded Butterfly to go to Howth Head with him one dull hot day when the town was empty and she had nothing better to do. No place could have been more fatally poetic than Howth. She wore her musquash. Not even the heat could part her from it.

—He never let up, she said, not once from the moment we boarded the bus on the quays. Poethry. I had my bellyful.

—Sure thing, said Jody.

—Any man, she said, that won't pay every time he performs is a man to keep a cautious eye on. Not that he's not generous. But at the wrong times. Money down or no play's my motto.

—Well I know that, Jody said.

—But Pike Hunter says that would make our love mercenary, whatever that is.

—You're a great girl, said Austin, to be able to pronounce it.

—Your middle name, said Jody, is mercenary.

—My middle name, thank you, is Imelda. And the cheek of Pike Hunter suggesting to me to go to a doctor because he noticed something wrong with himself, a kidney disorder, he said. He must wet the bed.

—Butterfly, said Austin, he might have been giving you good advice.

—Nevertheless. It's not for him to say.

When they saw from the bus the Bull Wall holding the northern sand back from clogging up the harbour, and the Bull Island, three miles long, with dunes, bent grass, golfers, bathers and skylarks, Pike told her about some fellow called Joyce—there was a Joyce in the Civic Guards, a Galwayman who played county football, but no relation—who had gone walking on the Island one fine day and laid eyes on a young one, wading in a pool, with her skirts well pulled up; and let a roar out of him. By all accounts this Joyce was no addition to the family for, as Pike told the story, Butterfly worked out that the young one was well under age.

Pike and Butterfly had lunch by the edge of the sea, in the Claremont Hotel, and that was all right. Then they walked in the grounds of Howth Castle, Pike had a special pass and the flowers and shrubs were a sight to see if only Pike had kept his mouth shut about some limey by the name of Spenser who landed there in the year of God, and wrote a poem as long as from here to Killarney about a fairy queen and a gentle knight who was pricking on the plain like the members of the Harp Cycling Club, Junior Branch, up above there in the Phoenix Park. He didn't get time to finish the poem, the poet that is, not Pike, for the Cork people burned him out of house and home and, as far as Butterfly was concerned, that was the only good deed she ever heard attributed to the Cork people.

The Phoenix Park and the Harp Club reminded her that one day Jody had said, meaning no harm, about the way Pike moped around the Dark Cow when Butterfly wasn't there, that Pike was the victim of a semi-horn and should go up to the Fifteen Acres and put it in the grass for a while and run around it. But when, for fun, she told this to Pike he got so huffed he didn't speak for half an hour, and they walked Howth Head until her feet were blistered and the heel of her right shoe broke, and the sweat, with the weight of the musquash and the heat of the day, was running between her shoulder-blades like a cloudburst down the gutter. Then the row and the ructions, as the song says, soon began. He said she should have worn flat-heeled shoes. She said that if she had known that he was conscripting her for a forced march over a mountain she'd have borrowed a pair of boots from the last soldier she gave it to at cut-price, for the soldiers, God help them, didn't have much money but they were more open-handed with what they had than some people who had plenty, and soldiers didn't waste time and breath on poetry: Be you fat or be you lean there is no soap like Preservene.

So she sat on the summit of Howth and looked at the light-house and the seagulls, while Pike walked back to the village to have the broken heel mended, and the sweat dried cold on her, and she was perished. Then when he came back, off he was again about how that white-headed old character that you'd see across the river there at the Abbey Theatre, and Madame Gone Mad McBride that was the age of ninety and looked it, and known to all as a roaring rebel, worse than Austin, had stood there on that very spot, and how the poet wrote a poem wishing for himself and herself to be turned into seagulls, the big dirty brutes that you'd see along the docks robbing the pigeons of their food. Butterfly would have laughed at him, except that her teeth by this time were tap-dancing with the cold like the twinkling feet of Fred Astaire. So she pulled her coat around her and said: Pike, I'm no seagull. For Janey's sake take me back to civilisation and Jody's where I know someone.

But, God sees, you never knew nobody, for at that moment the caveman came out in Pike Hunter, he that was always so backward on Jody's bed and, there and then, he tried to flatten her in the heather in full view of all Dublin and the coast of Ireland as far south as Wicklow Head and as far north as where the Mountains of Mourne sweep down to the sea.

—Oh none of that, Pike Hunter, she says, my good musquash will be crucified. There's a time and a place and a price for everything.

—You and your musquash, he tells her.

They were wrestling like Man Mountain Dean and Jack Doyle, the Gorgeous Gael.

—You've neither sense nor taste, says he, to be wearing a fur coat on a day like this.

—Bloody well for you to talk, says she, with your rolled umbrella and your woollen combinations and your wobbly ass that won't keep you straight in the chair, and your three witches of maiden aunts never touched, tasted or handled by mortal man, and plenty of money and everything your own way. This is my only coat that's decent, in case you haven't noticed, and I earned it hard and honest with Jody, a generous man but a monster on the bed, I bled after him.

That put a stop to the wrestling. He brought her back to the Dark Cow and left her at the door and went his way.

He never came back to the Dark Cow but once, and Butterfly wasn't on her throne that night. It was the night before the cattle-market. He was so lugubrious and woebegone that Jody and Austin and a few merry newspaper men, including myself, tried to jolly him up, take him out of himself, by making jokes at his expense that would force him to come alive and answer back. Our efforts failed. He looked at us sadly and said: Boys, Beethoven, when he was dying, said: Clap now, good friends, the comedy is done.

He was more than a little drunk and, for the first time, seemed lopsided when standing up; and untidy.

—Clap now indeed, said Jody.

Pike departed and never returned. He took to steady drinking in places like the Shelbourne Hotel or the Buttery in the Hibernian where it was most unlikely, even with Dublin being the democratic sort of town that it is, that he would ever encounter Madame Butterfly. He became a great problem for his colleagues and his superior officers in the civil service, and for his three aunts. After careful consultation they, all together, persuaded him to rest up in Saint Patrick's Hospital where, as you all may remember, Dean Swift died roaring. Which was I feel sure, why Pike wasn't there to pay the last respects to the dead when Jody dropped from a heart attack and was waked in the bedroom above the Dark Cow. The girls were there in force to say an eternal farewell to a good friend. Since the drink was plentiful and the fun and the mourning intense, somebody, not even Austin knew who, suggested that the part of the corpse that the girls knew best should be tastefully decorated with black crepe ribbon. The honour of tying on the ribbon naturally went to Madame Butterfly but it was Big Anne who burst into tears and cried out: Jody's dead and gone forever.

Austin met her, Butterfly not Big Anne, a few days afterwards at the foot of the Nelson Pillar. Jody's successor had routed the girls from the Dark Cow. Austin told her about Pike and where he was. She brooded a bit. She said it was a pity, but nobody could do nothing for him, that those three aunts had spoiled him for ever and, anyway, didn't Austin think that he was a bit astray in the head.

–Who knows, Butterfly? Who's sound or who's silly? Consider yourself for a moment.

—What about me, Austin?

—A lovely girl like you, a vision from the romantic east, and think of the life you lead. It can have no good ending. Let me tell you a story, Butterfly. There was a girl once in London, a slavey, a poor domestic servant. I knew a redcoat here in the old British days who said he preferred slaveys to anything else because they were clean, free and flattering.

—Austin, I was never a slavey.

—No Butterfly, you have your proper pride. But listen: this slavey is out one morning scrubbing the stone steps in front of the big house she works in, bucket and brush, carbolic soap and all that, in one of the great squares in one of the more classy parts of London Town. There she is on her bended knees when a gentleman walks past, a British army major in the Coldstream Guards or the Black Watch or something.

—I've heard of them, Austin.

—So this British major looks at her, and he sees the naked backs of her legs, thighs you know, and taps her on the shoulder or somewhere and he says: Oh, rise up, lovely maiden and come along with me, there's a better life in store for you somewhere else. She left the bucket and the brush, and the stone steps half-scrubbed, and walked off with him and became his girl. But there were even greater things in store for her. For, Butterfly, that slavey became Lady Emma Hamilton, the beloved of Lord Nelson, the greatest British sailor that ever sailed, and the victor of the renowned battle of Trafalgar. There he is up on the top of the Pillar.

—You wouldn't think to look at him, Austin, that he had much love in him.

—But, Butterfly, meditate on that story, and rise up and get yourself out of the gutter. You're handsome enough to be the second Lady Hamilton.

After that remark, Austin brought her into Lloyd's, a famous house of worship in North Earl Street under the shadow of Lord Nelson and his pillar. In Lloyd's he brought her a drink and out of the kindness of his great singing heart, gave her some money. She shook his hand and said: Austin, you're the nicest man I ever met.

Austin had, we may suppose, given her an image, an ideal. She may have been wearied by Pike and his sad attachment to poetry, but she rose to the glimmering vision of herself as a great lady beloved by a great and valiant lord. A year later she married a docker, a decent quiet hard-working fellow who had slowly sipped his pints of black porter and watched and waited all the time.

Oddly enough, Austin told me when the dignity of old age had gathered around him like the glow of corn-stubble in the afterwards of harvest.

He could still sing. His voice never grew old.

—Oddly enough, I never had anything to do with her. That way, I mean. Well you know me. Fine wife, splendid sons, nobody like them in the world. Fine daughters, too. But a cousin of mine, a ship's wireless operator who had been all round the world from Yokohama to the Belgian Congo and back again, and had had a ship burned under him in Bermuda and, for good value, another ship burned under him in Belfast, said she was the meanest whore he ever met. When he had paid her the stated price, there were some coppers left in his hand and she grabbed them and said: give us these for the gas-meter.

But he said, also, that at the high moments she had a curious and diverting way of raising and bending and extending her left leg—not her right leg which she kept as flat as a plumb-level. He had never encountered the like before, in any colour or in any country.

PHONEFUN LIMITED

Bernard MacLaverty

*Belfast-born Bernard MacLaverty (1942–) has in recent years won
an international reputation for his two dramatic and acclaimed
novels,* Cal *and* Lamb, *both of which have been filmed, plus his collections of short stories, hailed by* The Times *for their 'humour as
bleak and raw as the Irish landscape'. MacLaverty worked for almost
ten years in a medical laboratory before becoming a teacher. Then the
success of his books—which have won several major literary prizes
including a Scottish Arts Council Book Award and the Guardian Fiction Prize—enabled him to become a full-time writer, spreading his
remarkable talents between novels, short stories and screenplays.
Bernard MacLaverty's short tales range from such jokey fantasies as
'The Miraculous Candidate' to the Walter Mitty exploits of an artificial inseminator in 'The Bull with the Hard Hat' and the amusingly
upbeat events described in 'Language, Truth and Lockjaw'. For ribald humour, though, 'Phonefun Limited', the story of two former
prostitutes running a business in glamorous titillation against the
background of a seedy flat, is without equal in recent comic fiction.*

*   *   *

When she heard the whine of the last customer's fast spin—
a bearded student with what seemed like a year's supply of
Y-fronts—Sadie Thompson changed her blue nylon launderette
coat for her outdoor one and stood jingling the keys by the door
until he left. It was dark and wet and the streets reflected the lights
from the shop windows. She had to rush to get to the Spar before
it closed, and was out of breath—not that she had much to buy,
potatoes, sugar and tea-bags. In the corner shop she got her cigarettes, the evening paper and a copy of *Men Only*, which she
slipped inside the newspaper and put in her carrier bag. She slowly

climbed the steep street in darkness because the Army had put out most of the street lights. She turned in at Number Ninety-six. The door stuck momentarily on a large envelope lying on the mat.

She had the table set and the dinner ready for Agnes when she came in.

'Hello, Sadie, love,' she said and kissed her on the cheek. Beside Sadie, Agnes was huge. She wore an expensive silver-fox fur coat. Sadie did not like the coat and had said so. It was much too much for a woman whose only job was cleaning the local primary school.

'I'm knackered,' said Agnes, kicking off her shoes and falling into the armchair. There was a hole in the toe of her tights.

'Take off your coat, your dinner's ready,' said Sadie.

'Hang on. Let me have a fag first.'

She lit up a cigarette and put her head back in the chair. Sadie thought she looked a putty colour. She was grossly overweight but would do nothing about it, no matter what Sadie said.

'Are you all right?'

'I'll be all right in a minute. It's that bloody hill. It's like entering the Olympics.'

'If you ask me, you're carrying too much weight. When did you last weigh yourself?'

'This morning.'

'And what were you?'

'I don't know,' said Agnes laughing, 'I was afraid to look.'

With her head back like that her fat neck and chin were one. There were red arcs of lipstick on the cork-tip of her cigarette. Sadie served the mash and sausages.

'Sit over,' she said. Agnes stubbed her cigarette out and, groaning for effect, came to the table still wearing her coat.

'You'd think to hear you that you'd cleaned that school by yourself.'

'It feels like I did.' Agnes raised her fork listlessly to her mouth. 'Did the post come?'

'Yes.'

'Much?'

'It feels fat.'

'Aw God no.'

'You'll have to brighten up a bit. Don't be so glum.'

'God, that's a good one coming from you, Sadie. I don't think I've seen you smiling since Christmas.'

'I'm the brains. You're supposed to be the charm. I don't *have* to smile.' They ate in silence except for the sound of their forks making small screeches against the plate.

'I wish you'd take off your coat when you're eating. It looks that slovenly,' said Sadie. Agnes heaved herself to her feet, took off her coat and flung it on the sofa. She turned on the transistor. The news was on so she tuned it to some music.

'I need a wee doze before I brighten up. You know that, Sadie.'

'I suppose I'm not tired after a day in that bloody laundryette?'

Agnes nibbled her sausage at the front of her closed mouth, very quickly, like a rabbit. The music on the radio stopped and a foreign voice came on and babbled.

'That's a great programme you picked.'

'It's better than the Northern Ireland news.'

The foreign voice stopped and music came on again. Agnes finished what was on her plate.

'Is there anything for afters?'

'You can open some plums if you want.'

Agnes lurched out to the tiled kitchen and opened a tin of plums. She threw the circle of lid into the bucket and came back with the tin and a spoon.

'It's cold on your feet out there. There's a draught coming in under that door that would clean corn.' She ate the plums from the tin. Some juice trickled on to her chin.

'Want some?' She offered the half-finished tin to Sadie, but she refused.

'It's no wonder you're fat.'

'It oils my voice. Makes it nice for the phone.'

'I got you a *Men Only* if you run out of inspiration. It's there on the sideboard.'

'Thanks, love, but I don't think I'll need it.' Agnes drank off the last of the juice from the tin.

'You'll cut your lip one of these days,' said Sadie, 'don't say I didn't warn you.'

Agnes lit a cigarette and rolled one across the table to Sadie. She dropped the dead match into the tin.

'That was good,' she said. 'I'm full to the gunnels.' She slapped her large stomach with the flat of her hand in satisfaction. The foreigner began to speak gobbledegook again.

'Aw shut up,' said Sadie. 'Men are all the same no matter what they're speaking.' She twiddled the knob until she got another station with music. Almost immediately the music stopped and a man with a rich American drawl began to speak.

'Aw God, Sadie, do you remember the Yanks? He sounds just like one I had.'

'Will I ever forget them? They could spend money all right.'

'That's exactly like his voice. It's the spit of him.'

'Give us a light.' Agnes leaned over and touched Sadie's cigarette with her own. Sadie pulled hard until it was lit.

'I fancied him no end,' said Agnes. 'He was lovely. I think it was his first time but he pretended it wasn't.'

'I think you told me about him.'

'My Yankee Doodle Dandy, I called him. I can still feel the stubble of his haircut. It was like he had sandpapered up the back of his neck. Blondie. We sort of went together for a while.'

'You mean he didn't pay.'

'That kind of thing.'

'Better clear this table.' Sadie put the cigarette in her mouth, closing one eye against the trickle of blue smoke and began to remove the dirty plates. Ash toppled on to the cloth. She came back from the kitchen and gently brushed the grey roll into the palm of her other hand and dropped it into Agnes's tin. Agnes said,

'You wash and I'll dry.'

'What you mean is I'll wash and put them in the rack and then about ten o'clock you'll come out and put them in the cupboard.'

'Well, it's more hygienic that way. I saw in the paper that the tea-towels leaves germs all over them.'

'You only read what suits you.'

Sadie went out into the kitchen to wash up the dishes. She heard the programme on the radio finish and change to a service with an American preacher. It kept fading and going out of focus and was mixed up with pips of Morse Code. When she had finished she washed out the tea-towel in some Lux and hung it in the yard to dry. She could do her own washing at the launderette but she hated lugging the bagful of damp clothes home. There was such a weight in wet clothes. If she did that too often she would end up with arms like a chimpanzee. When she went back into the living room Agnes was asleep in her armchair beside the radio with a silly smile on her face.

Sadie picked up the large envelope off the sideboard and opened it with her thumb and spilled out the pile of envelopes on to the table. She began to open them and separate the cheques and money. On each letter she marked down the amount of money contained and then set it to one side. Agnes began to snore wetly, her head pitched forward on to her chest. When she had all the letters opened, Sadie got up and switched off the radio. In the silence Agnes woke with a start. Sadie said,

'So you're back with us again.'

'What do you mean?'

'You were sound asleep.'

'I was not. I was only closing my eyes. Just for a minute.'

'You were snoring like a drunk.'

'Indeed I was not. I was just resting my eyes.'

The ticking of the clock annoyed Agnes so she switched the radio on again just in time to hear 'The Lord is my Shepherd' being sung in a smooth American drawl. She tuned it to Radio One. Sadie said,

'Hymns give me the creeps. That Billy Graham one. Euchh!' She shuddered. 'You weren't in Belfast for the Blitz, were you?'

'No, I was still a nice country girl from Cookstown. My Americans all came from the camp out at Larrycormack. That's where my Yankee Doodle Dandy was stationed. You stuck it out here through the Blitz?'

'You can say that again. We all slept on the Cavehill for a couple of nights. Watched the whole thing. It was terrible—fires everywhere.'

'Sadie, will you do my hair?'

Sadie took the polythene bag bulging with rollers from under the table and began combing Agnes's hair.

'It needs to be dyed again. Your roots is beginning to show.'

'I think I'll maybe grow them out this time. Have it greying at the temples.'

Sadie damped each strand of hair and rolled it up right into Agnes's head, then fixed it with a hairpin. With each tug of the brush Agnes let her head jerk with it.

'I love somebody working with my hair. It's so relaxing.' Sadie couldn't answer because her mouth was bristling with hairpins. Agnes said,

'How much was there in the envelopes?'

'Hengy-hee oung.'

'How much?'

Sadie took the hairpins from her mouth.

'Sixty-eight pounds.'

'That's not bad at all.'

'You're right there. It's better than walking the streets on a night like this.'

'If it goes on like this I'm going to give up my job in that bloody school.'

'I think you'd be foolish. Anything could happen. It could all fall through any day.'

'How could it?'

'I don't know. It all seems too good to be true. The Post Office could catch on. Even the Law. Or the tax man.'

'It's not against the law?'

'I wouldn't be too sure.'

'It's against the law the other way round but not the way we do it.'

'There. That's you finished,' said Sadie, giving the rollers a final pat in close to her head. She held the mirror up for Agnes to see but before she put it away she looked at herself. Her neck was a dead give-away. That's where the age really showed. You could do what you liked with make-up on your face but there was no way of disguising those chicken sinews on your neck. And the back of the hands. They showed it too. She put the mirror on the mantelpiece and said,

'Are you ready, Agnes?'

'Let's have a wee gin first.'

'O.K.'

She poured two gins and filled them to the brim with tonic. Agnes sat over to the table. When she drank her gin she pinched in her mouth with the delightful bitterness.

'Too much gin,' she said.

'You say that every time.'

Agnes sipped some more out of her glass and then topped up with tonic. She began to sort through the letters. She laughed and nodded her head at some. At others she turned down the corners of her mouth.

'I suppose I better make a start.'

She lifted the telephone and set it beside her on the table. She burst out laughing.

'Have you read any of these, Sadie?'

'No.'

'Listen to this. "Dear Samantha, you really turn me on with that sexy voice of yours. Not only me but my wife as well. I get her to listen on the extension. Sometimes it's too much for the both of us." Good Gawd. I never thought there was any women listening to me.' She picked up the phone and snuggled it between her ear and the fat of her shoulder.

'Kick over that pouffe, Sadie.'

Sadie brought the pouffe to her feet. Agnes covered the hole in the toe of her tights with the sole of her other foot. She sorted through the letters and chose one.

'"Available at any time." He must be an oul' bachelor. O three one. That's Edinburgh isn't it? Dirty oul' kilty.'

She dialled the number and while she listened to the dialling tone she smiled at Sadie. She raised her eyebrows as if she thought she was posh. A voice answered at the other end. Agnes's voice changed into a soft purr which pronounced its -ings.

'Hello is Ian there? . . . Oh, I didn't recognise your voice. This is Samantha . . . Yes, I can hold on, but not too long.' She covered the mouthpiece with her hand and, exaggerating her lips, said to Sadie,

'The egg-timer.'

Sadie went out to the kitchen and came back with it. It was a cheap plastic one with pink sand. She set it on the table with the full side on top.

'Ah, there you are again, honey,' whispered Agnes into the mouthpiece, 'are you all ready now? Good. What would you like to talk about? . . . Well, I'm lying here on my bed. It's a lovely bed with black silk sheets . . . No, it has really. Does that do something for you? Mmm, it's warm. I have the heating turned up full. It's so warm all I am wearing are my undies . . . Lemon . . . Yes, and the panties are lemon too . . . All right, if you insist . . .' Agnes put the phone down on the table and signalled to Sadie to light her a fag. She made a rustling noise with her sleeve close to the mouthpiece then picked up the phone again.

'There, I've done what you asked . . . You're not normally breathless, are you, Ian? Have you just run up the stairs? . . . No, I'm only kidding . . . I know only too well what it's like to have asthma.'

She listened for a while, taking the lit cigarette from Sadie. She rolled her eyes to heaven and smiled across the table at her. She covered the mouthpiece with her hand.

'He's doing his nut.'

Sadie topped up her gin and tonic from the gin bottle.

'Do you really want me to do that? That might cost a little more money . . . All right, just for you love.' She laughed heartily and paused. 'Yes, I'm doing it now . . . Yes, it's fairly pleasant. A bit awkward . . . Actually I'm getting to like it. Ohhh, I love it now . . . Say what again? . . . Ohhh, I love it.'

She turned to Sadie.

'He's rung off. That didn't take long. He just came and went. Who's next?'

Sadie flicked another letter to her.

'London,' she said. 'Jerome. Only on Thursdays after eight.'

'That's today. Probably the wife's night out at the Bingo.'

She dialled the number and when a voice answered she said, 'Hello Jerome, this is Samantha.'

Sadie turned over the egg-timer.

'Oh, sorry love—say that again. Ger—o—mey. I thought it was Ger—ome. Like Ger-ome Cairns, the song writer. Would you like to talk or do you want me to . . . O.K., fire away . . . I'm twenty-four . . . Blonde . . . Lemon, mostly . . . Yes, as brief as possible. Sometimes they're so brief they cut into me.' She listened for a moment, then covering the mouthpiece said to Sadie,

'This one's disgusting. How much did he pay?'

Sadie looked at the letter.

'Ten pounds. Don't lose him. Do what he says.'

'Yes, this is still Samantha.' Her voice went babyish and her mouth pouted. 'How could a nice little girl like me do a thing like that? . . . Well, if it pleases you.' Agnes lifted her stubby finger and wobbled it wetly against her lips. 'Can you hear that? . . . Yes, I like it . . . Yes, I have *very* long legs.' She lifted her legs off the pouffe and looked at them disapprovingly. She had too many varicose veins. She'd had them out twice.

'You *are* a bold boy, but your time is nearly up.' The last of the pink sand was caving in and trickling through. Sadie raised a warning finger then signalled with all ten. She mouthed.

'Ten pounds. Don't lose him.'

'All right, just for you . . . Then I'll have to go,' said Agnes and she wobbled her finger against her lips again. 'Is that enough? . . . You just write us another letter. You know the box number?

Good . . . I love you too, Ger—o—mey. Bye-eee.' She put the phone down.

'For God's sake give us another gin,' she said. 'What a creep!'

'It's better than walking the street,' said Sadie. 'What I like about it is that they can't get near you.'

'Catch yourself on, Sadie. If anyone got near us now they'd run a mile.'

'I used to be frightened of them. Not all the time. But there was one every so often that made your scalp crawl. Something not right about them. Those ones gave me the heemy-jeemies, I can tell you. You felt you were going to end up in an entry somewhere—strangled—with your clothes over your head.'

Agnes nodded in agreement. 'Or worse,' she said.

Sadie went on, 'When I think of the things I've had to endure. Do you remember that pig that gave me the kicking? I was in hospital for a fortnight. A broken arm and a ruptured spleen—the bastard.'

Agnes began to laugh. 'Do you remember the time I broke my ankle? Jumping out of a lavatory window. Gawd, I was sure and certain I was going to be murdered that night.'

'Was that the guy with the steel plate in his head?'

'The very one. He said he would go mad if I didn't stroke it for him.'

'What?'

'His steel plate.'

'I can still smell some of those rooms. It was no picnic, Agnes, I can tell you.'

'The only disease you can get at this game is an ear infection. Who's next?'

Sadie passed another letter to her.

'Bristol, I think.'

'This one wants *me* to breathe. Good God, what will they think of next?'

'I hate their guts, every last one of them.'

'Do you fancy doing this one?' asked Agnes.

'No. You know I'm no good at it.'

'Chrissake, Sadie, you can breathe. I never get a rest. Why's it always me?'

'Because I told you. You are the creative one. I just look after the books. The business end. Would you know how to go about putting an ad in? Or wording it properly? Or getting a box number? You stick to the bit you're good at. You're really great, you know. I don't know how you think the half of them up.'

Agnes smiled. She wiggled her stubby toes on the pouffe. She said,

'Do you know what I'd like? With the money.'

'What? Remember that we're still paying off that carpet in the bedroom—and the suite. Don't forget the phone bills either.'

'A jewelled cigarette holder. Like the one Audrey Hepburn had in that picture—what was it called?'

'*The Nun's Story*?'

'No.'

'*Breakfast at Tiffany's*?'

'Yes, one like that. I could use it on the phone. It'd make me feel good.'

As Agnes dialled another number Sadie said,

'You're mad in the skull.'

'We can afford it. Whisht now.'

When the phone was answered at the other end she said,

'Hello, Samantha here,' and began to breathe loudly into the receiver. She quickened her pace gradually until she was panting, then said,

'He's hung up. Must have been expecting me. We should get a pair of bellows for fellas like him. Save my puff.'

'I'll go up and turn the blanket on, then we'll have a cup of tea,' said Sadie. Agnes turned another letter towards herself and dialled a number.

Upstairs Sadie looked round the bedroom with admiration. She still hadn't got used to it. The plush almost ankle-deepness of the mushroom-coloured carpet and the brown flock wallpaper, the brown duvet with the matching brown sheets. The curtains were of heavy velvet and were the most luxurious stuff she had ever touched. She switched on the blanket and while on her hands and knees she allowed her fingers to sink into the pile of the carpet. All her life she had wanted a bedroom like this. Some of the places she had lain down, she wouldn't have kept chickens in. She heard Agnes's voice coming blurred from downstairs. She owed a lot to her. Everything, in fact. From the first time they met, the night they were both arrested and ended up in the back of the same paddy-wagon, she had thought there was something awful good about her, something awful kind. She had been so good-looking in her day too, tall and stately and well-built. They had stayed together after that night—all through the hard times. As Agnes said, once you quit the streets it didn't qualify you for much afterwards. Until lately, when she had shown this amazing talent for talking on the phone. It had all started one night when a man got the wrong number and Agnes had chatted him up until he was doing his nut at the other end. They had both crouched over the phone wheezing and laughing their heads off at the puffs and pants of him. Then it was Sadie's idea to put the whole thing on a commercial basis and form the Phonefun company. She dug her fingers into the carpet and brushed her cheek against the crisp sheet.

'Agnes,' she said and went downstairs to make the tea.

She stood waiting for the kettle to boil, then transferred the tea-bag from one cup of boiling water to the other. Agnes laughed loudly at something in the living room. Sadie heard her say,

'But if I put the phone there you'll not hear me.'

She put some custard creams on a plate and brought the tea in.

'Here you are, love,' she said, setting the plate beside the egg-timer. 'He's over his time.' Agnes covered the mouthpiece and said,

'I forgot to start it.' Then back to the phone. 'I can get some rubber ones if you want me to . . . But you'll have to pay for them. Will you send the money through? . . . Goooood boy. Now I really must go . . . Yes, I'm listening.' She made a face, half laughing, half in disgust, to Sadie. 'Well done, love . . . Bye-eee, sweetheart.' She puckered her mouth and did a kiss noise into the mouthpiece, then put the phone down.

'Have your tea now, Agnes, you can do the others later.'

'There's only two more I can do tonight. The rest have special dates.'

'You can do those. Then we'll go to bed. Eh?'

'O.K.,' said Agnes. 'Ahm plumb tuckered out.'

'You're what?'

'Plumb tuckered out. It's what my Yankee Doodle Dandy used to say afterwards.'

'What started you on *him* tonight?'

'I don't know. I just remembered, that's all. He used to bring me nylons and put them on for me.'

She fiddled with the egg-timer and allowed the pink sand to run through it. She raised her legs off the pouffe and turned her feet outwards, looking at them.

'I don't like tights,' she said, 'I read somewhere they're unhygienic.'

'Do you want to hear the news before we go up? Just in case?'

'Just in case what?'

'They could be rioting all over the city and we wouldn't know a thing.'

'You're better not to know, even if they are. That tea's cold.'

'That's because you didn't drink it. You talk far too much.'

Agnes drank her tea and snapped a custard cream in half with her front teeth.

'I don't think I'll bother with these next two.'

'That's the way you lose customers. If you phone them once they'll come back for more—and for a longer time. Give them a short time. Keep them interested.' She lifted the crumbed plate and the cups and took them out to the kitchen. Agnes lit another cigarette and sat staring vacantly at the egg-timer. She said without raising her eyes,

'Make someone happy with a phone call.'

'I'm away on up,' said Sadie. 'I'll keep a place warm for you.'

Sadie was in bed when Agnes came up.

'Take your rollers out,' she said.

Agnes undressed, grunting and tugging hard at her roll-on. When she got it off she gave a long sigh and rubbed the puckered flesh that had just been released.

'That's like taking three Valium, to get out of that,' she said. She sat down on the side of the bed and began taking her rollers out, clinking the hairpins into a saucer on the dressing table. Sadie spoke from the bed.

'Were you really in love with that Yank?'

'Yes, as near as possible.'

Agnes shook her hair loose and rolled back into bed. She turned out the light and Sadie notched into her back. She began to stroke Agnes's soft upper arm, then moved to her haunch.

'I've got a bit of a headache, love,' said Agnes.

Sadie turned to the wall and Agnes felt her harsh skin touch her own.

'My God, Sadie,' she said, 'you've got heels on you like pumice stones.'

2

BATTLES OF WIT

Tales of Wordplay

'An Irish Scrimmage', by John Leech from *The Fortunes of Hector O'Halloran* by W. H. Maxwell.

BOB PENTLAND, OR THE
GAUGER OUTWITTED

William Carleton

By the nineteenth century, Irish wit and wordplay were already *proverbial throughout the English-speaking countries, although at home the tradition had been well-established for many years. This fact was due mainly to the emergence of people like William Carleton, John Philpot Curran and, later still, Oscar Wilde and Oliver St John Gogarty, whose reputation as writers and wits highlighted the natural talent of the nation as a whole. George Bernard Shaw, who was also born in Ireland, liked to give the credit for this facility to the Irish climate, though the Irishman's long-standing delight in wild humour is probably a more generally accepted explanation.*

The first of the great Anglo-Irish writers using wit and wordplay was William Carleton (1794–1869), the youngest of 14 children of an impoverished County Tyrone farmer, who first came to public notice in Dublin with a series of satires on Irish Catholicism, but is today best remembered for his two volumes of insight into native characteristics, Traits and Stories of the Irish Peasantry *(1830 and 1834). Although Carleton believed he deserved the same level of success as Dickens, Thackeray and even his own countryman, Charles Lever, he was often unscrupulous in his transactions and sly in his attacks on other literary figures, and probably deserves the epitaph given to him by Thomas Flanagan in* The Irish Novelists, 1800–1850 *(1958), of being 'the richest talent in nineteenth-century Ireland and the most prodigally wasted'. Yet whatever his failings as a man, Carleton's undeniable talent as a comic writer has survived. It sparkles in the names he gives to characters such as the land agent, Valentine McClutchy, the enforcer, Darby O'Drive, the corrupt attorney Solomon McSlime and the grasping preacher, the Reverend Phineas Lucre; and it shines in short stories such as 'Wildgoose Lodge' and 'Going to Maynooth', and in the* novella '*Larry M'Farland's Wake*', *which may well have influenced the composition of James Joyce's classic* Finnegans Wake. *The story of the gauger (excise man) Bob Pentland is a hilarious account of illegal whiskey-making and Irish quick-wittedness—and it comes as something of a bizarre postscript to the author's life to learn that he died of cancer of the tongue.*

*   *   *

That the Irish are a ready-witted people is a fact to the truth of which testimony has been amply borne both by their friends and enemies. Many causes might be brought forward to account for this questionable gift, if it were our intention to be philosophical; but, as the matter has been so generally conceded, it would be but a waste of logic to prove to the world that which the world cares not about, beyond the mere fact that it is so. On this or any other topic one illustration is worth twenty arguments, and, accordingly, instead of broaching a theory we shall relate a story.

Behind the hill, or rather mountain, of Altnaveenan lies one of those deep and almost precipitous valleys, on which the practised eye of an illicit distiller would dwell with delight, as a topography not likely to be invaded by the unhallowed feet of the gauger and his redcoats. In point of fact, the spot we speak of was, from its peculiarly isolated position, nearly invisible, unless to such as came very close to it. Being so completely hemmed in and concealed by the round and angular projections of the mountain hills, you could never dream of its existence at all, until you came upon the very verge of the little precipitous gorge which led into it. This advantage of position was not, however, its only one. It is true, indeed, that the moment you had entered it, all possibility of its being applied to the purposes of distillation at once vanished, and you consequently could not help exclaiming, 'What a pity that so safe and beautiful a nook should not have a single spot on which to erect a still-house, or rather on which to raise a sufficient stream of water to the elevation necessary for the process of distilling.' If a gauger actually came to the little chasm, and cast his scrutinising eye over it, he would immediately perceive that the erection of a private still in such a place was a piece of folly not generally to be found in the plans of those who have recourse to such practices.

This absence, however, of the requisite conveniences was only apparent, not real. To the right, about one hundred yards above the entrance to it, ran a ledge of rocks, some fifty feet high or so. Along the lower brows, near the ground, grew thick matted masses of long heath, which covered the entrance to a cave about as large and as high as an ordinary farmhouse. Through a series of small fissures in the rocks which formed its roof descended a stream of clear, soft water, precisely in body and volume such as was actually required by the distiller; but, unless by lifting up this mass of heath, no human being could for a moment imagine that there existed any such grotto, or so unexpected and easy an entrance to it. Here there was a private still-house made by the hand of nature herself, such as no art or ingenuity of man could equal.

Now it so happened that about the period we write of, there lived in our parish two individuals so antithetical to each other in their pursuits of life, that we question whether throughout all the instinctive antipathies of nature we could find any two animals more destructive of each other than the two we mean—to wit, Bob Pentland, the gauger, and little George Steen, the illicit distiller. Pentland was an old, staunch, well-trained fellow, of about fifty years or more, steady and sure, and with all the characteristic points of the high-bred gauger about him. He was a tallish man, thin, but lathy, with a hooked nose that could scent the tread of a distiller with the keenness of a sleuth-hound; his dark eye was deep-set, circumspect, and roguish in its expression, and his shaggy brow seemed always to be engaged in calculating whereabouts his inveterate foe, little George Steen, that eternally blinked him when almost in his very fangs, might then be distilling. To be brief, Pentland was proverbial for his sagacity and adroitness in detecting distillers, and little George was equally proverbial for having always baffled him, and that, too, sometimes under circumstances where escape seemed hopeless.

The incidents which we are about to detail occurred at that period of time when the collective wisdom of our legislators thought it advisable to impose a fine upon the whole townland in which the Still, Head, and Worm might be found; thus opening a door for knavery and fraud, and, as it proved in most cases, rendering the innocent as liable to suffer for an offence they never contemplated as the guilty who planned and perpetrated it. The consequence of such a law was, that still-houses were always certain to be erected either at the very verge of the neighbouring district, or as near them as the circumstances of convenience and situation would permit. The moment, of course, that the hue-and-cry of the gauger and his myrmidons was heard upon the wind, the whole apparatus was immediately heaved over the *mering** to the next townland, from which the fine imposed by Parliament was necessarily raised, whilst the crafty and offending district actually escaped. The state of society generated by such a blundering and barbarous statute as this was dreadful. In the course of a short time, reprisals, lawsuits, battles, murders, and massacres multiplied to such an extent throughout the whole country, that the sapient senators, who occasioned such commotion, were compelled to repeal their own act as soon as they found how it worked. Necessity, together with being the mother of invention, is also the cause of many an accidental discovery. Pentland had been so frequently defeated by little George, that he vowed never to rest until he had secured him; and George, on the other hand, frequently told him—for they were otherwise on the best terms—that he defied him, or, as he himself more quaintly expressed it, 'that he defied the devil, the world, and Bob Pentland'. The latter, however, was a very sore thorn in his side, and drove him from place to place, and from one haunt to another, until he began to despair of being able any longer to outwit him, or to find within the parish any spot at all suitable to distillation with which Pentland was not acquainted. In this state stood matters between them, when George fortunately discovered at the hip of Altnaveenan hill the natural grotto we have just sketched so briefly. Now, George was a man, as we have already hinted, of great fertility of resources; but there existed in the same parish another distiller who outstripped him in that far-sighted cunning which is so necessary in misleading or circumventing such a sharp-scented old hound as Pentland. This was little Mickey M'Quade, a short-necked, squat, little fellow, with bow legs, who might be said rather to creep in his motion than to walk. George and Mickey were intimate friends, independently of their joint antipathy against the gauger, and, truth to tell, much of the mortification and many of the defeats which Pentland experienced at George's hands were, *sub rosa*, to be attributed to Mickey. George was a distiller from none of the motives which generally actuate others of

* boundary.

that class. He was in truth an analytic philosopher—a natural chemist never out of some new experiment—and we have reason to think might have been the Kane, or Faraday, or Dalton, of his day, had he only received a scientific education. Not so honest Mickey, who never troubled his head about an experiment, but only thought of making a good running, and defeating the gauger. The first thing, of course, that George did was to consult Mickey, and both accordingly took a walk up to the scene of their future operations. On examining it, and fully perceiving its advantages, it might well be said that the look of exultation and triumph which passed between them was not unworthy of their respective characters.

'This will do,' said George. 'Eh—don't you think we'll put our finger in Pentland's eye yet?' Mickey spat sagaciously over his beard, and after a second glance gave one grave grin which spoke volumes. 'It'll do,' said he; 'but there's one point to be got over that maybe you didn't think of; an' you know that half a blink, half a point, is enough for Pentland.'

'What is it?'

'What do you intend to do with the smoke when the fire's lit? There's be no keepin' *that* down. Let Pentland see but as much smoke risin' as would come out of an ould woman's dudeen, an' he'd have us.'

George started, and it was clear by the vexation and disappointment which were visible on his brow that unless this untoward circumstance could be managed their whole plan was deranged, and the cave of no value.

'What's to be done?' he enquired of his cooler companion. 'If we can't get over this, we may bid goodbye to it.'

'Never mind,' said Mickey; 'I'll manage it, and *do* Pentland still.'

'Ay, but how?'

'It's no matter. Let us not lose a minute in settin' to work. Lave the other thing to me; an' if I don't account for the smoke without discoverin' the entrance to the still, I'll give you lave to crop the ears off my head.'

George knew the cool but steady self-confidence for which Mickey was remarkable, and, accordingly, without any further interrogatory, they both proceeded to follow up their plan of operations.

In those times when distillation might be truly considered as almost universal, it was customary for farmers to build their out-houses with secret chambers and other requisite partitions neces-sary for carrying it on. Several of them had private stores built between false walls, the entrance to which was only known to a few, and many of them had what were called *Malt-steeps* sunk in hidden recesses and hollow gables, for the purpose of steeping the barley, and afterwards of turning and airing it, until it was sufficiently hard to be kiln-dried and ground. From the mill it was usually conveyed to the still-house upon what were termed *Slipes*, a kind of car that was made without wheels, in order the more easily to pass through morasses and bogs which no wheeled vehicle could encounter.

In the course of a month or so, George and Mickey, aided by their friends, had all the apparatus of keeve, hogshead, etc., together with Still, Head, and Worm, set up and in full work.

'And now, Mickey,' enquired his companion, 'how will you manage about the smoke? For you know that the two worst informers against a private distiller, barrin' a *stag*, is a smoke by day an' a fire by night.'

'I know that,' replied Mickey; 'an' a rousin' smoke we'll have for 'fraid a little puff wouldn't do us. Come, now, an' I'll show you.'

They both ascended to the top, where Mickey had closed all the open fissures of the roof with the exception of that which was directly over the fire of the still. This was at best not more than six inches in breadth, and about twelve long. Over it he placed a piece of strong plate-iron perforated with holes, and on this he had a fire of turf, beside which sat a little boy who acted as a vidette. The thing was simple but effective. Clamps of turf were at every side of them, and the boy was instructed, if the gauger, whom he well knew, ever appeared, to heap on fresh fuel, so as to increase the smoke in such a manner as to induce him to suppose that *all* he saw of it proceeded merely from the fire before him. In fact, smoke from the cave below was so completely identified with and lost in that which was emitted from the fire above, that no human being could penetrate the mystery, if not made previously acquainted with it. The writer of this saw it during the hottest process of distillation, and failed to make the discovery, although told that the still-house was within a circle of three hundred yards, the point he stood on being considered the centre. On more than one occasion has he absconded from home, and spent a whole night in the place, seized with that indescribable fascination which such a scene holds forth to youngsters, as well as from his irrepressible anxiety to hear the old stories and legends with the recital of which they generally pass the night.

In this way, well provided against the gauger—indeed, much better than our readers are yet aware of, as they shall understand by-and-bye—did George, Mickey, and their friends proceed for the greater part of a winter without a single visit from Pentland. Several successful runnings had come off, which had, of course, turned out highly profitable, and they were just now preparing to commence their last, not only for the season, but the last they should ever work together, as George was making preparations to go early in the spring to America. Even this running was going on to their satisfaction, and the singlings had been thrown again into the still, from the worm of which projected the strong medicinal *first-shot* as the doubling commenced— this last term meaning the spirit in its pure and finished state. On this occasion the two worthies were more than ordinarily anxious, and certainly doubled their usual precautions against a surprise, for they knew that Pentland's visits resembled the pounces of a hawk or the springs of a tiger more than anything else to which they could compare them. In this they were not disappointed. When the doubling was about half finished he made his appearance, attended by a strong party of reluctant soldiers—for, indeed, it is due to the military to state that they never took delight in harassing the country people at the command of a keg-hunter, as they generally nicknamed the gauger. It had been arranged that the vidette at the iron plate should whistle a particular tune the moment that the gauger or a redcoat, or, in fact, any person whom he did not know, should appear. Accordingly, about eight o'clock in the morning they heard the little fellow in his highest key whistling up that well-known and very significant old Irish air called 'Go to the devil and shake yourself'—which in this case was applied to the gauger in anything but an allegorical sense.

'Be the pins,' which was George's usual oath—'be the pins, Mickey, it's over with us—Pentland's here, for there's the sign.'

Mickey paused for a moment and listened very gravely; then squirting out a tobacco spittle, 'Take it easy,' said he; 'I have half-a-dozen fires about the hills, any one as like this as your right hand is to your left. I didn't spare trouble, for I knew that if we'd get over *this* day, we'd be out of his power.'

'Well, my good lad,' said Pentland, addressing the vidette, 'what's this fire for?'

'What is it for, is it?'

'Yes; if you don't let me know instantly I'll blow your brains out, and get you hanged and transported afterwards.'

This he said with a thundering voice, cocking a large horse-pistol at the same time.

'Why, sir,' said the boy, 'it's watchin' a still I am; but be the hole o' my coat if you tell upon me, it's broilin' upon these coals I'll be soon.'

'Where is the still, then? An' the still-house, where is it?'

'Oh, begorra, as to where the still or still-house is, they wouldn't tell *me* that.'

'Why, sirra, didn't you say this moment you were watching a still?'

'I meant, sir,' replied the lad, with a face that spoke of pure idiocy, 'that it was the gauger I was watchin', an' I was to whistle upon my fingers to let the boy at that fire on the hill there above know he was comin'.'

'Who told you to do so?'

'Little George, sir, an' Mickey M'Quade.'

'Ay, ay, right enough there, my lad—two of the most notorious schemers unhanged, they are both. But now, like a good boy, tell me the truth, an' I'll give you the price of a pair of shoes. Do you know where the still or still-house is? Because, if you do, an' won't tell me, here are the soldiers at hand to make a prisoner of you; an' if they do, all the world can't prevent you from being hanged, drawn and quartered.'

'Oh, bad cess may seize the morsel o' me knows that; but, if you'll give me the money, sir, I'll tell you who can bring you to it, for he tould me yesterday mornin' that he knew, an' offered to bring me there last night, if I'd steal him a bottle that my mother keeps the holy water in at home, tal he'd put whiskey in it.'

'Well, my lad, who is this boy?'

'Do you know "Harry Neil, or Mankind," sir?'

'I do, my good boy.'

'Well, it's a son of his, sir; an, look, sir; do you see the smoke farthest up to the right, sir?'

'To the right? Yes.'

'Well, 'tis there, sir, that Darby Neil is watchin'; and he *says* he knows.'

'How long have you been watching here?'

'This is only the third day, sir, for *me*, but the rest, them boys above, has been here a good while.'

'Have you seen nobody stirring about the hills since you came?'

'Only once, sir, yesterday, I seen two men, havin' an empty sack or two, runnin' across the hill there above.'

At this moment the military came up, for he had himself run forward in advance of them, and he repeated the substance of his conversation with our friend the vidette. Upon examining the stolidity of his countenance, in which there certainly was a woeful deficiency of meaning, they agreed among themselves that his appearance justified the truth of the story which he told the gauger, and upon being still further interrogated, they were confirmed that none but a stupid lout like himself would entrust to his keeping any secret worth knowing. They now separated themselves into as many detached parties as there were fires burning on the hills about them, the gauger himself resolving to make for that which Darby Neil had in his keeping, for he could not help thinking that the vidette's story was too natural to be false. They were just in the act of separating themselves to pursue their different routes when the lad said:

'Look, sir! Look, sir! Bad scran be from me but there's a still, anyway. Sure I often seen a still: that's just like the one that Philip Hagan, the tinker, mended in George Steen's barn.'

'Hollo, boys,' exclaimed Pentland, 'stoop! Stoop! They are coming this way, and don't see us: no, hang them, no! They have discovered us now, and are off towards Mossfield. By Jove, this will be a bitter trick if they succeed; confound them, they are bent for Ballagh, which is my own property; and may I be hanged, but if we do not intercept them it is I myself who will have to pay the fine.'

The pursuit instantly commenced with a speed and vigour equal to the ingenuity of this singular act of retaliation on the gauger. Pentland himself being long-winded from much practice in this way, and being further stimulated by the prospective loss which he dreaded, made as beautiful a run of it as any man of his years could do. It was all in vain, however. He merely got far enough to see the Still, Head, and Worm, heaved across the march ditch into his own property, and to reflect after seeing it, that he was certain to have the double consolation of being made a standing joke of for life, and of paying heavily for the jest out of his own pocket. In the meantime, he was bound, of course, to seize the still, and report the caption; and as he himself farmed the townland in question, the fine was levied to the last shilling, upon the very natural principle that if he had been sufficiently active and vigilant, no man would have attempted to set up a still so convenient to his own residence and property.

This manoeuvre of keeping in reserve an old or second set of apparatus, for the purpose of acting the lapwing and misleading the gauger, was afterwards often practised with success; but the first discoverer of it was undoubtedly Mickey M'Quade, although the honour of the discovery was attributed to his friend George Steen. The matter, however, did not actually end here, for in a few days afterwards some malicious wag—in other words, George himself—had correct information sent to Pentland touching the locality of the cavern and the secret of its entrance. On this occasion the latter brought a larger military party than usual along with him, but it was only to make him feel that he stood in a position, if possible, still more ridiculous than the first. He found, indeed, the marks of recent distillation in the place, but nothing else. Every vessel and implement connected with the process had been removed, with the exception of one bottle of whiskey, to which was attached, by a bit of twine, the following friendly note:

Mr Pentland, Sir—Take this bottle home and drink your own health. You can't do less. It was distilled *under your nose*, the first day you came to look for us, and bottled for you while you were speaking to the little boy that made a hare of you. Being distilled, then, under your nose, let it be drunk in the same place, and don't forget while doing so to drink the health of

G. S.

The incident went abroad like wildfire, and was known everywhere. Indeed, for a long time it was the standing topic of the parish; and so sharply was it felt by Pentland that he could never keep his temper if asked, 'Mr Pentland, when did you see little George Steen?'—a question to which he was never known to give a civil reply.

THE LAW OF LAUGHTER

John Philpot Curran

Ireland has given the world many great wits, but few have been the equal of John Philpot Curran (1750–1817), the nation's acknowledged master of the art of wordplay and also 'the wittiest man I ever met', according to Lord Byron. Born at Newmarket in County Cork, Curran was educated at Trinity College, Dublin, and there 'his merciless satirising of the reigning vices shaped him into an orator and legal counsel,' according to his son, W. H. Curran, in his biography, Life of Curran *(1822). His spontaneous wit soon made him famous throughout the courts of the land, though some of his sarcastic retorts involved him in being challenged to duels by enraged victims. He is said to have fought five—fortunately escaping from all of them without serious harm.*

Curiously, Curran wrote very little himself, apart from a few essays on Irish law and some verses of poetry, but he has still been immortalised in literature as 'Fillthepot Curran' (by James Joyce) and credited with being the father of Irish legal wit. As Vivian Mercier has observed, 'The witty and humorous cross-examination of witnesses who match their own wit and humour against the barrister's is a part of Irish legal tradition; John Philpot Curran was considered a past master at this art. To this day, obtaining information from an Irishman or Irishwoman about the simplest matters of fact often involves a battle of wits.' Here are just a few surviving examples of the courtroom wit which inaugurated Curran's legend and began an enduring tradition . . .

*   *   *

Mr Curran was engaged in a legal argument in court one day. Behind him stood his colleague, a gentleman whose person was remarkably tall and slender and who had originally intended to take holy orders.

The judge observed that the case under discussion involved a question of ecclesiastical law.

'Then,' said Mr Curran, 'I can refer your lordship to a higher authority behind me who was once intended for the Church, though (in a whisper to another friend beside him) in my opinion he was fitter for the *steeple*.'

*

An officer of one of the courts named Halfpenny having frequently interrupted Mr Curran, the judge peremptorily ordered him to be silent and sit down.

'I thank your lordship,' said the counsel, 'for having at length *nailed that rap to the counter*.' [A rap was a counterfeit halfpenny.]

*

'I can't tell you, Curran,' observed an Irish nobleman who had voted for the Union, 'how frightful our old House of Commons appears to me.'

'Ah! my Lord,' replied the other, 'it is only natural for murderers to be afraid of ghosts.'

*

An elderly judge had a defect in one of his limbs from which, when he walked, one foot described almost a circle round the other. Mr Curran, being asked how his lordship still contrived to walk so fast, answered,

'Don't you see that one leg goes before like a tipstaff and clears the way for the other?'

*

A miniature portrait-painter being cross-examined by Mr Curran was made to confess that he had carried his improper advances with a young lady so far as to attempt to put his arm around her waist.

'Then, sir,' said the counsel, 'I suppose you took that waist [*waste*] for a *common*!'

*

'No man,' said a wealthy but weak-headed barrister, 'should be admitted to the Bar who has not an independent landed property.'

'May I ask, sir,' said Mr Curran, 'how many acres make a *wise-acre*?'

*

'Would you not have known this boy to be my son from his resemblance to me?' asked a gentleman of counsel.

Mr Curran answered, 'Yes, sir. The maker's name is stamped upon the *blade*.'

*

At a public dinner, Mr Curran was defending his countrymen against the imputation of being a naturally vicious race.

'Many of our faults, for instance,' he said, 'arise from our too free use of wine and spirits—but I never yet heard of an Irishman being *born drunk*.'

*

A gigantic and ignorant barrister once half-seriously threatened to put Mr Curran in his pocket after suffering from his wit. The counsel, being of stunted stature and size, quickly retorted, 'Do! and you'll have more law in your pocket than you ever had in your head!'

*

Another huge barrister named Egan who was to fight a duel with Mr Curran complained that his opponent offered too small a target while he was too large a one.

To which Curran replied, 'Very true, my good fellow. Suppose that we chalk my size upon your person and every bullet outside the outline shall count for nothing!'

THE CANTERVILLE GHOST

Oscar Wilde

While John Philpot Curran may have been one of the earliest of Ireland's great wits, the most famous was surely Oscar Fingal O'Flahertie Wills Wilde (1854–1900), the novelist, poet, dramatist and a key cultural influence. Born in Dublin the son of the president of the Irish Academy, Sir William Wilde, and the literary figure Lady 'Speranza' Wilde, Oscar displayed his literary ability and genius for self-publicity from an early age and soon became one of the leading lights in the Aesthetic Movement. His biting wit and brilliant epigrams illuminated both his social life and much of his writing, before he was pilloried for his homosexuality and driven into exile in Paris, where he died. 'The Canterville Ghost' is the story of a puritanical American Ambassador who purchases a haunted house and refuses to believe it has a ghost. It is an example of Wilde's humorous writing at its best.

✶   ✶   ✶

I

When Mr Hiram B. Otis, the American Minister, bought Canterville Chase, everyone told him he was doing a very foolish thing, as there was no doubt at all that the place was haunted. Indeed, Lord Canterville himself, who was a man of the most punctilious honour, had felt it his duty to mention the fact to Mr Otis when they came to discuss terms.

'We have not cared to live in the place ourselves,' said Lord Canterville, 'since my grand-aunt, the Dowager Duchess of Bolton, was frightened into a fit, from which she never really recovered, by two skeleton hands being placed on her shoulders as she was dressing for dinner, and I feel bound to tell you, Mr Otis, that the ghost has been seen by several living members of my family, as well as by the rector of the parish, Rev. Augustus Dampier, who is a Fellow of King's College, Cambridge. After the unfortunate accident to the Duchess, none of our younger servants would stay with us, and Lady Canterville often got very little sleep at night, in consequence of the mysterious noises that came from the corridor and the library.'

'My Lord,' answered the Minister, 'I will take the furniture and the ghost at a valuation. I come from a modern country, where we have everything that money can buy; and with all our spry young fellows painting the Old World red, and carrying off your best actors and prima-donnas, I reckon that if there were such a thing as a ghost in Europe, we'd have it at home in a very short time in one of our public museums, or on the road as a show.'

'I fear that the ghost exists,' said Lord Canterville, smiling, 'though it may have resisted the overtures of your enterprising impresarios. It has been well known for three centuries, since 1584 in fact, and always makes its appearance before the death of any member of our family.'

'Well, so does the family doctor for that matter, Lord Canterville. But there is no such thing, sir, as a ghost, and I guess the laws of Nature are not going to be suspended for the British aristocracy.'

'You are certainly very natural in America,' answered Lord Canterville, who did not quite understand Mr Otis's last observation, 'and if you don't mind a ghost in the house, it is all right. Only you must remember I warned you.'

A few weeks after this, the purchase was concluded, and at the close of the season the Minister and his family went down to Canterville Chase. Mrs Otis, who, as Miss Lucretia R. Tappan, of West 53rd Street, had been a celebrated New York belle, was now a very handsome, middle-aged woman, with fine eyes, and a superb profile. Many American ladies on leaving their native land adopt an appearance of chronic ill-health, under the impression that it is a form of European refinement, but Mrs Otis had never fallen into this error. She had a magnificent constitution, and a really wonderful amount of animal spirits. Indeed, in many respects, she was quite English, and was an excellent example of the fact that we have really everything in common with America nowadays, except, of course, language. Her eldest son, christened Washington by his parents in a moment of patriotism, which he never ceased to regret, was a fair-haired, rather good-looking young man, who had qualified himself for American diplomacy by leading the German at the Newport Casino for three successive seasons, and even in London was well known as an excellent dancer. Gardenias and the peerage were his only weaknesses. Otherwise he was extremely sensible. Miss Virginia E. Otis was a little girl of fifteen, lithe and lovely as a fawn, and with a fine freedom in her large blue eyes. She was a wonderful amazon, and had once raced old Lord Bilton on her pony twice round the park, winning by a length and a half, just in front of the Achilles statue, to the huge delight of the young Duke of Cheshire, who proposed for her on the spot, and was sent back to Eton that very night by his guardians, in floods of tears. After Virginia came the twins, who were usually called the 'Stars and Stripes', as they were always getting swished. They were delightful boys, and with the exception of the worthy Minister the only true republicans of the family.

As Canterville Chase is seven miles from Ascot, the nearest railway station, Mr Otis had telegraphed for a wagonette to meet them, and they started on the drive in high spirits. It was a lovely July evening, and the air was delicate with the scent of the pine-woods. Now and then they heard a wood pigeon brooding over its own sweet voice, or saw, deep in the rustling fern, the burnished breast of the pheasant. Little squirrels peered at them from the beech-trees as they went by, and the rabbits scudded away through the brushwood and over the mossy knolls, with their white tails in the air. As they entered the avenue of Canterville Chase, however, the sky became suddenly overcast with clouds, a curious stillness seemed to hold the atmosphere, a great flight of rooks passed silently over their heads, and, before they reached the house, some big drops of rain had fallen.

Standing on the steps to receive them was an old woman, neatly dressed in black silk, with a white cap and apron. This was Mrs Umney, the housekeeper, whom Mrs Otis, at Lady Canterville's earnest request, had consented to keep on in her former position. She made them each a low courtesy as they alighted, and said in a quaint, old-fashioned manner, 'I bid you welcome to Canterville Chase.' Following her, they passed through the fine Tudor hall into the library, a long, low room, panelled in black oak, at the end of which was a large stained-glass window. Here they found tea laid out for them, and, after taking off their wraps, they sat down and began to look round, while Mrs Umney waited on them.

Suddenly Mrs Otis caught sight of a dull red stain on the floor just by the fireplace and, quite unconscious of what it really signified, said to Mrs Umney, 'I am afraid something has been spilt there.'

'Yes, madam,' replied the old housekeeper in a low voice, 'blood has been spilt on that spot.'

'How horrid,' cried Mrs Otis; 'I don't at all care for blood-stains in a sitting-room. It must be removed at once.'

The old woman smiled, and answered in the same low, mysterious voice, 'It is the blood of Lady Eleanore de Canterville, who was murdered on that very spot by her own husband, Sir Simon de Canterville, in 1575. Sir Simon survived her nine years, and disappeared suddenly under very mysterious circumstances. His body has never been discovered, but his guilty spirit still haunts the Chase. The blood-stain has been much admired by tourists and others, and cannot be removed.'

'That is all nonsense,' cried Washington Otis; 'Pinkerton's Champion Stain Remover and Paragon Detergent will clean it up in no time,' and before the terrified housekeeper could interfere he had fallen upon his knees, and was rapidly scouring the floor with a small stick of what looked like a black cosmetic. In a few moments no trace of the blood-stain could be seen.

'I knew Pinkerton would do it,' he exclaimed triumphantly, as he looked round at his admiring family; but no sooner had he said these words than a terrible flash of lightning lit up the sombre room, a fearful peal of thunder made them all start to their feet, and Mrs Umney fainted.

'What a monstrous climate!' said the American Minister calmly, as he lit a long cheroot. 'I guess the old country is so over-populated that they have not enough decent weather for everybody. I have always been of opinion that emigration is the only thing for England.'

'My dear Hiram,' cried Mrs Otis, 'what can we do with a woman who faints?'

'Charge it to her like breakages,' answered the Minister; 'she won't faint after that'; and in a few moments Mrs Umney certainly came to. There was no doubt, however, that she was extremely upset, and she sternly warned Mr Otis to beware of some trouble coming to the house.

'I have seen things with my own eyes, sir,' she said, 'that would make any Christian's hair stand on end, and many and many a night I have not closed my eyes in sleep for the awful things that are done here.' Mr Otis, however, and his wife warmly assured the honest soul that they were not afraid of ghosts, and, after invoking the blessings of Providence on her new master and mistress, and making arrangements for an increase of salary, the old housekeeper tottered off to her own room.

II

The storm raged fiercely all that night, but nothing of particular note occurred. The next morning, however, when they came down to breakfast, they found the terrible stain of blood once again on the floor. 'I don't think it can be the fault of the Paragon Detergent,' said Washington, 'for I have tried it with everything. It must be the ghost.' He accordingly rubbed out the stain a second time, but the second morning it appeared again. The third morning also it was there, though the library had been locked up at night by Mr Otis himself, and the key carried upstairs. The whole family were now quite interested; Mr Otis began to suspect that he had been too dogmatic in his denial of the existence of ghosts, Mrs Otis expressed her intention of joining the Psychical Society, and Washington prepared a long letter to Messrs Myers and Podmore on the subject of the Permanence of Sanguineous Stains when connected with Crime. That night all doubts about the objective existence of phantasmata were removed for ever.

The day had been warm and sunny; and, in the cool of the evening, the whole family went out to drive. They did not return home till nine o'clock, when they had a light supper. The conversation in no way turned upon ghosts, so there were not even those primary conditions of receptive expectation which so often precede the presentation of psychical phenomena. The subjects discussed, as I have since learned from Mr Otis, were merely such as form the ordinary conversation of cultured Americans of the better class, such as the immense superiority of Miss Fanny Davenport over Sara Bernhardt as an actress; the difficulty of obtaining green corn, buckwheat cakes, and hominy, even in the best English houses; the importance of Boston in the development of the world-soul; the advantages of the baggage check system in railway travelling; and the sweetness of the New York accent as compared to the London drawl. No mention at all was made of the supernatural, nor was Sir Simon de Canterville alluded to in any way. At eleven o'clock the family retired, and by half-past all the lights were out. Some time after, Mr Otis was awakened by a curious noise in the corridor, outside his room. It sounded like the clank of metal, and seemed to be coming nearer every moment. He got up at once, struck a match, and looked at the time. It was exactly one o'clock. He was quite calm, and felt his pulse, which was not at all feverish. The strange noise still continued, and with it he heard distinctly the sound of footsteps. He put on his slippers, took a small oblong phial out of his dressing-case, and opened the door. Right in front of him he saw, in the wan moonlight, an old man of terrible aspect. His eyes were as red as burning coals; long grey hair fell over his shoulders in matted coils; his garments, which were of antique cut, were soiled and ragged, and from his wrists and ankles hung heavy manacles and rusty gyves.

'My dear sir,' said Mr Otis, 'I really must insist on your oiling those chains, and have brought you for that purpose a small bottle of the Tammany Rising Sun Lubricator. It is said to be completely efficacious upon one application, and there are several testimonials to that effect on the wrapper from some of our most eminent native divines. I shall leave it here for you by my bedroom candles, and will be happy to supply you with more should you require it.' With these words the United States Minister laid the bottle down on a marble table, and, closing the door, retired to rest.

For a moment the Canterville ghost stood quite motionless in natural indignation; then, dashing the bottle violently upon the polished floor, he fled down the corridor, uttering hollow groans, and emitting a ghastly green light. Just, however, as he reached the top of the great oak staircase, a door was flung open, two little white-robed figures appeared, and a large pillow whizzed past his head! There was evidently no time to be lost, so, hastily adopting the Fourth Dimension of Space as a means of escape, he vanished through the wainscoting, and the house became quite quiet.

On reaching a small secret chamber in the left wing, he leaned up against a moonbeam to recover his breath, and began to try and realise his position. Never, in a brilliant and uninterrupted career of three hundred years, had he been so grossly insulted. He thought of the Dowager Duchess, whom he had frightened into a fit as she stood before the glass in her lace and diamonds; of the four housemaids, who had gone off into hysterics when he merely grinned at them through the curtains of one of the spare bedrooms; of the rector of the parish, whose candle he had blown out as he was coming late one night from the library, and who had been under the care of Sir William Gull ever since, a perfect martyr to nervous disorders; and of old Madame de Tremouillac, who, having wakened up one morning early and seen a skeleton seated in an armchair by the fire reading her diary, had been confined to her bed for six weeks with an attack of brain fever, and, on her recovery, had become reconciled to the Church, and broken off her connection with that notorious sceptic Monsieur de Voltaire. He remembered the terrible night when the wicked Lord Canterville was found choking in his dressing-room, with the knave of diamonds halfway down his throat, and confessed, just before he died, that he had cheated Charles James Fox out of £50,000 at Crockford's by means of that very card, and swore that the ghost had made him swallow it. All his great achievements came back to him again, from the butler who had shot himself in the pantry because he had seen a green hand tapping at the window pane, to the beautiful Lady Stutfield, who was always obliged to wear a black velvet band round her throat to hide the mark of five fingers burnt upon her white skin, and who drowned herself at last in the carp-pond at the end of the King's Walk. With the enthusiastic egotism of the true artist he went over his most celebrated performances, and smiled bitterly to himself as he recalled to mind his last appearance as 'Red Reuben, or the Strangled Babe', his *début* as 'Gaunt Gibeon, the Blood-sucker of Bexley Moor', and the *furore* he had excited one lovely June evening by merely playing ninepins with his own bones upon the lawn-tennis ground. And after all this, some wretched modern Americans were to come and offer him the Rising Sun Lubricator, and throw pillows at his head! It was quite unbearable. Besides, no ghost in history had ever been treated in this manner. Accordingly, he determined to have vengeance, and remained till daylight in an attitude of deep thought.

III

The next morning, when the Otis family met at breakfast, they discussed the ghost at some length. The United States Minister was naturally a little annoyed to find that his present had not been accepted. 'I have no wish,' he said, 'to do the ghost any personal injury, and I must say that, considering the length of time he has been in the house, I don't think it is at all polite to throw pillows at him'—a very just remark, at which I am sorry to say, the twins burst into shouts of laughter. 'Upon the other hand,' he continued, 'if he really declines to use the Rising Sun Lubricator, we shall have to take his chains from him. It would be quite impossible to sleep, with such a noise going on outside the bedrooms.'

For the rest of the week, however, they were undisturbed, the only thing that excited any attention being the continual renewal of the blood-stain on the library floor. This certainly was very strange, as the door was always locked at night by Mr Otis, and the windows kept closely barred. The chameleon-like colour, also, of the stain excited a good deal of comment. Some mornings it was a dull (almost Indian) red, then it would be vermilion, then a rich purple, and once when they came down for family prayers, according to the simple rites of the Free American Reformed Episcopalian Church, they found it a bright emerald-green. These kaleidoscopic changes naturally amused the party very much, and bets on the subject were freely made every evening. The only person who did not enter into the joke was little Virginia, who, for some unexplained reason, was always a good deal distressed at the sight of the blood-stain, and very nearly cried the morning it was emerald-green.

The second appearance of the ghost was on Sunday night. Shortly after they had gone to bed they were suddenly alarmed by a fearful crash in the hall. Rushing downstairs, they found that a large suit of old armour had become detached from its stand, and had fallen on the stone floor, while, seated in a high-backed chair, was the Canterville ghost, rubbing his knees with an expression of acute agony on his face. The twins, having brought their pea-shooters with them, at once discharged two pellets on him, with that accuracy of aim which can only be attained by long and careful practice on a writing-master, while the United States Minister covered him with a revolver, and called upon him, in accordance with Californian etiquette, to hold up his hands! The ghost started up with a wild shriek of rage, and swept through them like a mist, extinguishing Washington Otis's candle as he passed, and so leaving them all in total darkness. On reaching the top of the staircase he recovered himself, and determined to give his celebrated peal of demoniac laughter. This he had on more than one occasion found extremely useful. It was said to have turned Lord Raker's wig grey in a single night, and had certainly made three of Lady Canterville's French governesses give warning before their month was up. He accordingly laughed his most horrible laugh, till the old vaulted roof rang and rang again, but hardly had the fearful echo died away when a door opened, and Mrs Otis came out in a light blue dressing-gown. 'I am afraid you are far from well,' she said, 'and have brought you a bottle of Dr Dobell's tincture. If it is indigestion, you will find it a most excellent remedy.' The ghost glared at her in fury, and began at once to make preparations for turning himself into a large black dog, an accomplishment for which he was justly renowned, and to which the family doctor always attributed the permanent idiocy of Lord Canterville's uncle, the Hon. Thomas Horton. The sound of approaching footsteps, however, made him hesitate in his fell purpose, so he contented himself with becoming faintly phosphorescent, and vanished with a deep churchyard groan, just as the twins had come up to him.

On reaching his room he entirely broke down, and became a prey to the most violent agitation. The vulgarity of the twins, and the gross materialism of Mrs Otis, were naturally extremely annoying, but what really distressed him most was, that he had been unable to wear the suit of mail. He had hoped that even modern Americans would be thrilled by the sight of a Spectre In Armour, if for no more sensible reason, at least out of respect for their national poet Longfellow, over whose graceful and attractive poetry he himself had whiled away many a weary hour when the Cantervilles were up in town. Besides, it was his own suit. He had worn it with great success at the Kenilworth tournament, and had been highly complimented on it by no less a person than the Virgin Queen herself. Yet when he had put it on, he had been completely overpowered by the weight of the huge breastplate and steel casque, and had fallen heavily on the stone pavement, barking both his knees severely, and bruising the knuckles of his right hand.

For some days after this he was extremely ill, and hardly stirred out of his room at all, except to keep the blood-stain in proper repair. However, by taking great care of himself, he recovered, and resolved to make a third attempt to frighten the United States Minister and his family. He selected Friday, the 17th of August, for his appearance, and spent most of that day in looking over his wardrobe, ultimately deciding in favour of a large slouched hat with a red feather, a winding-sheet frilled at the wrists and neck, and a rusty dagger. Towards evening a violent storm of rain came on, and the wind was so high that all the windows and doors in the old house shook and rattled. In fact, it was just such weather as he loved. His plan of action was this. He was to make his way quietly to Washington Otis's room, gibber at him from the foot of the bed, and stab himself three times in the throat to the sound of low music. He bore Washington a special grudge, being quite aware that it was he who was in the habit of removing the famous Canterville blood-stain, by means of Pinkerton's Paragon Detergent. Having reduced the reckless and foolhardy youth to a condition of abject terror, he was then to proceed to the room occupied by the United States Minister and his wife, and there to place a clammy hand on Mrs Otis's forehead, while he hissed into her trembling husband's ear the awful secrets of the charnel-house. With regard to little Virginia, he had not quite made up his mind. She had never insulted him in any way, and was pretty and gentle. A few hollow groans from the wardrobe, he thought, would be more than sufficient, or, if that failed to wake her, he might grabble at the counterpane with palsy-twitching fingers. As for the twins, he was quite determined to teach them a lesson. The first thing to be done was, of course, to sit upon their chests, so as to produce the stifling sensation of nightmare. Then, as their beds were quite close to each other, to stand between them in the form of a green, icy-cold corpse, till they became paralysed with fear, and finally, to throw off the winding-sheet, and crawl round the room, with white, bleached bones and one rolling eyeball, in the character of 'Dumb Daniel, or the Suicide's Skeleton', a role in which he had on more than one occasion produced a great effect, and which he considered quite equal to his famous part of 'Martin the Maniac, or the Masked Mystery'.

At half-past ten he heard the family going to bed. For some time he was disturbed by wild shrieks of laughter from the twins, who with the light-hearted gaiety of schoolboys, were evidently amusing themselves before they retired to rest, but at a quarter past eleven all was still, and, as midnight sounded, he sallied forth. The owl beat against the window panes, the raven croaked from the old yew-tree, and the wind wandered moaning round the house like a lost soul; but the Otis family slept unconscious of their doom, and high above the rain and storm he could hear the steady snoring of the Minister of the United States. He stepped stealthily out of the wainscoting, with an evil smile on his cruel, wrinkled mouth, and the moon hid her face in a cloud as he stole past the great oriel window, where his own arms and those of his murdered wife were blazoned in azure and gold. On and on he glided, like an evil shadow, the very darkness seeming to loathe him as he passed. Once he thought he heard something call, and stopped; but it was only the baying of a dog from the Red Farm, and he went on, muttering strange sixteenth-century curses, and ever and anon brandishing the rusty dagger in the midnight air. Finally he reached the corner of the passage that led to luckless Washington's room. For a moment he paused there, the wind blowing his long grey locks about his head, and twisting into grotesque and fantastic folds the nameless horror of the dead man's shroud. Then the clock struck the quarter, and he felt the time was come. He chuckled to himself, and turned the corner; but no sooner had he done so, than, with a piteous wail of terror, he fell back, and hid his blanched face in his long, bony hands. Right in front of him was standing a horrible spectre, motionless as a carven image, and monstrous as a madman's dream! Its head was bald and burnished; its face round, and fat, and white; and hideous laughter seemed to have writhed its features into an eternal grin. From the eyes streamed rays of scarlet light, the mouth was a wide well of fire, and a hideous garment, like to his own, swathed with its silent snows the Titan form. On its breast was a placard with strange writing in antique characters, some scroll of shame it seemed, some record of wild sins, some awful calendar of crime, and, with its right hand, it bore aloft a falchion of gleaming steel.

Never having seen a ghost before, he naturally was terribly frightened, and, after a second hasty glance at the awful phantom, he fled back to his room, tripping up in his long winding sheet as he sped down the corridor, and finally dropping the rusty dagger into the Minister's jackboots, where it was found in the morning by the butler. Once in the privacy of his own apartment, he flung himself down on a small pallet-bed, and hid his face under the clothes. After a time, however, the brave old Canterville spirit asserted itself, and he determined to go and speak to the other ghost as soon as it was daylight. Accordingly, just as the dawn was touching the hills with silver, he returned towards the spot where he had first laid eyes on the grisly phantom, feeling that, after all, two ghosts were better than one, and that, by the aid of his new friend, he might safely grapple with the twins. On reaching the spot, however, a terrible sight met his gaze. Something had evidently happened to the spectre, for the light had entirely faded from its hollow eyes, the gleaming falchion had fallen from its hand, and it was leaning up against the wall in a strained and uncomfortable attitude. He rushed forward and seized it in his arms, when, to his horror, the head slipped off and rolled on the floor, the body assumed a recumbent posture, and he found himself clasping a white dimity bedcurtain, with a sweeping-brush, a kitchen cleaver, and a hollow turnip lying at his feet! Unable to understand this curious transformation, he clutched the placard with feverish haste, and there, in the grey morning light, he read these fearful words:

YE OTIS GHOSTE.
Ye onlie True and Originale Spook.
Beware of Ye Imitationes.
All others are Counterfeite.

The whole thing flashed across him. He had been tricked, foiled, and outwitted! The old Canterville look came into his eyes; he ground his toothless gums together; and, raising his withered hands high above his head, swore, according to the picturesque phraseology of the antique school, that when Chanticleer had sounded twice his merry horn, deeds of blood would be wrought, and Murder walk abroad with silent feet.

Hardly had he finished this awful oath when, from the red-tiled roof of a distant homestead, a cock crew. He laughed a long, low, bitter laugh, and waited. Hour after hour he waited, but the cock, for some strange reason, did not crow again. Finally, at half-past seven, the arrival of the housemaids made him give up his fearful vigil, and he stalked back to his room, thinking of his vain oath and baffled purpose. There he consulted several books of ancient chivalry, of which he was exceedingly fond, and found that, on every occasion on which this oath had been used, Chanticleer had always crowed a second time. 'Perdition seize the naughty fowl,' he muttered, 'I have seen the day when, with my stout spear, I would have run him through the gorge, and made him crow for me an 'twere in death!' He then retired to a comfortable lead coffin, and stayed there till evening.

IV

The next day the ghost was very weak and tired. The terrible excitement of the last four weeks was beginning to have its effect. His nerves were completely shattered, and he started at the slightest noise. For five days he kept his room, and at last made up his mind to give up the point of the blood-stain on the library floor. If the Otis family did not want it, they clearly did not deserve it. They were evidently people on a low, material plane of existence, and quite incapable of appreciating the symbolic value of sensuous phenomena. The question of phantasmic apparitions, and the development of astral bodies, was of course quite a different matter, and really not under his control. It was his solemn duty to appear in the corridor once a week, and to gibber from the large oriel window on the first and third Wednesdays in every month, and he did not see how he could honourably escape from his obligations. It is quite true that his life had been very evil, but, upon the other hand, he was most conscientious in all things connected with the supernatural. For the next three Saturdays, accordingly, he traversed the corridor as usual between midnight and three o'clock, taking every possible precaution against being either heard or seen. He removed his boots, trod as lightly as possible on the old worm-eaten boards, wore a large black velvet cloak, and was careful to use the Rising Sun Lubricator for oiling his chains. I am bound to acknowledge that it was with a good deal of difficulty that he brought himself to adopt this last mode of protection. However, one night, while the family were at dinner, he slipped into Mr Otis's bedroom and carried off the bottle. He felt a little humiliated at first, but afterwards was sensible enough to see that there was a great deal to be said for the invention, and, to a certain degree, it served his purpose. Still, in spite of everything, he was not left unmolested. Strings were continually being stretched across the corridor, over which he tripped in the dark, and on one occasion, while dressed for the part of 'Black Isaac, or the Huntsman of Hogley Woods', he met with a severe fall, through treading on a butter-slide, which the twins had constructed from the entrance of the Tapestry Chamber to the top of the oak staircase. This last insult so enraged him, that he resolved to make one final effort to assert his dignity and social position, and determined to visit the insolent young Etonians the next night in his celebrated character of 'Reckless Rupert, or the Headless Earl'.

He had not appeared in this disguise for more than seventy years: in fact, not since he had so frightened pretty Lady Barbara Modish by means of it, that she suddenly broke off her engagement with the present Lord Canterville's grandfather, and ran away to Gretna Green with handsome Jack Castletown, declaring that nothing in the world would induce her to marry into a family that allowed such a horrible phantom to walk up and down the terrace at twilight. Poor Jack was afterwards shot in a duel by Lord Canterville on Wandsworth Common, and Lady Barbara died of a broken heart at Tunbridge Wells before the year was out, so, in every way, it had been a great success. It was, however, an extremely difficult 'make-up', if I may use such a theatrical expression in connection with one of the greatest mysteries of the supernatural, or, to employ a more scientific term, the higher-natural world, and it took him fully three hours to make his preparations. At last everything was ready, and he was very pleased with his appearance. The big leather riding-boots that went with the dress were just a little too large for him, and he could only find one of the two horse-pistols, but, on the whole, he was quite satisfied, and at a quarter past one he glided out of the wainscoting and crept down the corridor. On reaching the room occupied by the twins, which I should mention was called the Blue Bed Chamber, on account of the colour of its hangings, he found the door just ajar. Wishing to make an effective entrance, he flung it wide open, when a heavy jug of water fell right down on him, wetting him to the skin, and just missing his left shoulder by a couple of inches. At the same moment he heard stifled shrieks of laughter proceeding from the four-post bed. The shock to his nervous system was so great that he fled back to his room as hard as he could go, and the next day he was laid up with a severe cold. The only thing that at all consoled him in the whole affair was the fact that he had not brought his head with him, for, had he done so, the consequences might have been very serious.

He now gave up all hope of ever frightening this rude American family, and contented himself, as a rule, with creeping about the passages in list slippers, with a thick red muffler round his throat for fear of draughts, and a small arquebuse, in case he should be attacked by the twins. The final blow he received occurred on the 19th of September. He had gone downstairs to the great entrance-hall, feeling sure that there, at any rate, he would be quite unmolested, and was amusing himself by making satirical remarks on the large Saroni photographs of the United States Minister and his wife, which had now taken the place of the Canterville family pictures. He was simply but neatly clad in a long shroud, spotted with churchyard mould, had tied up his jaw with a strip of yellow linen, and carried a small lantern and a sexton's spade. In fact, he was dressed for the character of 'Jonas the Graveless, or the Corpse-Snatcher of Chertsey Barn', one of his most remarkable impersonations, and one which the Cantervilles had every reason to remember, as it was the real origin of their quarrel with their neighbour, Lord Rufford. It was about a quarter past two o'clock in the morning, and, as far as he could ascertain, no one was stirring. As he was strolling towards the library, however, to see if there were any traces left of the blood-stain, suddenly there leaped out on him from a dark corner two figures, who waved their arms wildly above their heads, and shrieked out 'BOO!' in his ear.

Seized with a panic, which, under the circumstances, was only natural, he rushed for the staircase, but found Washington Otis waiting for him there with the big garden-syringe; and being thus hemmed in by his enemies on every side, and driven almost to bay, he vanished into the great iron stove, which, fortunately for him, was not lit, and had to make his way home through the flues and chimneys, arriving at his own room in a terrible state of dirt, disorder, and despair.

After this he was not seen again on any nocturnal expedition. The twins lay in wait for him on several occasions, and strewed the passages with nutshells every night to the great annoyance of their parents and the servants, but it was of no avail. It was quite evident that his feelings were so wounded that he would not appear. Mr Otis consequently resumed his great work on the history of the Democratic Party, on which he had been engaged for some years; Mrs Otis organised a wonderful clam-bake, which amazed the whole county; the boys took to lacrosse, euchre, poker, and other American national games; and Virginia rode about the lanes on her pony, accompanied by the young Duke of Cheshire, who had come to spend the last week of his holidays at Canterville Chase. It was generally assumed that the ghost had gone away, and, in fact, Mr Otis wrote a letter to that effect to Lord Canterville, who, in reply, expressed his great pleasure at the news, and sent his best congratulations to the Minister's worthy wife.

The Otises, however, were deceived, for the ghost was still in the house, and though now almost an invalid, was by no means ready to let matters rest, particularly as he heard that among the guests was the young Duke of Cheshire, whose grand-uncle, Lord Francis Stilton, had once bet a hundred guineas with Colonel Carbury that he would play dice with the Canterville ghost, and was found next morning lying on the floor of the card-room in such a helpless paralytic state, that though he lived on to a great age, he was never able to say anything again but 'Double Sixes'. The story was well known at the time, though, of course, out of respect to the feelings of the two noble families, every attempt was made to hush it up; and a full account of all the circumstances connected with it will be found in the third volume of Lord Tattle's *Recollections of the Prince Regent and his Friends*. The ghost, then, was naturally very anxious to show that he had not lost his influence over the Stiltons, with whom, indeed, he was distantly connected, his own first cousin having been married *en secondes noces* to the Sieur de Bulkeley, from whom, as everyone knows, the Dukes of Cheshire are lineally descended. Accordingly, he made arrangements for appearing to Virginia's little lover in his celebrated impersonation of 'The Vampire Monk, or the Bloodless

Benedictine', a performance so horrible that when old Lady Startup saw it, which she did on one fatal New Year's Eve, in the year 1764, she went off into the most piercing shrieks, which culminated in violent apoplexy, and died in three days, after disinheriting the Cantervilles, who were her nearest relations, and leaving all her money to her London apothecary. At the last moment, however, his terror of the twins prevented his leaving his room, and the little Duke slept in peace under the great feathered canopy in the Royal Bedchamber, and dreamed of Virginia.

V

A few days after this, Virginia and her curly-haired cavalier went out riding on Brockley meadows, where she tore her habit so badly in getting through a hedge, that, on their return home, she made up her mind to go up by the back staircase so as not to be seen. As she was running past the Tapestry Chamber, the door of which happened to be open, she fancied she saw someone inside, and thinking it was her mother's maid, who sometimes used to bring her work there, looked in to ask her to mend her habit. To her immense surprise, however, it was the Canterville Ghost himself! He was sitting by the window, watching the ruined gold of the yellowing trees fly through the air, and the red leaves dancing madly down the long avenue. His head was leaning on his hand, and his whole attitude was one of extreme depression. Indeed, so forlorn, and so much out of repair did he look, that little Virginia, whose first idea had been to run away and lock herself in her room, was filled with pity, and determined to try and comfort him. So light was her footfall, and so deep his melancholy, that he was not aware of her presence till she spoke to him.

'I am so sorry for you,' she said, 'but my brothers are going back to Eton tomorrow, and then, if you behave yourself, no one will annoy you.'

'It is absurd asking me to behave myself,' he answered, looking round in astonishment at the pretty little girl who had ventured to address him, 'quite absurd. I must rattle my chains, and groan through keyholes, and walk about at night, if that is what you mean. It is my only reason for existing.'

'It is no reason at all for existing, and you know you have been very wicked. Mrs Umney told us, the first day we arrived here, that you had killed your wife.'

'Well, I quite admit it,' said the Ghost petulantly, 'but it was a purely family matter, and concerned no one else.'

'It is very wrong to kill anyone,' said Virginia, who at times had a sweet Puritan gravity, caught from some old New England ancestor.

'Oh, I hate the cheap severity of abstract ethics! My wife was very plain, never had my ruffs properly starched, and knew nothing about cookery. Why, there was a buck I had shot in Hogley Woods, a magnificent pricket, and do you know how she had it sent up to table? However, it is no matter now, for it is all over, and I don't think it was very nice of her brothers to starve me to death, though I did kill her.'

'Starve you to death? Oh, Mr Ghost, I mean Sir Simon, are you hungry? I have a sandwich in my case. Would you like it?'

'No, thank you, I never eat anything now; but it is very kind of you, all the same, and you are much nicer than the rest of your horrid, rude, vulgar, dishonest family.'

'Stop!' cried Virginia stamping her foot, 'it is you who are rude, and horrid, and vulgar, and as for dishonesty, you know you stole the paints out of my box to try and furbish up that ridiculous blood-stain in the library. First you took all my reds, including the vermilion, and I couldn't do any more sunsets, then you took the emerald-green and the chrome-yellow, and finally I had nothing left but indigo and Chinese white, and could only do moonlight scenes, which are always depressing to look at, and not at all easy to paint. I never told on you, though I was very much annoyed, and it was most ridiculous, the whole thing; for who ever heard of emerald-green blood?'

'Well, really,' said the Ghost, rather meekly, 'what was I to do? It is a very difficult thing to get real blood nowadays, and, as your brother began it all with his Paragon Detergent, I certainly saw no reason why I should not have your paints. As for colour, that is always a matter of taste: the Cantervilles have blue blood, for instance, the very bluest in England; but I know you Americans don't care for things of this kind.'

'You know nothing about it, and the best thing you can do is to emigrate and improve your mind. My father will be only too happy to give you a free passage, and though there is a heavy duty on spirits of every kind, there will be no difficulty about the Custom House, as the officers are all Democrats. Once in New York, you are sure to be a great success. I know lots of people there who would give a hundred thousand dollars to have a grandfather, and much more than that to have a family ghost.'

'I don't think I should like America.'

'I suppose because we have no ruins and no curiosities,' said Virginia satirically.

'No ruins! No curiosities!' answered the Ghost; 'You have your navy and your manners.'

'Good evening; I will go and ask papa to get the twins an extra week's holiday.'

'Please don't go, Miss Virginia,' he cried; 'I am so lonely and so unhappy, and I really don't know what to do. I want to go to sleep and I cannot.'

'That's quite absurd! You have merely to go to bed and blow out the candle. It is very difficult sometimes to keep awake, especially at church, but there is no difficulty at all about sleeping. Why, even babies know how to do that, and they are not very clever.'

'I have not slept for three hundred years,' he said sadly, and Virginia's beautiful blue eyes opened in wonder; 'for three hundred years I have not slept, and I am so tired.'

Virginia grew quite grave, and her little lips trembled like rose-leaves. She came towards him, and kneeling down at his side, looked up into his old withered face.

'Poor, poor Ghost,' she murmured; 'have you no place where you can sleep?'

'Far away beyond the pinewoods,' he answered, in a low dreamy voice, 'there is a little garden. There the grass grows long and deep, there are the great white stars of the hemlock flower, there the nightingale sings all night long. All night long he sings, and the cold, crystal moon looks down, and the yew-tree spreads out its giant arms over the sleepers.'

Virginia's eyes grew dim with tears, and she hid her face in her hands.

'You mean the Garden of Death,' she whispered.

'Yes, Death. Death must be so beautiful. To lie in the soft brown earth, with the grasses waving above one's head, and listen to silence. To have no yesterday, and no tomorrow. To forget time, to forgive life, to be at peace. You can help me. You can open for me the portals of Death's house, for Love is always with you, and Love is stronger than Death is.'

Virginia trembled, a cold shudder ran through her, and for a few moments there was silence. She felt as if she was in a terrible dream.

Then the Ghost spoke again, and his voice sounded like a sighing of the wind.

'Have you ever read the old prophecy on the library window?'

'Oh, often,' cried the little girl, looking up; 'I know it quite well. It is painted in curious black letters, and is difficult to read. There are only six lines:

> *When a golden girl can win*
> *Prayer from out the lips of sin,*
> *When the barren almond bears,*
> *And a little child gives away its tears,*
> *Then shall all the house be still*
> *And peace come to Canterville.*

But I don't know what they mean.'

'They mean,' he said sadly, 'that you must weep with me for my sins, because I have no tears, and pray with me for my soul, because I have no faith, and then, if you have always been sweet, and good, and gentle, the Angel of Death will have mercy on me. You will see fearful shapes in darkness and wicked voices will whisper in your ear, but they will not harm you, for against the purity of a little child the powers of Hell cannot prevail.'

Virginia made no answer, and the Ghost wrung his hands in wild despair as he looked down at her bowed golden head. Suddenly she stood up, very pale, and with a strange light in her eyes. 'I am not afraid,' she said, firmly, 'and I will ask the Angel to have mercy on you.'

He rose from his seat with a faint cry of joy, and taking her hand bent over it with old-fashioned grace and kissed it. His fingers were as cold as ice, and his lips burned like fire, but Virginia did not falter, as he led her across the dusky room. On the faded green tapestry were broidered little huntsmen. They blew their tasselled horns and with their tiny hands waved to her to go back. 'Go back! Little Virginia,' they cried, 'go back!' but the Ghost clutched her hand more tightly, and she shut her eyes against them. Horrible animals with lizard tails, and goggle eyes, blinked at her from the carven chimney-piece, and murmured, 'Beware! Little Virginia, beware! We may never see you again,' but the Ghost glided on more swiftly, and Virginia did not listen. When they reached the end of the room he stopped, and muttered some words she could not understand. She opened her eyes, and saw the wall slowly fading away like a mist, and a great black cavern in front of her. A bitter cold wind swept round them, and she felt something pulling at her dress. 'Quick, quick,' cried the Ghost, 'or it will be too late,' and, in a moment, the wainscoting had closed behind them, and the Tapestry Chamber was empty.

VI

About ten minutes later, the bell rang for tea, and, as Virginia did not come down, Mrs Otis sent up one of the footmen to tell her. After a little time he returned and said that he could not find Miss Virginia anywhere. As she was in the habit of going out to the garden every evening to get flowers for the dinner-table, Mrs Otis was not at all alarmed at first, but when six o'clock struck, and Virginia did not appear, she became really agitated, and sent the boys out to look for her, while she herself and Mr Otis searched every room in the house. At half-past six the boys came back and said that they could find no trace of their sister anywhere. They were all now in the greatest state of excitement, and did not know what to do, when Mr Otis suddenly remembered that, some few days before, he had given a band of gypsies permission to camp in the park. He accordingly at once set off for Blackfell Hollow, where he knew they were, accompanied by his eldest son and two of the farm-servants. The little Duke of Cheshire, who was perfectly frantic with anxiety, begged hard to be allowed to go too, but Mr Otis would not allow him, as he was afraid there might be a scuffle. On arriving at the spot, however, he found that the gypsies had gone, and it was evident that their departure had been rather sudden, as the fire was still burning, and some plates were lying on the grass. Having sent off Washington and the two men to scour the district, he ran home, and despatched telegrams to all the police inspectors in the county, telling them to look out for a little girl who had been kidnapped by tramps or gypsies. He then ordered his horse to be brought round, and, after insisting on his wife and the three boys sitting down to dinner, rode off down the Ascot road with a groom. He had hardly, however, gone a couple of miles, when he heard somebody galloping after him, and, looking round, saw the little Duke coming up on his pony, with his face very flushed and no hat. 'I'm awfully sorry, Mr Otis,' gasped out the boy, 'but I can't eat any dinner as long as Virginia is lost. Please don't be angry with me; if you had let us be engaged last year, there would never have been all this trouble. You won't send me back, will you? I can't go! I won't go!'

The Minister could not help smiling at the handsome young scapegrace, and was a good deal touched at his devotion to Virginia, so leaning down from his horse, he patted him kindly on the shoulders, and said, 'Well, Cecil, if you won't go back I suppose you must come with me, but I must get you a hat at Ascot.'

'Oh, bother my hat! I want Virginia!' cried the little Duke, laughing, and they galloped on to the railway station. There Mr Otis inquired of the station-master if anyone answering to the description of Virginia had been seen on the platform, but could get no news of her. The station-master, however, wired up and down the line, and assured him that a strict watch would be kept for her, and, after having bought a hat for the little Duke from a linen-draper, who was just putting up his shutters, Mr Otis rode off to Bexley, a village about four miles away, which he was told was a well-known haunt of the gypsies, as there was a large common next to it. Here they roused up the rural policeman, but could get no information from him, and, after riding all over the common, they turned their horses' heads homewards, and reached the Chase about eleven o'clock, dead-tired and almost heart-broken. They found Washington and the twins waiting for them at the gate-house with lanterns, as the avenue was very dark. Not the slightest trace of Virginia had been discovered. The gypsies had been caught on Brockley meadows, but she was not with them, and they had explained their sudden departure by saying that they had mistaken the date of Chorton Fair, and had gone off in a hurry for fear they might be late. Indeed, they had been quite distressed at hearing of Virginia's disappearance, as they were very grateful to Mr Otis for having allowed them to camp in his park, and four of their number had stayed behind to help in the search. The carp-pond had been dragged, and the whole Chase thoroughly gone over, but without any result. It was evident that, for that night at any rate, Virginia was lost to them; and it was in a state of the deepest depression that Mr Otis and the boys walked up to the house, the groom following behind with the two horses and the pony. In the hall they found a group of frightened servants, and lying on a sofa in the library was poor Mrs Otis, almost out of her mind with terror and anxiety, and having her forehead bathed with eau-de-cologne by the old housekeeper. Mr Otis at once insisted on her having something to eat, and ordered up supper for the whole party. It was a melancholy meal, as hardly anyone spoke, and even the twins were awestruck and subdued, as they were very fond of their sister. When they had finished, Mr Otis, in spite of the entreaties of the little Duke, ordered them all to bed, saying that nothing more could be done that night, and that he would telegraph in the morning to Scotland Yard for some detectives to be sent down immediately. Just as they were passing out of the dining-room, midnight began to boom from the clock tower, and when the last stroke sounded they heard a crash and a sudden shrill cry; a dreadful peal of thunder shook the house, a strain of unearthly music floated through the air, a panel at the top of the staircase flew back with a loud noise, and out on the landing, looking very pale and white, with a little casket in her hand, stepped Virginia. In a moment they had all rushed up to her. Mrs Otis clasped her passionately in her arms, the Duke smothered her with violent kisses, and the twins executed a wild war-dance round the group.

'Good heavens! child, where have you been?' said Mr Otis, rather angrily, thinking that she had been playing some foolish trick on them. 'Cecil and I have been riding all over the country looking for you, and your mother has been frightened to death. You must never play these practical jokes any more.'

'Except on the Ghost! Except on the Ghost!' shrieked the twins, as they capered about.

'My own darling, thank God you are found; you must never leave my side again,' murmured Mrs Otis, as she kissed the trembling child, and smoothed the tangled gold of her hair.

'Papa,' said Virginia quietly, 'I have been with the Ghost. He is dead, and you must come and see him. He had been very wicked, but he was really sorry for all that he had done, and he gave me this box of beautiful jewels before he died.'

The whole family gazed at her in mute amazement, but she was quite grave and serious; and, turning round, she led them through the opening in the wainscoting down a narrow secret corridor, Washington following with a lighted candle, which he had caught up from the table. Finally, they came to a great oak door, studded with rusty nails. When Virginia touched it, it swung back on its heavy hinges, and they found themselves in a little low room, with a vaulted ceiling, and one tiny grated window. Imbedded in the wall was a huge iron ring, and chained to it was a gaunt skeleton, that was stretched out at full length on the stone floor, and seemed to be trying to grasp with its long fleshless fingers an old-fashioned trencher and ewer, that were placed just out of its reach. The jug had evidently been once filled with water, as it was covered inside with green mould. There was nothing on the trencher but a pile of dust. Virginia knelt down beside the skeleton, and, folding her little hands together, began to pray silently, while the rest of the party looked on in wonder at the terrible tragedy whose secret was now disclosed to them.

'Hallo!' suddenly exclaimed one of the twins, who had been looking out of the window to try and discover in what wing of the house the room was situated. 'Hallo! the old withered almond-tree has blossomed. I can see the flowers quite plainly in the moonlight.'

'God has forgiven him,' said Virginia gravely, as she rose to her feet, and a beautiful light seemed to illumine her face.

'What an angel you are!' cried the young Duke, and he put his arm round her neck, and kissed her.

VII

Four days after these curious incidents a funeral started from Canterville Chase at about eleven o'clock at night. The hearse was drawn by eight black horses, each of which carried on its head a great tuft of nodding ostrich-plumes, and the leaden coffin was covered by a rich purple pall, on which was embroidered in gold the Canterville coat-of-arms. By the side of the hearse and the coaches walked the servants with lighted torches, and the whole procession was wonderfully impressive. Lord Canterville was the chief mourner, having come up specially from Wales to attend the funeral, and sat in the first carriage along with little Virginia. Then came the United States Minister and his wife, then Washington and the three boys, and in the last carriage was Mrs Umney. It was generally felt that, as she had been frightened by the ghost for more than fifty years of her life, she had a right to see the last of him. A deep grave had been dug in the corner of the churchyard, just under the old yew-tree, and the service was read in the most impressive manner by the Rev. Augustus Dampier. When the ceremony was over, the servants, according to an old custom observed in the Canterville family, extinguished their torches, and, as the coffin was being lowered into the grave, Virginia stepped forward, and laid on it a large cross made of white and pink almond-blossoms. As she did so, the moon came out from behind a cloud, and flooded with its silent silver the little churchyard, and from a distant copse a nightingale began to sing. She thought of the ghost's description of the Garden of Death, her eyes became dim with tears, and she hardly spoke a word during the drive home.

The next morning, before Lord Canterville went up to town, Mr Otis had an interview with him on the subject of the jewels the ghost had given to Virginia. They were perfectly magnificent, especially a certain ruby necklace with old Venetian setting, which was really a superb specimen of sixteenth-century work, and their value was so great that Mr Otis felt considerable scruples about allowing his daughter to accept them.

'My lord,' he said, 'I know that in this country mortmain is held to apply to trinkets as well as to land, and it is quite clear to me that these jewels are, or should be, heirlooms in your family. I must beg you, accordingly, to take them to London with you, and to regard them simply as a portion of your property which has been restored to you under certain strange conditions. As for my daughter, she is merely a child, and has as yet, I am glad to say, but little interest in such appurtenances of idle luxury. I am also informed by Mrs Otis, who, I may say, is no mean authority upon Art—having had the privilege of spending several winters in Boston when she was a girl—that these gems are of great monetary worth, and if offered for sale would fetch a tall price. Under these circumstances, Lord Canterville, I feel sure that you will recognise how impossible it would be for me to allow them to remain in the possession of any member of my family; and, indeed, all such vain gauds and toys, however suitable or necessary to the dignity of the British aristocracy, would be completely out of place among those who have been brought up on the severe, and I believe immortal, principles of Republican simplicity. Perhaps I should mention that Virginia is very anxious that you should allow her to retain the box, as a memento of your unfortunate but misguided ancestor. As it is extremely old, and consequently a good deal out of repair, you may perhaps think fit to comply with her request. For my own part, I confess I am a good deal surprised to find a child of mine expressing sympathy with mediaevalism in any form, and can only account for it by the fact that Virginia was born in one of your London suburbs shortly after Mrs Otis had returned from a trip to Athens.'

Lord Canterville listened very gravely to the worthy Minister's speech, pulling his grey moustache now and then to hide an involuntary smile, and when Mr Otis had ended, he shook him cordially by the hands, and said, 'My dear sir, your charming little daughter rendered my unlucky ancestor, Sir Simon, a very important service, and I and my family are much indebted to her for her marvellous courage and pluck. The jewels are clearly hers, and, egad, I believe that if I were heartless enough to take them from her, the wicked old fellow would be out of his grave in a fortnight, leading me the devil of a life. As for their being heirlooms, nothing is an heirloom that is not so mentioned in a will or legal document, and the existence of these jewels has been quite unknown. I assure you I have no more claim on them than your butler, and when Miss Virginia grows up I daresay she will be pleased to have pretty things to wear. Besides, you forget, Mr Otis, that you took the furniture and the ghost at a valuation, and anything that belonged to the ghost passed at once into your possession, as, whatever activity Sir Simon may have shown in the corridor at night, in point of law he was really dead, and you acquired his property by purchase.'

Mr Otis was a good deal distressed at Lord Canterville's refusal, and begged him to reconsider his decision, but the good-natured peer was quite firm, and finally induced the Minister to allow his daughter to retain the present the ghost had given her, and when, in the spring of 1890, the young Duchess of Cheshire was presented at the Queen's first drawing-room on the occasion of her marriage, her jewels were the universal theme of admiration. For Virginia received the coronet, which is the reward of all good little American girls, and was married to her boy-lover as soon as he came of age. They were both so charming, and they loved each other so much, that everyone was delighted at the match, except the old Marchioness of Dumbleton, who had tried to catch the Duke for one of her seven unmarried daughters, and had given no less than three expensive dinner-parties for that purpose, and, strange to say, Mr Otis himself. Mr Otis was extremely fond of the young Duke personally, but, theoretically, he objected to titles, and, to use his own words, 'was not without apprehension lest amid the enervating influences of a pleasure-loving aristocracy, the true principles of Republican simplicity should be forgotten.' His objections, however, were completely overruled, and I believe that when he walked up the aisle of St George's, Hanover Square, with his daughter leaning on his arm, there was not a prouder man in the whole length and breadth of England.

The Duke and Duchess, after the honeymoon was over, went down to Canterville Chase, and on the day after their arrival they walked over in the afternoon to the lonely churchyard by the pine-woods. There had been a great deal of difficulty at first about the inscription on Sir Simon's tombstone, but finally it had been decided to engrave on it simply the initials of the old gentleman's name, and the verse from the library window. The Duchess had brought with her some lovely roses, which she strewed upon the grave, and after they had stood by it for some time they strolled into the ruined chancel of the old abbey. There the Duchess sat down on a fallen pillar, while her husband lay at her feet smoking a cigarette and looking up at her beautiful eyes. Suddenly he threw his cigarette away, took hold of her hand, and said to her, 'Virginia, a wife should have no secrets from her husband.'

'Dear Cecil! I have no secrets from you.'

'Yes, you have,' he answered, smiling, 'you have never told me what happened to you when you were locked up with the ghost.'

'I have never told anyone, Cecil,' said Virginia gravely.

'I know that, but you might tell me.'

'Please don't ask me, Cecil, I cannot tell you. Poor Sir Simon! I owe him a great deal. Yes, don't laugh, Cecil, I really do. He made me see what Life is, and what Death signifies, and why Love is stronger than both.'

The Duke rose and kissed his wife lovingly.

'You can have your secret as long as I have your heart,' he murmured.

'You have always had that, Cecil.'

'And you will tell our children some day, won't you?'

Virginia blushed.

LIQUID ASSETS

Oliver St John Gogarty

Oliver St John Gogarty (1878–1957), another Dublin-born wit, is widely remembered for his bons mots and was immortalised by his friend James Joyce in Ulysses *as Buck Milligan. His versatile sense of humour suffuses both his early poetry and stage plays, and his later novels, autobiographical tales and essays (in particular his discussion on wit and humour, 'Start From Somewhere Else'). He was a member of the literary circle that included W. B. Yeats, George Moore and Joyce, and his witticisms are reported to have been even more spontaneous in person. He is credited with having originated the famous comment about a Dublin river bank which was a favourite spot with lovers. 'The trees along the Dodder,' he remarked, 'are more sinned against than sinning.' Gogarty also took a serious interest in politics and was a senator in Dublin from 1922 to 1936. City life was, in fact, the setting for much of his best humorous writing—as is the case with 'Liquid Assets' (1950), a hilarious tale about a bank manager who is actually delighted to be giving out money . . .*

*   *   *

The branch office of the Munster and Leinster Bank was empty, not because of an economic war with England (that is another story) but because it was the lunch hour. I had come to see the manager; but he was at lunch. He would be back 'any minute now'. Delays were becoming a treat to me. Had I not already waited two months and seven days for a seat on a Transatlantic plane that was to take off 'any minute now'? That minute was approaching: it might be tomorrow. You never could tell. To judge by the advertisements, it was quicker to go to New York than to

Cork, from actual experience of the train. So I lolled about the branch office, which was decorated by a calendar and a clock. The sound of an adding machine being tuned somewhere off carried the life of the bank over the lunch hour. Behind some vertical brass bars I thought I heard a sound of breathing. I crept close, taking the utmost precaution not to alarm whomever it might be. I stood still, hardly daring to respire. I glanced at the clock. Its hands were together. It was ten past two. I moved so that I could see diagonally through the bars. A blond young man was leaning over a black box of japanned metal. Fascinated, I stared transfixed. My gaze must have aroused him. Without lifting his eyes from the contents of the box, he murmured, 'Any minute now.'

A sound behind me broke the tension. A hand must have moved from outside, for one half of the swing door was thrust open and a man entered with rapid strides and two raincoats. He was spare, with square shoulders and a broad, red face. He took one look round the bank. The adding machine opened up; its staccato speech filled the air with sound. The newcomer turned and eyed me. I felt that the youth behind the bars had suddenly risen to his feet. He was coming closer as the man with the raincoats approached. I was between the two, with the adding machine on my right under the screened window. Abruptly the man with the overcoats removed his hat, changed it to his left hand and, holding his right hand out in greeting, stood and said with a slow smile:

'The poetry of motion!'

It was McWilliam Lynch, the sprinter. He referred to our days on the track when I used to compete in cycling events and he did the hundred yards dash.

A voice behind me whispered in awestruck tones:

'That's the manager!'

The manager and I shook hands. He seized me by the elbow and, rushing me across the floor, led the way to an inner room which a quick glance at the flying door marked 'Manager' told me was his office. The door swung to behind us. The manager hung up his hat. He pointed to a chair with polished arms.

'It must be fifty years ago,' he said.

I was about to assent when he held up his hand in a gesture that indicated silence and conveyed a warning at the same time. He tiptoed to a large safe or strong room embedded in the wall, swung the combination and produced two glasses and a bottle of

Tullamore Dew. He spun the bottle in his hand, making a movie of the label.

'Twenty years old,' he said. 'I wish I was twenty years old again. I would be doing better than around twelve for the hundred.'

'Metres,' I inquired.

'Not likely. The hundred yards dash. I did that the other day in the Veterans' race.'

'By heavens, you're not a day older. What age are you, anyway?'

He said nothing, but raised his eyes to a clock over my head on the wall behind me. He filled himself another shot. I thought it an opportune moment to ask his help.

'What can I do for you?' he asked.

'I have run out of cash; but I have a cheque-book . . .'

'Fill it in! Fill it in! Any amount. You see that clock? I shall be retired in ten minutes. Fifty years of service! Fill it in!'

'I have run out only of English money. This is a dollar cheque-book.'

'And what's wrong with that? Fill it in, and hurry up.'

'Well, of all the banks I have ever come across, this one beats Banagher.'

He pressed a bell. The blond young man appeared.

'How do you want it?' the manager asked me. 'Small denominations? Cash that.'

The blond youth went out gazing at the cheque.

While he was gone we resumed our conversation. It was the manager's last day, last hour, in the Bank. He had bought a house on the river. He had all he wanted. He would make way for younger blood: give the boys a chance.

'When I came in and found the bank empty it put me in mind of the famous bank in the Midlands during the so-called economic war.'

'I know the bank. What did you hear?'

'I heard that there was no report from that branch for three weeks. None of the letters from Headquarters was answered, so they sent an Inspector down. He arrived and, right enough, the bank was empty. He had not expected to see any customers; but he did expect to see the staff. There was no sign of any of them anywhere. He rapped on a door. No answer. He tried a second door. It was locked. He went behind the rails and tried another door. Locked. Behind the third door he thought he heard voices. He listened. After a while he heard someone say:

' "Have a heart? I pass."

'Indignantly he tried the handle, but the door was locked. He hammered on the panel.

' "Who's there?" a voice asked.

' "The Inspector."

' "Well, the gas meter's in the cellar."

' "But—but I'm the bank Inspector."

'Silence. Then a voice: "The books are on the shelf. Inspect away."

'He was speechless. At last his eye fell on the fire alarm. To teach the young pups a lesson, he pulled it. That would get them out. For a minute nothing happened. He looked out of the window, and in front of his eyes a pot-boy from the hotel across the street came hurrying with four pints of Guinness on a tray.'

McWilliam Lynch slapped his thigh. His eyes sparkled.

'That bank had liquid assets all right.'

The blond clerk came in with the change. When he had gone, McWilliam Lynch put the bottle and the glasses in the pockets of his raincoat.

'This bank has liquid assets *go leor* without this!' he remarked as we steered for the door.

A DAY ON THE BOG

Lord Dunsany

Amidst a nation of characters, Edward John Moreton Drax Plunkett, the 18th Baron Dunsany (1878–1957), certainly features prominently. He was a larger-than-life figure who prided himself on the title, 'The Worst Dressed Man in Ireland', wrote all of his fiction and essays with a quill pen, and in order to pursue his great obsession with cricket laid out his own pitch in the grounds of his ancestral home, a castle in County Meath. Dunsany was also a soldier, big game hunter, chess champion of Ireland, bon vivant and natural wit, as well as a master of humorous fiction. His great comedy creation was Jorkens, a plausible, Munchausen-type character who delighted in telling the tallest of tall stories to the members of the Billiards Club in London, usually in return for a free drink—as you might guess from the titles of two of the most popular collections of these stories: Jorkens Has a Large Whiskey *(1940) and* Jorkens Borrows Another Whiskey *(1954).*

Lord Dunsany was also a regular contributor to Punch *magazine with stories that revealed the wit of his fellow countrymen. 'A Day on the Bog', which appeared in the magazine in December 1947, is a typical example of his wonderfully humorous style.*

* * *

There was gentlemen in Ireland in the old days, said Mickey Tuohey, such as you very seldom see now. Severals of them there were, and all of them great gentlemen. And I'll tell you what they used to do: when they'd go out shooting grouse on the bog they'd take silver flasks with them that held as much as a quart of whiskey. A quart of whiskey in one flask. Sure, you never see anything like that nowadays. The old stock are nearly all gone, more's the pity.

I mind the time when Mr Fitzcharles (the light of Heaven to him, for he is dead long ago) went out on the red bog one day, and he takes me with him to mind the dog. And the bog went right to the horizon and over the other side of it. And we walked all day, and when it got near to one o'clock, and we had a fine bag of snipe and a few grouse, he says to me, 'What about a bit of lunch, Tuohey?'

And I says to him, 'Sir, it was the very thing I was thinking myself.'

And we sits down on the heather and eats a few sandwiches, and that sort of stuff, that I had in the game-bag. And then he says to me, 'Did you happen to remember to bring my flask, Tuohey?'

Remember it! Sure I remember it to this day.

And I says, 'I did, sir.'

And I brings out the great silver flask that used to hold a quart.

'Then shall we have a little whiskey,' he says, 'to keep our throats from getting dry?'

And I had two tumblers in the game-bag, made of horn, the way that they wouldn't break. And our throats never got dry that morning. It was the best of old whiskey that Mr Fitzcharles used to have in those days, mild as milk, and did you no more harm nor milk, and a great deal more good. And Mr Fitzcharles gave me half of it for myself, and he drinks his half straight off, without taking a breath. That's the kind of grand old gentleman that he was. We sat there in the sun resting and feeling the good that the whiskey was doing us, and the red bog round us as far as the eye could see. And a leprechaun comes over the bog and he runs straight up to us, the only time in my life I ever seen a leprechaun close, though I'd often heard tell of them; a little brown lad not half the height of a man. And he stands there on a patch of bright-red moss and looks at us. And he says to us, 'You are the two grandest men ever I seen.'

And Mr Fitzcharles says to him, 'Is there anything I can do for you?'

And the leprechaun says, 'Sure, there is. Would your honour give me your soul, that I may become a mortal and go about on the dry land, and see towns and wear boots and a fine glossy hat?'

And I was terrified for the sake of Mr Fitzcharles, for he was the most generous-hearted man in the world, one of the great gentlemen, and he would never refuse anyone anything; and I was afraid that he would give up his soul and be damned. But he thinks for a moment before he answers, as a man should. And then he says to the leprechaun, 'I'm afraid I'm only a Protestant.'

'Ah, well,' says the leprechaun, 'what matter? But never mind now. Sure, I'll ask you for it some other time.'

And then I was more frightened than ever, for I was afraid he would ask me for mine. And I couldn't refuse him, if he did, in the presence of Mr Fitzcharles, on account of him being one of the most generous-hearted men in the world, as I'm just after telling you. I couldn't refuse anybody anything when I was out with him, whatever I might do at another time. So I sat there trying to look the other way. But the leprechaun hops round in front of the way I was looking, quicker nor I could turn my eyes away from him. And he says to me, 'Will you lend me your soul?'

Well, you know the way it is when anyone asks you to lend him something: it is harder to refuse nor when he asks you to give it. But the result is the same either way. And I thought for a moment or two, the same as Mr Fitzcharles had done; and then I says to him, 'I'll lend you my soul for so long as you like, if you'll give me your crock of gold.'

And, mind you, it isn't that I valued the crock of gold more nor my soul. Sure, it would be a great mistake to do that. But I knew that he'd never part with his crock. And, sure, he wouldn't. And what he says is, 'Sure, I wouldn't pay you all that for it.'

'You and your crock of gold,' I says to him. 'Sure, you've not enough in it to buy a pig, let alone a good Catholic soul.'

'Begob,' he says to me, 'I've enough in it to buy a herd of cattle, and your soul as well, and another one like it thrown in for luck. And you'll not find my crock, for I'm going to run away in the opposite direction from where it is, so as not to lead you to it.'

Well, we hunted most of the evening for that crock in the opposite direction from the one in which he had run. But after a bit I says to Mr Fitzcharles, 'Maybe he's not so simple as he appeared. What if the little devil has been telling a lie to us?'

'And so he might,' says Mrs Fitzcharles. 'I would never trust a leprechaun.'

And that was perfectly right, for there was nothing Mr Fitzcharles didn't know.

So we hunted in the other direction, the one in which he *had* run. But very soon the good that the whiskey had done us seemed to begin to run out of us, and there was no more left in the flask to keep us going; and it was like looking for a snipe, without a dog, that has fallen a long way off. Sure, the red bog has a great knack of hiding things. So we give it up. The cheek of him, saying that he wouldn't make the exchange! Ah, but those were the good days. You can't get enough for two shillings to moisten your lips now.

THE MARTYR'S CROWN

Flann O'Brien

Few lovers of humour require an introduction to the work of Flann O'Brien (1911–1966), yet the fact remains that the greatest work by this master of wordplay, An Beal Bocht *(The Poor Mouth), was written in Gaelic in 1941 but not translated into English for thirty years, until 1973. O'Brien, whose real name was Brian O Nuallain, was born in Strabane, County Tyrone, one of two literary brothers. His first novel,* At Swim-Two-Birds, *appeared in 1939 and although praised by James Joyce received little attention until the Sixties, when it at last became a cult classic.* An Beal Bocht, *its successor, immediately achieved two distinctions. It was one of the few Irish-language books which had to be immediately reprinted and was condemned by the Irish Catholic hierarchy—a fact that ensured several more reprints. The title, which translates from the Irish as 'to put on the poor mouth', means to make a pretence of being poor or in bad circumstances in order to gain advantage from creditors. The book itself was a merciless and uproarious comment on Irish life and is now recognised by many critics as the great classic of Irish literary humour. In 1973, Patrick Power of Cork University undertook the difficult task of translating the originality and subtlety of O'Brien's prose into English, and not least his parody of the styles and clichés of other Irish-language writers.*

Apart from a few other novels, O'Brien also wrote a very popular column, 'Cruiskeen Lawn', about the humours of local life, for the Irish Times. *'The Martyr's Crown' is one of his few short stories, but is typical of his mastery of wit and wordplay.*

*   *   *

Mr Toole and Mr O'Hickey walked down the street together in the morning.

Mr Toole had a peculiarity. He had the habit, when accompanied by another person, of saluting total strangers; but only if these strangers were of important air and costly raiment. He meant thus to make it known that he had friends in high places, and that he himself, though poor, was a person of quality fallen on evil days through some undisclosed sacrifice made in the interest of immutable principle early in life. Most of the strangers, startled out of their private thoughts, stammered a salutation in return. And Mr Toole was shrewd. He stopped at that. He said no more to his companion, but by some little private gesture, a chuckle, a shake of the head, a smothered imprecation, he nearly always extracted the one question most melodious to his ear: '*Who was that?*'

Mr Toole was shabby, and so was Mr O'Hickey, but Mr O'Hickey had a neat and careful shabbiness. He was an older and a wiser man, and was well up to Mr Toole's tricks. Mr Toole at his best, he thought, was better than a play. And he now knew that Mr Toole was appraising the street with beady eye.

'Gorawars!' Mr Toole said suddenly.

We are off, Mr O'Hickey thought.

'Do you see this hop-off-my-thumb with the stick and the hat?' Mr Toole said.

Mr O'Hickey did. A young man of surpassing elegance was approaching; tall, fair, darkly dressed; even at fifty yards his hauteur seemed to chill Mr O'Hickey's part of the street.

'Ten to one he cuts me dead,' Mr Toole said. 'This is one of the most extraordinary pieces of work in the whole world.'

Mr O'Hickey braced himself for a more than ordinary impact. The adversaries neared each other.

'*How are we at all, Sean a chara?*' Mr Toole called out.

The young man's control was superb. There was no glare, no glance of scorn, no sign at all. He was gone, but had left in his wake so complete an impression of his contempt that even Mr Toole paled momentarily. The experience frightened Mr O'Hickey.

'Who . . . who was *that?*' he asked at last.

'I knew the mother well,' Mr Toole said musingly. 'The woman was a saint.' Then he was silent.

Mr O'Hickey thought: there is nothing for it but bribery—again. He led the way into a public house and ordered two bottles of stout.

'As you know,' Mr Toole began, 'I was Bart Conlon's right-hand man. Bart, of course, went the other way in 'twenty-two.'

Mr O'Hickey nodded and said nothing. He knew that Mr Toole had never rendered military service to his country.

'In any case,' Mr Toole continued, 'there was a certain day early in 'twenty-one and orders come through that there was to be a raid on the Sinn Fein office above in Harcourt Street. There happened to be a certain gawskogue of a cattle jobber from the County Meath had an office on the other side of the street. And he was well in with a certain character be the name of Mick Collins. I think you get me drift?'

'I do,' Mr O'Hickey said.

'There was six of us,' Mr Toole said, 'with meself and Bart Conlon in charge. Me man the cattle jobber gets an urgent call to be out of his office accidentally on purpose at four o'clock, and at half-four the six of us is parked inside there with two machine guns, the rifles, and a class of a homemade bomb that Bart used to make in his own kitchen. The military arrived in two lurries on the other side of the street at five o'clock. That was the hour in the orders that come. I believe that man Mick Collins had lads working for him over in the War Office across in London. He was a great stickler for the British being punctual on the dot.'

'He was a wonderful organiser,' Mr O'Hickey said.

'Well, we stood with our backs to the far wall and let them have it through the open window and then getting down off the lurries. Sacred godfathers! I never seen such murder in me life. Your men didn't know where it was coming from, and a lot of them wasn't worried very much when it was all over, because there was no heads left on some of them. Bart then gives the order for retreat down the back stairs; in no time we're in the lane, and five minutes more the six of us upstairs in Martin Fulham's pub in Camden Street. Poor Martin is dead since.'

'I knew that man well,' Mr O'Hickey remarked.

'Certainly you knew him well,' Mr Toole said, warmly. 'The six of us was marked men, of course. In any case, fresh orders come at six o'clock. All hands was to proceed in military formation, singly, be different routes to the house of a great skin in the

Cumann na mBan, a widow be the name of Clougherty that lived on the south side. We were all to lie low, do you understand, till there was fresh orders to come out and fight again. Sacred wars, they were very rough days them days; will I ever forget Mrs Clougherty! She was certainly a marvellous figure of a woman. I never seen a woman like her to bake bread.'

Mr O'Hickey looked up.

'Was she,' he said, 'was she . . . all right?'

'She was certainly nothing of the sort,' Mr Toole said loudly and sharply. 'By God, we were all thinking of other things in them days. Here was this unfortunate woman in a three-storey house on her own, with some quare fellow in the middle flat, herself on the ground floor, and six bloodthirsty pultogues hiding above on the top floor, every manjack ready to shoot his way out if there was trouble. We got feeds there I never seen before or since, and the *Independent* every morning. Outrage in Harcourt Street. The armed men then decamped and made good their excape. I'm damn bloody sure we made good our excape. There was one snag. We couldn't budge out. No exercise at all—and that means only one thing . . .'

'Constipation?' Mr O'Hickey suggested.

'The very man,' said Mr Toole.

Mr O'Hickey shook his head.

'We were there a week. Smoking and playing cards, but when nine o'clock struck, Mrs Clougherty come up, and, Protestant, Catholic, or Jewman, all hands had to go down on the knees. A very good . . . strict . . . woman, if you understand me, a true daughter of Ireland. And now I'll tell you a damn good one. About five o'clock one evening I heard a noise below and peeped out of the window. Sanctified and holy godfathers!'

'What was it—the noise?' Mr O'Hickey asked.

'What do you think, only two lurries packed with military, with my nabs of an officer hopping out and running up the steps to hammer at the door, and all the Tommies sitting back with their guns at the ready. Trapped! That's a nice word—*trapped!* If there was ever rats in a cage, it was me unfortunate brave men from the battle of Harcourt Street. God!'

'They had you at what we call a disadvantage,' Mr O'Hickey conceded.

'She was in the room herself with the teapot. She had a big

silver satteen blouse on her; I can see it yet. She turned on us and
gave us all one look that said: *Shut up, ye nervous lousers.* Then
she foostered about a bit at the glass and walks out of the room
with bang-bang-bang to shake the house going on downstairs. And
I seen a thing . . .'

'What?' asked Mr O'Hickey.

'She was a fine—now you'll understand me, Mr O'Hickey,' Mr
Toole said carefully; 'I seen her fingers on the buttons of the
satteen, if you follow me, and she leaving the room.'

Mr O'Hickey, discreet, nodded thoughtfully.

'I listened at the stairs. Jakers I never got such a drop in me
life. She clatters down and flings open the hall door. This young
pup is outside, and asks—awsks—in the law-de-daw voice, "Is
there any men in this house?" The answer took me to the fair
altogether. She puts on the guttiest voice I ever heard outside
Moor Street and says, "Sairtintly not at this hour of the night; I
wish to God there was. Sure, how could the poor unfortunate
women get on without them, officer?" Well lookat. I nearly fell
down the stairs on top of the two of them. The next thing I hear
is, "Madam this and madam that" and "Sorry to disturb and I beg
your pardon," "I trust this and I trust that," and then the whispering starts, and at the windup the hall door is closed and into the
room off the hall with the pair of them. This young bucko out of
the Borderers in a room off the hall with a headquarters captain
of the Cumann na mBan! *Give us two more stouts there, Mick!*'

'That is a very queer one, as the man said,' Mr O'Hickey said.

'I went back to the room and sat down. Bart had his gun out,
and we were all looking at one another. After ten minutes we
heard another noise.'

Mr Toole poured out his stout with unnecessary care.

'It was the noise of the lurries driving away,' he said at last.
'She'd saved our lives, and when she come up a while later she
said, "We'll go to bed a bit earlier tonight, boys; kneel down all."
That was Mrs Clougherty the saint.'

Mr O'Hickey, also careful, was working at his own bottle, his
wise head bent at the task.

'What I meant to ask you was this,' Mr O'Hickey said, 'that's
an extraordinary affair altogether, but what has that to do with
that stuck-up young man we met in the street, the lad with all the
airs?'

'Do you not see it, man?' Mr Toole said in surprise. 'For seven hundred year, thousands—no, I'll make it millions—of Irish men and women have died for Ireland. We never rared jibbers; they were glad to do it, and will again. But that young man was *born* for Ireland. There was never anybody else like him. Why wouldn't he be proud?'

'The Lord save us!' Mr O'Hickey cried.

'A saint I called her,' Mr Toole said, hotly. 'What am I talking about—she's a martyr and wears the martyr's crown today!'

THE CORNCRAKE

Sean O'Casey

'Captain' Boyle in Sean O'Casey's famous play about Dublin low life, Juno and the Paycock *(1924), has been described as one of the most uproariously comic characters in the Irish theatre: the nearest rival to Falstaff, in fact, in contemporary literature. Indeed, although O'Casey (1884–1964) is probably best known for his experimental and expressionistic dramas, he never forgot the people who came from the same kind of poor Dublin background as himself, with their love of wordplay and sense of the absurd, and examples of them are to be found in several of his other plays and short stories. In dramas such as* Juno, The Shadow of a Gunman *(1923) and* The Plough and the Stars *(1926) he often deliberately set out to make his audiences laugh at society.*

Among the short stories, several were to prove forerunners of later works. 'The Seamless Coat of Kathleen', for instance, is a political allegory that satirises the efforts of various groups to control the Irish Free State in 1922 and foreshadows the phantasy of 'Kathleen Listens In'; while in 'The Corncrake', which is reprinted here, the central figures of Ginger and Lanky are just the same kind of argumentative characters as those to be found in O'Casey's plays from Nannie's Night Out *to* The Drums of Father Ned.

*   *   *

It was raining heavily and, though the business of the market was almost over, there were still a few standing in the square of Ballycoolin with a fading hope in their hearts that someone would come to relieve them of their vigil and the pig or the cow they had to sell.

Ginger Gilligan, with his shoulder leaning lovingly against the doorframe of the little village tavern, dreamily watched the little group lingering in the narrow street, eager to seek shelter from the fast-falling rain, but yet determined to endure it till fortune should take their wares and give them a fair exchange.

Ginger was enjoying the exquisite sensation of a complex joy; the failure of the others gave the contemplation of his own successful sale a richer satisfaction; the consciousness of being safe in shelter while others were being beaten by the driving rain was a sensual source of pleasure; and Ginger smoked his pipe—for life patted him on the back, and Ginger smiled at life—for the time being.

Ginger, with his short perky body, his sallow cheeks, his aggressive way of talking, his self-conscious display of conceit when he was arguing the point—which was very often indeed—was a celebrated unit in the life of Ballycoolin. Indeed, there was only one man who dared to oppose Ginger in an argument, and that was Lanky Lonergan, a long, thin, spare, stick of a man, with a thin pipe-like neck, supporting a heavy head, large-eyed and lantern-jawed, with an indescribably comical look of melancholy on his immovable face.

Whenever Lanky met Ginger, or Ginger encountered Lanky, there was an end of harmony and good fellowship. It was considered impossible, and it was never expected by the people of Ballycoolin, that Lanky and Ginger could ever agree, in this world or the next, upon any subject that interested the sons of men. Lanky's scorn for Ginger's opinion was only equalled by Ginger's contempt for the opinions of Lanky.

Ponderous and difficult were the questions they discussed, from why a dog turned three times before he lay down, to the settlement of the question whether the hen came before the egg, or the egg came before the hen.

Well, free from care, Ginger was blissfully smoking, when who should come along but Lanky, anxious to have a drink, with a pig's cheek under his arm.

'God save us,' said Lanky, with an ominous gleam in his eye that was nearest to Ginger, 'isn't it terrible weather we're havin'?'

'Oh, it's fine an' soft, anyhow, thanks be to God,' replied Ginger, with an equally ominous gleam in his eye that was nearest to Lanky.

'Come in out o' the rain, anyhow,' said Lanky, and accompanied by six or seven others who had been at the fair, they entered the pub, and soon began to drink each other's health with anxious sincerity, while they were waiting for the weather to clear.

But the rain continued to fall steadily, and the dreary prospect of a drearier walk home that confronted most of them, induced them to continue their mellow expressions of fellowship, which expressions were expanded and developed with additional drinks.

Everybody was waiting for the coming dispute between Lanky and Ginger; how it was to commence nobody knew, but that it was an ultimate certainty everyone was convinced.

'I heard the corncrake this mornin' for the first time this season,' said a little man, as he thoughtfully took a drink from his tumbler of stout; 'it's a curious bird with a curious call; I don't mind if anybody ever seen it.'

'I seen it,' said Ginger, 'not once but hundreds of times.'

'I wonder what way does he be when he gives out that comical call o' his,' said the little man again.

Lanky's eyes held an expression of pity as he answered, 'That's the simplest thing in the world for anyone to tell who has kept his eyes open. Sure everyone ought to know that the corncrake makes the comical noise when he calls by sticking his bake in the ground.'

'Well,' said Ginger, as he carefully deposited on the counter the glass from which he was drinking, 'I don't mind what everybody knows, for they mostly know wrong; it's sickenin' the foolish things some people say; his bake stuck in the ground! Anyone who has ever seen the corncrake knows that when the bird is givin' its call it does be stretched on the broad of its back with its legs kickin' in the air.'

Then the battle started, Lanky trying to convince Ginger, and Ginger determined to convince Lanky, and you may be sure they got all the help they needed from the surrounding company.

One minute you would hear, 'I knew Lanky would see that point, an' it puts the kybosh on you, Ginger'; and the next minute, 'You took them words out o' me mouth, Ginger; sure I often seen the corncrake doin' it meself, an' he's got the kinch on you there, Lanky.'

More and more animated the discussion grew; graphic descriptions were recklessly whirled around the corncrake's habits, customs, manners, legs, wings, beak and plumage. Ginger exhausted all the local science of ornithology concerning every known bird, and vigorously applied it all to the corncrake. Lanky recounted all he had ever read, and a good deal he had never read—nor anybody else—about the corncrake till the shades of evening fell upon them, and the time came for the reluctant master of the tavern to bid farewell to his guests.

And the worthy landlord ushered them out—'themselves and their corncrake'—telling them that the question would have to be settled elsewhere, and reminding them the good people at home would be wondering what was keeping them.

It's a singular thing, by the way, how anxious the owners of taverns become about the people at home when the time arrives for the closing of the shop.

The assembly, still disputing about the corncrake, poured themselves out into the street, and gradually, for it was still raining heavily, departed, some this way, some that, till nobody was left in the now lonely vicinity of the public house but Ginger and Lanky, still arguing about the call of the corncrake.

The melancholy moon began to peer through thinning clouds, and the rain began to fall more timidly as the pair at last began to move slowly and tentatively homewards—Lanky with the pig's cheek still under his arm.

It was painfully puzzling to Ginger and Lanky that the width—or rather the narrowness—of the road put more difficulties in their way than its length. The hedges, too, seemed to be in a playful mood, continually leaping around them, and bumping into them in a way that was far from reassuring. The very road, as well, seemed to be packed with hills and hollows in a way that never troubled them before, or, let us hope, never will again; but through it all they still continued to discuss the evolution of the corncrake's call.

'Arrah, look here,' said Lanky, 'you can talk till the tongue falls out of your head, but you'll have to admit that she sticks her gob in the ground.'

'Whisht, whisht, man,' responded Ginger, 'and don't let anybody hear you talkin' that way; how could the creature stick his gob in—look out, here's the hedge again—supposin' she was standin' on a rock how could she—mind that hole there—stick her bake in the ground? It's on her back she does be, I'm tellin' you.'

'Now, listen to me,' said Lanky, 'I don't like to be arguin', but if you have the least bit of sense in your thick head'—suddenly both of them stopped dead in the middle of the road and began to listen intently, wearing an expression of awe that was comical to behold.

'Creek, crawk, creek, crawk,' came with startling insistence from the middle of a field on the side of the road.

'The b----y bird itself,' ejaculated Lanky.

'There, now, what did I tell you,' said Ginger, in a tone of dogmatic scorn. 'Maybe you're satisfied at last.'

Lanky made no rejoinder, but softly murmured to himself, 'Blessin' o' God on me eyesight; look now where's his gob?'

'Man,' rejoined Ginger fiercely, 'don't you see her legs?'

'What are you tryin' to say,' retorted Lanky. 'Is it blindness that's on you or what?' And the two of them glared at each other in a menacing manner.

'It's my opinion,' said Ginger, slowly and decisively, 'that you never seen a corncrake in your life.'

'The gentleman that's talkin',' rejoined Lanky, 'wouldn't know a corncrake from a hen.'

'Here,' said Ginger, with a vicious decision, 'I'll bring you to the bird an' show you him makin' his call lyin' on the broad of his back with his legs stickin' up in the air.'

'An' I'll show you him,' said Lanky, 'with his bake stuck down in the ground.'

As the little corncrake continued to lustily give forth her cry, the pair excitedly crossed the hedge, and began to steal towards the place from which the call came. But the certainty of their ears was a fallible guide, for a difference quickly arose about the right locality. 'This way, man, this way,' muttered Lanky.

'Over here, man, over here,' responded Ginger, as they stood in the centre of the field, disputing violently, their noses almost touching each other.

The corncrake evidently heard the disturbances, for her call suddenly ceased, and the two stood trembling to fear that they had frightened her away.

'Why couldn't you keep quiet for a minute?' remonstrated Lanky; 'your row would wake a dead man out o' the grave.'

'Yourself ye mean,' retorted Ginger. 'Sure, anything wud see that ugly face o' yours on your long pole of a neck stuck up among the clouds.'

Just as Lanky was about to retort, they heard the 'creek, crawk' of the bird coming from another part of the field.

Away they went again; and so as not to be seen, as they thought, they began the journey on their hands and knees. The corn was more than a foot and a half high, dripping with moisture as well from the recent rains, so that before very long they were as wet as the saturated corn.

But they didn't care a pin; there was a question to be settled, and settle it they would, even at the imminent peril of their lives.

Now there were two mischievous gossoons in Ballycoolin, named Shawn Beag and Sheumas Ruadh, who by some chance, good or bad, were always in the place where they were least expected. If a person was quietly gathering a few heads of cabbage from a neighbour's garden, or a few sods of turf from a heap that was not his own, it was as certain as the sun was in the heavens that the young devils should be near, and the whole story bruited about the village before you could have time to bless yourself, and it was the great and irreparable misfortune that Ginger and Lanky should be seen by these two young rascals. Wondering what could be going on in the field in the middle of the night, they crept to the hedge and watched the antics of the pair who were chasing the corncrake. But they no longer wondered when they saw that Ginger and Lanky always crept towards the place from which they thought the call of the corncrake came.

'Bedad, we'll have a bit o' fun now,' said Shawn to Sheumas, and away he went to the end of the field furthest from where were Lanky and Ginger, while Sheumas remained where he was.

Inside were the benighted pair, creeping carefully on their hands and knees through the dripping corn, Lanky leading, his long head and neck lifted above the surrounding corn, murmuring softly, 'We're not a mile from her now'; when suddenly the call ceased again. They stopped, listened, looked at each other, and were about to launch into mutual abuse again, when they heard the 'creek, crawk' more distinctly than ever before, from the other end of the field. Away with them again towards the place from which the call came, moving now as rapidly as they could go on their hands and knees, for, becoming excited in the chase, each was anxious to be the first to catch a glimpse of the corncrake.

But it wasn't long before Shawn ceased his mimicking cry, and

Sheumas took up the cry far away behind them, and turning swiftly, Ginger and Lanky moved madly in the opposite direction.

Back and forth, from left to right, from right to left, went the now frantic couple, ay, till the whole cornfield had been traversed on hands and knees for more than fifty times. Exhausted and teeming with sweat from their exertions, they still continued to creep at a mad miniature gallop towards any place in which they heard the cry of the mysterious bird.

At last, as they paused together in the middle of the field waiting to hear the call again, the two birds began to cry together. This was puzzling, and Ginger and Lanky were immediately in a state of mental disorder. Each chose a different corncrake to follow, and then the dispute arose in an effort of each to persuade the other to follow the bird of his choice.

'The one over forninst us,' said Lanky.

'The one that's right behind us,' said Ginger.

But Lanky refused to go up the field, and Ginger was equally determined not to go down. The difficulty was at last overcome by each following, in a burst of anger, his own particular corncrake.

Down the field went Lanky, and who should the corncrake be but my bould Sheumas Ruadh. When Lanky came near to him he stopped the call, but he didn't stop Lanky; and away fled Sheumas to the other side of the field, and, unfortunately for Lanky, he recommenced the call. Over the hedge jumped Lanky into the adjoining potato field, stumbling through the ridges and splashing through the water that had gathered in the hollows between the ridges, till, reaching the centre of the field exhausted and half dead, he lay down in one of the hollows, and the vigorous cries of the corncrake failed to arouse him again, for Lanky was dead to the world.

Meanwhile Ginger was in hot pursuit of his own bird. When he came to the ditch he heard the call out in the bog. With the heedlessness of a madman he went over the ditch in one bound and raced towards the bog. He was on a hot scent now, and gathering together all his remaining energy, he rushed forward and plunged headlong into a cold and brimming bog-hole, giving vent to an agonising yell as he disappeared beneath the surface.

Shawn Beag ran to his assistance, and, catching hold of him by the collar, tried to pull him out, but his effort was in vain. So he had to bellow for Sheumas, who, running up, lent a hand, and their united efforts withdrew poor Ginger from his perilous position. Poor Ginger never let a whimper out of him. All the corncrakes in the world might call their loudest, but Ginger wouldn't pay the slightest attention to them. Like Lanky, he was dead to the world.

Sheumas and Shawn, each catching hold of an arm, half carried, half dragged him to the door of his house. After knocking loudly at the door, they left Ginger standing stupidly before it and fled. The wife of Ginger came and opened the door, and astonishment was writ large on the face of Ginger when he saw the wonder on the face of his wife.

'Oh,' said he, 'is it asleep you were?'

'Ay,' said she, 'the sleep of the corncrake,' and stretching out her hand, she gripped Ginger by the collar, and the poor man passed away from the world's ken.

'Where did you leave Lanky?' enquired Shawn, as they were returning to the scene of the hunt for the corncrake.

'Asleep in Peg's potato field, and the last trump wouldn't waken him,' responded Sheumas. 'We'll have to go and waken him, too; but he's too heavy to carry.'

They thought of the problem for a few moments, and at last decided to commandeer old Farmer Dermody's yellow mule cart. Having secured the cart, they brought it to the potato field, and put in Lanky, with his two long legs streeling out from the back of the cart, and in this manner conveyed the unconscious man home. They kicked violently at the door, and hearing the approach of Lanky's wife, they fled, and left Lanky to explain as best he could what he was doing in Farmer Dermody's yellow mule cart.

'Well, well,' said old Mihaul to his friends in the little pub of Ballycoolin a few days later, 'you should have seen the state o' me corn, an' all the roads destroyed, an' the curiousest thing about it all was that the divil a sign of anyone or anything I ever found there, save a pig's cheek an' it wrapped in paper.'

I MEET A SHEIK

Brendan Behan

Brendan Behan (1923–1964) was also a larger-than-life character, totally irreverent and unpredictable, who has drawn comparison with some of Ireland's greatest modern writers—in particular, the last contributor, Sean O'Casey. Writing in 1963, the English critic Kenneth Tynan declared, 'If the English hoard words like misers, the Irish spend them like sailors; and Brendan Behan, Dublin's obstreperous poet-playwright, is one of the biggest spenders in this line since the young Sean O'Casey. Behan sends language out on a swaggering spree, ribald, flushed and spoiling for a fight.' Born in Dublin, Behan became an international celebrity after the success of his play, The Quare Fellow, *in 1956, a reputation confirmed by his classic account of prison life,* Borstal Boy (1958). *Despite the drinking and turmoil which ended in a tragically early death, there was no disguising Behan's talent, nor his understanding of all the idiosyncrasies of human nature, those of the Irish in particular. Also no one loved a tall story more than he did—or told them better, as he demonstrates in this sly yarn contributed to* The Irish Press *in 1953.*

*　　*　　*

I was in the Strand recently—I should have said the Strand, London, in case people thought I meant the North Strand and I didn't get the credit of my travels.

Irish people, who for some reason have the reputation of being insular, have great *meas** for the traveller.

It's almost a competition. A man from Ballyhaunis will, no

---

* respect.

doubt, get great credit for his weekly run to Sligo or Athlone. But he has to shut up about the glories of both places, when Micky Fitz that's working above in Dublin, comes down in the summer holidays.

And the Dubliner, on a visit to smaller centres in the west, or south, will almost certainly be introduced to some mild old man who stands innocently at the counter, and plies your man with questions about the wonders of the great metropolis, listening with wide-eyed astonishment to descriptions of traffic-lights and buses, and the flashing jewels of neon signs that shine across the width of O'Connell Street to one another.

The old man greets the account of metropolitan majesty, from Store Street Station to O'Keefe's the knacker's, with 'Oh' and 'Ah' and 'Glory be' and your gills is condescendingly pleased to have brought a hint at least, of the colour and bursting life of urban civilisation into the old man's last days, until he discovers that the old pig-minder has been getting it up for him, rich and rare. That he spent forty year in a saloon on Broadway, or drove a truck for Al Capone in Chicago, and that he performs this Simple Simon act on every visiting Dubliner for the benefit of his friends and neighbours, who are in no way averse to seeing the jackeen being made look a gilly.

For some reason, the old fellow who has been to America is better thought of than the fellow who only got as far as Liverpool. I think they must sit up with maps measuring the distance, so as to know to what honours the returning exile is entitled.

In hotels and bars, in Youghal, Caherciveen, Donaghadee, Tallaght, Camden Town, Inisheer, and Kilburn—in any place where our people have gathered—I have bested them all.

If someone said he had been to Texas, and hunted cattle, I was hot on his heels with my story of a week-end spent with a sheik in East Tunis.

By the same token I met the sheik under rather peculiar circumstances. He fancied himself as something of a huntsman, but there was very little to be hunted in his own country, unless you count the sand-flies.

So when he was invited by the French Government to shoot deer in the Vosges he was delighted, and would hardly go to bed the night before the hunt was to begin.

But in the field he proved a very bad shot. The only deer he would have got a direct hit on would have been the one in the hall, and they wanted that for a hat-rack.

The French were very anxious to keep on the right side of the old sheik, and they didn't know what to do, till the next morning he sneaked out on his own, and they heard the bang and the crash of his guns, and squeals of delight in Arabic, not to mention the thud of falling bodies as his victims hit the dust.

He ran in ecstatically, and screeching in his own language:

'All of them have I killed, the woolly white deer.'

And when they followed him out they discovered about twenty tons of dead prime mutton belonging to the neighbouring farmer.

He was duly fixed up with a sum of money that more than compensated him for the loss of his 'woolly white deer', and the old sheik returned home with a shipload of stuffed sheep's heads, which trophies of the chase now line the walls of his castle in Beni Rah Kosi.

How did I come into the story? I tied the fifty-six-pound weights on the legs of the sheep the previous night, with the man who owned them, a chap from Granamore, County Wicklow, by the name of Mike Burke.

I nearly drove a man in this city mad with yarns the like of that the other night.

He was standing at the counter with his friends, and smiled when he heard my accent. His own was an Irish one heavily mixed with Paddington. He paid tribute to the country of his adoption with the vowels, but the 'th's' betrayed the land of his birth.

''Ello, you're from Ahland. Just come oveh, Paddy?'

'That's right. Guilty on both counts.'

He smiled indulgently. 'Ah bin ere nah abaht fifteen years. Dow now when Ah was 'ome last.'

'I got in today from Baghdad.'

'From wheah?'

'Baghdad. I'm over here for an operation.'

'From Baghdad? For an operation? For what?'

'Leprosy. I'll tell how I got it. There was this sheik I knew. Man be the name of Mohammed Ali Bababa. Lived in a place be the name of Beni Rah Kosi . . .'

DAN DOONAN'S WAKE

Spike Milligan

Irish wakes have been famous for centuries—indeed so notorious were these riotous and drunken gatherings held in the same room as the corpse of a man or woman on the night before their burial that they were frequently referred to as 'Wake Orgies'. Instances of the ancient tradition are to be found in many Irish novels and stories, but rarely handled with such outlandish humour as in this next story by Spike Milligan (1919–   ), famous, of course, as one of creators of the immortal Goon Show. Though he was actually born in India, Spike came from Irish stock—the O'Maolagains and O'Higgins—and has always professed a strong affinity with the country, as he explained in a recent interview in the Sunday Telegraph: *'My father told me incredible stories about himself, from how he and his six brothers, fresh from Ireland in the 1900s, were set upon by bully boys, to how he won the Battery light-heavyweight championship. From him flowed an endless stream of wonderful tales, from fighting Arabs in Mesopotamia in World War I to being a cowboy on a big ranch in Brownsville, Texas. This was pure Irish fantasy, springing from the kind of mind that created leprechauns and banshees.' Spike has undoubtedly inherited this same gift for outlandish humour and witticism, as he shows in the story of 'Dan Doonan's Wake' . . .*

*   *   *

Dr Goldstein pulled the sheet over the face of Dan Doonan. Mrs Doonan took the news dry-eyed. She'd only stayed with him for the money. Twenty years before she had tried to get a separation. The solicitor listened to her attentively. 'But Mrs Doonan, just because you don't like him, that's no grounds for separation.'

'Well, make a few suggestions,' she said.

'Has he ever struck you?'

'No. I'd kill him if he did.'

'Has he ever been cruel to the children?'

'Never.'

'Ever left you short of money, then?'

'No, every Friday on the nail.'

'I see.' The solicitor pondered. 'Ah, wait, think hard now, Mrs Doonan, has he ever been unfaithful to you?'

Her face lit up. 'By God, I tink we got him there, I know for sure he wasn't the father of me last child!'

The solicitor had advised her accordingly. 'Get out of my office,' he told her and charged six and eightpence for the advice.

Now Dan was dead. 'I wonder how much he's left me,' the widow wondered. Money couldn't buy friends but you got a better class of enemy.

Messrs Quock, Murdle, Protts and Frigg, solicitors and Commissioners for Oaths, pondered dustily over the grey will papers; at 98, Dan Doonan had died leaving all his money to himself. The quartet of partners shook their heads, releasing little showers of legal dandruff. They had thumbed carefully through the 3,000 pages of *Morell on Unorthodox Wills*, and no light was cast on the problem. Murdle took a delicate silver Georgian snuff box from his waistcoat, dusted the back of his hand with the fragrant mixture of Sandalwood and ground Sobrani, sniffed into each nostril, then blew a great clarion blast into a crisp white handkerchief.

'This will take years of work to unravel,' he told his companions; 'we must make sure of that,' he added with a sly smile, wink, and a finger on the nose. They were, after all, a reputable firm built up on impeccable business principles, carefully doctored books and sound tax avoidance.

Only the last paragraph of the said will was clear. Doonan wanted a hundred pounds spent on a grand 'Wake' in honour of himself. Senior partner, Mr Protts, stood up, drew a gold engraved pocket watch to his hand, snapped it closed, '4.32 exactly, gentlemen—Time for Popeye,' he said switching on the TV.

The inebriated chanting of professional mourners came wailing from 44 Cloncarragah Terrace. Inside the front room, propped

by the fireplace, was the flower-bedecked coffin of Dan Doonan.
Grouped around admiringly, reverently clutching their drinks,
were friends and foes alike, and with drink they were all very
much alike. Funeral clichés were flying in the teeth of the dear
departed.

'A fine man, ma'am, it's a great day for him.'

'You must be proud of him, Mrs Doonan.'

'One of the finest dead men ter ever walk the earth.'

'I was sorry ter see him go!'

'So was I—he owed me a pound.'

'It's hard to believe he's dead.'

'Oh he's *dead* is he?' said Foggerty, who'd been speaking to
him all evening.

The corpse looked fine, fine, fine. New suit, hair cut and
greased, his boots highly polished and loaned by an anonymous
donor were firmly nailed to the coffin for additional security. The
tables in the next room were swollen high with the food. Two
wooden tubs steamed with baked potatoes, their earthy jackets
split and running with rivulets of melting butter. Hot pig slices, a
quarter inch thick, were piled high on seventeen plates. In the
middle, was one huge dish of brown pork sausages, and bacon,
still bubbling from the pan. On the floor, floating in a bucket of
vinegar, was a minefield of pickled onions. The temporary bar was
serving drinks as fast as O'Toole could pour them.

'God, there hasn't been a night like this since the signing of the
Treaty.'

Many people die of thirst but the Irish are born with one.

O'Connor the piper tucked his kilt between his legs, puffed the
bladder of his pipes and droned them into life; soon the floor was
lost in a sea of toiling, reeling legs. Uppity-hippity-juppity-ippity-
dippity-dippity shook the house. The centre bulb danced like a
freshly hanged man. There was a clapping a stamping-and-cries-of-
encouragement. The faithful few in Dan's parlour soon deserted
him for the dance. Alone in his room he stood, his body jerking
to the rhythm now shaking the house. The party was swelled
by the arrival of the victorious Puckoon Hurley team, many
still unconscious from the game. These were dutifully laid on the
floor beside Dan's coffin—the rest joined into the frenzied
dance.

The Milligan pulled his trousers up and leaped into the middle, but he observed his legs and stopped. 'Hey, you said me legs would develop with the plot.'

'They will.'

'Den why are they still like a pair of dirty old pipe cleaners?'

'It's a transitional period.'

'Look, I don't want transitional legs.' He stood in the middle of the leaping bodies and spoke, 'What's dis book all about, here we are on page-page—' he looked down, 'on page 180—and all these bloody people comin' and goin', where's it all going to end?'

'I don't know. Believe me, I'm just as worried as you are.'

'Tell me why?—tell me—give me a sign!'

A bottle bounced off Milligan's head.

'The Queen,' he shouted and fell sideways like a poleaxed ox.

Three fights had broken out in the midst of the dancers but the difference was hard to tell. The whole house now trembled from roof to foundations. In the next room the great family bible shook from the shelf above the coffin and struck Dan Doonan, throwing him from the coffin and catapulting him from his boots. His wig, a life-long secret, shot from his head and slid under the table next to the cat. He fell among the unconscious members of the Hurley team, who were starting to recover. 'He's drunk as a lord,' they said, dragging him across the hall and tucking him in bed.

'Good God, look at the size of that rat,' one said, seeing the cat pass with a wig in its jaws. 'He mustha' put up a fight.'

Placing a bottle of whiskey by the bed they drank it and stumbled from the room.

It was 4.32 in the morning as the crow flies. The last mourners had slobbered out their drunken farewells, their voices and great posterior blasts mingling into the night. Mrs Doonan drained an empty bottle, scratched her belly, and made for her bed.

Somewhere in the night, Milligan, drunk and with lumps on his head, was wandering through the braille-black countryside: in his path a carefully written well. Splash! it went on receipt of his body.

At 4.56 in the morning, the quietly patrolling constable Oaf was reduced to a kneeling-praying holy man by a leg-weakening shriek. The door of number 33 burst open and out screamed Mrs Doonan in unlaced corsets.

'There's a man in me bed, get him out!' she yelled, restraining her abounding bosoms.

'Madame, if you can't frighten him in that get up, I certainly can't!'

'Do yer duty,' she said, ladling her bosoms back.

The constable unclipped his torch, took a firm grip on his truncheon and entered the house.

'In that room,' she whispered.

'Leave him to me,' said Oaf, pushing her in front. He shone his torch on the bed. Mrs Doonan gasped and let fall her bosoms. 'Holy Mary!' she gasped, 'It's me husband.'

She fainted, clutching the policeman's legs as she fell, bringing his trousers to the ground. Now then, who would have thought a constable would use green knotted string for garters, and have red anchors tattooed on his knees? Ah, Ireland is still a land of mystery.

3

FIGURES OF FUN

Stories of Parody

'Dr Finucane and the Grey Mare', 'Phiz' (Hablot K. Browne) from *The Confessions of Harry Lorrequer* by Charles Lever.

THE CLAN THOMAS

David O Bruadair

Ireland has a rich tradition of parody that can be traced back as far as the twelfth century and a Gaelic manuscript, The Vision of Mac Conglinne, *which Robin Flower in* The Irish Tradition *(1947) has described as 'one long parody of the literary methods used by the clerical scholars'. It was in the middle years of the seventeenth century, however, that Irish parody really began to flower with the* Pairlement Chlainne Tomas—'The Clan Thomas' *(c.1650)—which was followed in 1689 by James Farewell's* The Irish Hudibras, *a burlesque of the sixth book of the* Aeneid *in which a comical Irishman visits Purgatory.*

The story of the clownish behaviour of the Clan Thomas is regarded as an important document in the history of Irish humour, although there is some disagreement as to whether the poet David O Bruadair (c.1625–1698) was the author. Born the son of a wealthy family in County Cork, O Bruadair earned the patronage of Sir John Fitzgerald for his mainly politically inspired poetry, but was later persecuted by the English and died in hiding. The first English translator of 'The Clan Thomas', Francis MacManus, has, though, no doubt about the talent of the creator, as he wrote in 1943, 'Our author, whoever he was, had a powerful command of language, both literary and colloquial . . . in addition he burlesques the style of heroic romances, and has a certain gusty, Tailor-and-Anstyish zest and humour and the words to convey it.' I would go even further than MacManus, for in his theme and hilarious naming of characters (Johnny O'Hollowgut, Bustler Brian O'Smellyslut and Bridget O'Ballsey, to name just three), O Bruadair—if it was he—is clearly a forerunner of such modern masters as Tolkien, Mervyn Peake and Terry Pratchett. As to the parody itself, there is no doubt that its influence on Irish humour has been widespread and will be seen running like a thread through the pages of this book . . .

*   *   *

1

Wherein the origin and destiny of the Clan are established for ever and ever.

Once upon a time the rabblement and rioting of war arose among the infernal demons concerning which of them should inhabit the territory between the River Styx and the River Acheron; and Hell's broods being assembled from every abode on the rivers, under the high leadership of Beelzebub, Abiron and Satan, and a blood-swilling butchering battle being waged between them, defeat fell to Beelzebub and his kin, all of whom were routed over the diverse kingdoms and regions of the great world where the harvests of the nations were universally ravaged and razed. This demoniacal kindred, it was, who, doling out dreadful destruction, spread widely over the four-pointed universe.

Now, this Beelzebub had a son named Dragonmaggot, whose son was Putridpelt. These were harrying the men of Ireland till the time when Laoghaire, son of Niall of the Nine Hostages, held Irish sovereignty. Laoghaire had a worthy steward, wealthy and prosperous both in householding and husbandry, who was Swaggerstinker son of Gluttongut. This Swaggerstinker had a daughter, Beasty by name, and she was married to Putridpelt and between them a family was generated. It was a son of that family who exceeded in repulsiveness and unnaturalness the kin from whom he had come, and he was uncouth, unclean Big Thomas, son of Putridpelt.

This was the time and the season during which Saint Patrick came to Ireland with many venerable disciples to sow piety and faith among the heathen gentiles who were in the land in those days. Then it was that Patrick gathered the venerable disciples and saints and their followers to one place, and the resolution they agreed upon was to eject all the diabolical races from Ireland. They went about proclaiming them from every district to the peak of Croagh Patrick whence Patrick banished them to the Lake of Demons, all except Thomas alone.

The reason Thomas was not banished was that, on his mother's side, he belonged to the corporeal human race and, on his father's, to the spiritual devil's breed. It happened that Patrick was informed of how Thomas was being educated by his grandfather, that is, Rotten Royster. So, Thomas was brought to Patrick and with difficulty did he accept the Faith from the Saint because the Faith, with Christ as Master, did not mix well with Thomas. For it was impossible to bind a divine mystery to the diabolical nature he possessed from his father, as is still evident from the generations succeeding him who cannot be taught either Christian doctrine or the manner of Confession, Commandments or Sacraments, pleading or praising.

Therefore, Patrick left to Thomas and his posterity these behests and counsels: superiority in bawling, brawling, codology and cudgelling; their food and fodder to be thus: the skull-sinews and shanks of beasts, the blood, clots and guts of dumb animals; their bread and sauce to be rude raw barley dough, pasty pottages of buttermilk and oatmeal, skim-milk, and the bristly, worm-nibbed, blue, rancid butter of goats and sheep; and, in like manner, their music and melody to be the screeches and screams of hags, hounds and infants, the grunts, cackles and bleats of pigs, hens and kids; and their bedding and quilting to be weeds and pease plants, beanstalks and thistles, and a full pack of red bugs and fleas to be under their splayveined, calloused, swarthy skins. While none of them would love the other, their power and prime were to be spent in toiling, ploughing and husbandry for the support of their noble elders in all kingdoms of the country, and the best of their sustenance was to be saved and set aside for the provisionment of all others. And he who would do them good and defend them, him they would account least; and he who would beat and tax them, him they would love the most of all men on earth. As the poet aptly says:

> *Rustica gens est optima flens et pessima gaudens,*
> *Unguentem pungit, pungentem rusticus ungit.*

The execrable progeny and tribe that were under every king in power from that time onward in Ireland, sprang from Big Thomas. The same Thomas had twenty-four sons by Snobby, daughter of

Barney Bunghole, son of Blubber who was brother to Swaggerstinker. Thomas divided the clan variously among the four
provinces of Ireland and the pleasant, level, lovely plain of Meath.
Wonderful surnames were composed for every one of his family.

Here are the four who were sent to reside in Meath: Fawner
O'Flattery, Brian O'Blubber, Johnny O'Hollowgut and Surly
Bobby O'Sorrel.

Some more of them were sent to red-handed Ulster, such
as, Malachy O'Hairy, Bustler Brian O'Smellyslut, Loughlin
O'Lopshoe and Gilly Patrick O'Belcherbuster.

To the fair, gentle province of Connacht were sent Gilly Bride
MacKisscracker, Yellow Sneezer O'Hollowgut, Wry Richard
O'Rottenrump and Dirty John O'Dryblubber.

To the province of Leinster were sent awkward, big-buttocked
Malbottom Murphy O'Meggybeard, Droning Dinny O'Dullard
and Licklapper Hugh O'Hocker.

And the rest of them to the proud province of Munster, such
as, Hollowgut Conn O'Plumage, Wideboned Cairbre O'Waxy,
Maggoty Marcus O'Muddler, Doltish Denis O'Dryguts and
Maladroit Tim O'Trailbottom.

Clan Thomas and their progeny spent their time merrily, well-
fed and with light minds as Patrick had ordained for them. They
did not use savoury succulent foods nor sweet intoxicating drinks,
nor clean well-fitting clothes, but crude canvas shirts, slimy coarse
swallow-tail coats woven of the foul hair of puck-goats and other
animals, stinking boots of untanned leather, crooked long-
lappeted caps without make or shape, bedunged, bare, rusty, slippery clogs; while, as Patrick had bade them, they watched and
waited, served and ploughed and slaved for the nobles and gentry
of Christian kind during the reign of every King from time
immemorial, and they were craven before the kingly decrees as
was their duty.

2

Wherein Widower Mangledlug Murphy makes a match for himself.

Thus they remained until the time when Felimy MacCriffin was
the proud and powerful prince of Munster. And there was, then,
a chieftain who surpassed all of the generations that sprang from

Thomas, by name, Mangledlug Murphy O'Muddle, and the town in which this Murphy lived was Clonmacnoise. It was when Felimy MacCriffin was making the royal circuit of the Province of Munster that fortune and wealth fell to the lot of this Murphy.

He, therefore, sent messengers to the four provinces of Ireland to assemble from them to Clonmacnoise all of the Clan Thomas who were men of learning or men of authority. So they came to the one place. Murphy bade them welcome. He spoke to them, and this is what he said:

'My beloved brethren,' said he, 'and dear, wise, far-seeing, exceedingly gentle kinsmen of Big Thomas, son of Putridpelt, son of Filthyfork, son of Dragonmaggot, son of Beelzebub: the reason why I sent for ye is that ye may advise me which worthy woman I may take to wife, because it's time for me to take a wife after the death of my darling loving spouse, Bridgey O'Ballsey, daughter of Blubbery Mahon O'Ballsey and Gawky Duckfoot O'Goatsmeg from Mouth-of-the-two-Muzzles.'

After uttering those words, a snotty stream of tears fell from him, and a fit and failure of mind took him so that he could not speak for an hour.

'And I hear,' continued Murphy, 'that in the fair gentle province of Connacht there's a wealthy noble, Manus O'Maddigan. We believe that we've been too long without ennobling our blood, we being in slavery and serving others to this very day. Now, this Manus has a beautiful single daughter and I've made up my mind to send messengers, with your advice, asking for her from her Da.'

Everyone declared that it was a clever and sensible idea, and that it was proper to carry it out. The four variously experienced men of Clan Thomas who were sent were Mightybum Mahon, Barney Bigbelly, Niall O'Nettles and Crookedcrown Con O'Hollowgut.

As they took their leave, Niall recited this lay learnedly:

> Farewell, Murphy, mighty Chief,
> Counsellor in blubberblab,
> May your house be crammed with beans,
> Children, swank and gobblegab.
>
> Farewell, men, whose shearing blades
> Reap both wheat and cockle dirt,
> Never were you glum or grave,
> Clodheeled, sour, malign or curt.

Farewell, merry Brian O'Knave,
Babbling in his babby's ear,
Farewell, Mureann, likewise Maeve,
Who belcheth not, nor muncheth meal;

Also Barney, proudly bold;
Loughlin, too, who claws no bone:
Farewell all, wise guileless host
Of paunches packed as tight as stone.

Murphy and everyone else praised this poem. The princes and
people of the house vowed and swore that never had there been
made in the world a poem as good as that, in point of learning,
craft, sweetness, harmony and wit.

Thereupon a truly wise sage of the Clan came before him and
his name was Blackguardly Brian O'Lard. Mighty, indeed, were
the knowledge, craft and genuine wisdom of this man. He pronounced that it was the chief Ollamh of the High King of Ireland
who originally composed that poem, and that appreciation of the
concluding verse was tremendous. The name Brian gave to the
effort was the Queer Quatrain.

(The Wedding and the Wedding Feast take place, but ends in
a mighty fight, described in burlesque of the heroic sagas. When
the casualties have been collected and the bawling and the laments,
the bleatings and the lowings, have subsided, Murphy speaks.)

3

Wherein Mangledlug Murphy makes a speech for peace, and peace,
strangely enough, is made.

Here follows Murphy's Oration:

'My beloved brethren,' says he, 'and wise, farseeing kinsmen
of Big Thomas, son of Putridpelt, son of Filthyfork, son of
Dragonmaggot, son of Beelzebub, my considered advice to ye and
my prayer to ye and your direct descendants, is that, till the day
of doom or the last gasp of life, ye should not trust the nobility
of this country. For your circumstances are not the same, and your
various customs are enemy to one another. Give your care to

learning, to the teaching of honour to your families, and to placing them on the road of the law and lofty knowledge. All of them that attain to rank or authority, may they be enemies of the nobility for ever.

'Cast off from ye, brethren,' continues he, 'your hide coats, your loplappeted fleacy bonnets, your rip-knives, your clogs, your reaping-hooks, your smelly flappy trousers, and all the execrable amazing articles of bad dress that ye have practised. Put away from ye, also, your foul, filthy, bestial, brutish habits. Let there be food and fodder always for your women and children. Do ye your best to provide bread and sauce, and be it known to ye that ye cannot have bread without a stock of beans, nor a stock of beans without manure; and there's no manure without cattle, and no cattle without a herdsman. Plough, whether you plough all Ireland or one field. A little is better than nothing. Weigh well these words of my own grandma,' says Murphy, 'and someday ye'll achieve prosperity and plenty, and with the power of your prosperity, mix your most lowly blood with the blood of nobles. And every one of ye who'll possess rank or authority, let him not allow the nobility to raise their heads if he can help it. Cleave close together. Populate farmsteads and townlands for yourselves. Have neither lord nor master but your own selves. Make the land dear for the nobility. Put brown and red and blue on your clothes, and wear collars, ruffs, and gloves, and always use half-spurs, half-pillions and pomes.'

This counsel Clan Thomas praised exceedingly and thanked Murphy cordially. Then every man of them returned to his own house and place.

They spent their lives in servitude during the reign of every king, waiting on the nobles, in which manner they existed till the time of Elizabeth, daughter of Henry, the eighth King of that name, and during her reign, they were, in truth, full of spunk and swelled head, pride and impudence, because of their abundant prosperity and plenty . . .

OSCAR OF THE FLAIL

Douglas Hyde

St Patrick, who featured in 'The Clan Thomas', has subsequently appeared in numerous other Irish parodies, and notably in 'Oscar of the Flail', which apparently originated as an oral tradition but was later collected by Douglas Hyde (1862–1949), the Gaelic scholar and first President of Ireland. Born the son of an Anglican clergyman at French Park in County Roscommon, Hyde did much to help revive Gaelic culture and founded the Gaelic League in 1893. He gathered many of the stories and poems for his books from folklore sources, and among the most popular of these is a series of humorous tales related by an old tramp named William Grady who came from County Galway. Hyde also wrote an amusing though little-known one-act play, The Bursting of the Bubble *(Dublin n.d.), in which he parodied a group of Irish professors who had expressed hostility towards the teaching of Gaelic in schools.*

The evidence suggests that Hyde had a particular affection for the next story—although he published it, curiously, in one of his more obscure collections, The Religious Songs of Connacht *(1906). He himself suggested, 'No doubt the following tale had its rise from the depth of the people's sorrow when they heard from the clergy that their loved Ossian and the Fenians in whom they so much delighted, were damned, and that some clever person invented this manner of saving them from perdition.'*

*   *   *

Saint Patrick came to Ireland, and Ossian met him in Elphin and he carrying stones.

And whatever time it might be that he got the food,
It would be long again till he would get the drink.

'Ossian,' says he, 'let me baptise you.'

'Oh, what good would that do me?' says Ossian.

'Ossian,' says St Patrick, 'unless you let me baptise you, you will go to hell where the rest of the Fenians are.'

'If,' says Ossian, 'Diarmaid and Goll were alive for us, and the king that was over the Fenians, if they were to go to hell they would bring the devil and his forge up out of it on their back.'

'Listen, O grey and senseless Ossian, think upon God, and bow your knee, and let me baptise you.'

'Patrick,' says Ossian, 'for what did God damn all that of people?'

'For eating the apple of commandment,' says St Patrick.

'If I had known that your God was so narrow-sighted that he damned all that of people for one apple, we would have sent three horses and a mule carrying apples to God's heaven to Him.'

'Listen, O grey and senseless Ossian, think upon God and bow your knee, and let me baptise you.'

Ossian fell into a faint, and the clergy thought that he had died. When he woke up out of it, 'O Patrick, baptise me,' says he—he saw something in his faint, he saw the thing that was before him. The spear was in St Patrick's hand, and he thrust it into Ossian's foot purposely; and the ground was red with his share of blood.

'Oh,' says St Patrick to Ossian, 'you are greatly cut.'

'Oh, isn't that for my baptism?' says Ossian.

'I hope in God that you are saved,' says St Patrick, 'you have undergone baptism and . . .'

'Patrick,' says Ossian, 'would you not be able to take the Fenians out of hell'—he saw them there when he was in his sleep.

'I could not,' says St Patrick, 'and any one who is in hell, it is impossible to bring him out of it.'

'Patrick,' says Ossian, 'are you able to take me to the place where Finn and the Fenians of Erin are?'

'I cannot,' says St Patrick.

'As much as the humming gnat
Or a scintilla of the beam of the sun,
Unknown to the great powerful king
Shall not pass in beneath my shield.'

'Can you give them relief from the pain?' says Ossian.

St Patrick then asked it as a petition from God to give them a relief from their pain, and he said to Ossian that they had found relief. This is the relief they got from God. Oscar got a flail, and he requested a fresh thong to be put into the flail, and there went a green rush as a thong in it, and he got the full of his palm of green sand, and he shook the sand on the ground, and as far as the sand reached the devils were not able to follow; but if they were to come beyond the place where the sand was strewn, Ossian was able to follow *them*, and to beat them with the flail. Oscar and all the Fenians are on this side of the sand, and the devils are on the other side, for St Patrick got it as a request from God that they should not be able to follow them where the sand was shaken—and the thong that was in the flail never broke since!

THE FIRST LORD LIEUTENANT

Percy French

Although he has been referred to as 'Ireland's greatest troubadour' and one of the finest writers of parodies in song and prose of his generation, William Percy French (1854–1922) is far less well-known internationally than three of the comic tunes he wrote: 'Phil the Fluter's Ball', 'Come Back Paddy Reilly to Ballyjamesduff' and 'Abdullah Bulbul Ameer'. So famous have these ditties become that they are often believed to be anonymous folk-tunes, and the fact that 'Abdullah Bulbul Ameer' was plagiarised without any form of credit to the author by a London firm before French could establish copyright has only added to this legend.

French, whom Vivian Mercier has called 'the successor to the medieval gleeman', was born in Cloonyquin House in County Roscommon and went to Trinity College, Dublin, where he was evidently more interested in entertaining fellow students on the banjo than in studying for his Civil Engineering degree. He actually wrote 'Abdullah' while at Trinity, and it then became a staple of his repertoire when he forsook a career in engineering for the precarious world of entertainment and became a sell-out attraction all over Ireland with his one-night stands, singing his own comic songs. He later entertained audiences with equal success in England and Scotland as well as across the Atlantic in America and Canada. French was also a writer of occasional lines of poetry and parodies such as 'The First Lord Lieutenant', which he described on its first publication as 'An historical sketch as related by Andrew Geraghty (Philomath)'.

*   *   *

'Essex,' said Queen Elizabeth, as the two of them sat at breakwhist in the back parlour of Buckingham Palace; 'Essex, me haro, I've got a job that I think would suit you. Do you know where Ireland is?'

'I'm no great fist at jografy,' says his Lordship, 'but I know the place you mane. Population, three million; exports, emigrants.'

'Well,' says the Queen, 'I've been reading the Dublin *Evening Mail*, and the *Telegraft*, for some time back, and sorra one o' me can get at the troot o' how things is goin', for the leadin' articles is as contradictory as if they wor husband and wife.'

'That's the way wid papers all the world over,' says Essex. 'Columbus told me it was the same in Amirikay when he was there, abusin' and contradictin' each other at every turn—it's the way they make their livin'. Thrubble you for an egg spoon.'

'It's addled they have me betune them,' says the Queen. 'Not a know I know what's going on. So now what I want you to do is to run over to Ireland, like a good fella, and bring me word how matters stand.'

'Is it me?' says Essex, leppin' up off his chair. 'It's not in airnest ye are, ould lady. Sure it's the hoight of the London season. Everyone's in town, and Shake's new fairy piece, "The Midsummer's Night Mare", billed for next week.'

'You'll go when yer told,' says the Queen, fixin' him with her eye, 'if you know which side yer bread's buttered on. See here, now,' says she, seein' him chokin' wid vexation and a slice of corned beef, 'you ought to be as pleased as Punch about it, for you'll be at the top of the walk over there as vice-regent representin' me.'

'I ought to have a title or two,' says Essex, pluckin' up a bit. 'His Gloriosity of Great Panjanthrum, or the like o' that.'

'How would "His Excellency the Lord Lieutenant of Ireland" strike you?' says Elizabeth.

'First class,' cries Essex. 'Couldn't be betther; it doesn't mean much, but it's allitherative, and will look well below the number on me hall door.'

Well, boys, it didn't take him long to pack his clothes and start away for the Island o' Saints. It took him a good while to get there though, through not knowing the road; but by means of a pocket compass, and a tip to the steward, he was landed at last contagious to Dalkey Island.

Going up to an ould man who was sitting on a rock he took off his hat, and says he:

'That's grand weather we're havin'?'

'Good enough for the times that's in it,' says the ould man, cockin' one eye at him.

'Any divarshan goin' on?' says Essex.

'You're a stranger in these parts, I'm thinkin',' says the ould man, 'or you'd know this was a "band night" in Dalkey.'

'I wasn't aware of it,' says Essex. 'The fact is,' says he, 'I only landed from England just this minute.'

'Aye,' says the old man, bitterly, 'it's little they know about us over there. I'll howld you,' says he, with a slight thrimble in his voice, 'that the Queen herself doesn't know there's to be fireworks in the Sorrento Gardins this night.'

Well, whin Essex heard that, he disremembered entirely that he was sent over to Ireland to put down rows and ructions, and haway wid him to see the fun and flirt with all the pretty girls he could find.

And he found plenty of them—thick as bees they were, and each one as beautiful as the day and the morra.

He wrote two letters home next day—one to Queen Elizabeth and the other to Lord Montaigle, a playboy like himself.

I'll read you the one to the Queen first.

Dame Street,
April 16, 1599.

Fair Enchantress,

I wish I was back in London, baskin' in your sweet smiles and listenin' to your melodious voice once more. I got the consignment of men and the post office order all right. I was out all morning looking for the inimy, but sorra a taste of Hugh O'Neill or his men can I find. A policeman at the corner of Nassau Street told me they were hiding in Wicklow. So I am making up a party to explore the Dargle on Easther Monda. The girls here are as ugly as sin, and every minite of the day I do be wishing it was your good-looking self I was gazin' at instead of these ignorant scare-crows.

Hoppin' soon to be back in ould England, I remain, your loving subjec,

Essex

P.S.—I hear Hugh O'Neill was seen on the top of the Donnybrook tram yesterday mornin'. If I have any luck the head'll be off him before you get this.—E.

The other letter read this way.

Dear Monty,

This is a great place all out. Come over here if you want fun. Divil
such playboys ever I seen, and the girls—oh, don't be talkin'—'pon
me secret honour you'll see more loveliness at a tay and supper ball
in Ra'mines than there is in the whole of England. Tell Ned Spenser
to send me a love-song to sing to a young girl who seems taken wid
my appearance. Her name's Mary, and she lives in Dunlary, so he
oughtent to find it hard.

I hear Hugh O'Neill's a terror, and hits a powerful welt, especially
when you're not lookin'. If he tries any of his games on wid me, I'll
give him in charge. No brawling for yours truly,

Essex

Well, me bould Essex stopped for odds of six months in Dublin,
purtending to be very busy subjugatin' the country, but all the
time only losin' his time and money without doin' a hand's turn,
and doin' his best to avoid a ruction with 'Fightin' Hugh'.

If a messenger came in to tell him that O'Neill was campin' out
on the North Bull, Essex would up stick and away for Sandycove,
where, after draggin' the Forty-foot Hole, he'd write off to Elizabeth, sayin' 'that owing to their suparior knowledge of the country,
the dastard foe had once more eluded him.'

The Queen got mighty tired of these letters, especially as they
always ended with a request to send stamps by return, and told
Essex to finish up his business, and not to be makin' a fool of
himself.

'Oh, that's the talk, is it?' says Essex. 'Very well, me ould sauce-
box' (that was the name he had for her ever since she gev him the
clip on the ear for turnin' his back on her). 'Very well, me ould
sauce-box,' says he, 'I'll write off to O'Neill this very minit, and
tell him to send in his lowest terms for peace at ruling prices.'
Well, the treaty was a bit of a one-sided one.

The terms proposed were:

1. Hugh O'Neill to be King of Great Britain.
2. Lord Essex to return to London and remain there as Viceroy
of England.
3. The O'Neill family to be supported by Government, with
free passes to all theatres and places of entertainment.
4. The London markets to buy only from Irish dealers.

5. All taxes to be sent in stamped envelope, directed to H.
O'Neill, and marked 'private'. Cheques crossed and made payable
to H. O'Neill. Terms cash.

Well, if Essex had had the sense to read through this treaty,
he'd have seen it was of too graspin' a nature to pass with any
sort of a respectable sovereign, but he was that mad that he just
stuck the document in the pocket of his pot-metal overcoat, and
haway wid him hot foot for England.

'Is the Queen within?' says he to the butler, when he opened
the door of the palace. His clothes was that dirty and disorthered
wid travellin' all night, and his boots that muddy, that the butler
was for not littin' him in at the first go-off. So says he very grand:

'Her Meejisty is abow stairs, and can't bee seen till she'd had
her brekwish.'

'Tell her the Lord Liftinant of Oirland desires an enterview,'
says Essex.

'Oh, beg pardon, me lord,' says the butler, steppin' to one side.
'I didn't know 'twas yourself was in it; come inside, sir; the
Queen's in the dhrawin' room.'

Well, Essex leps up the stairs, and into the dhrawin' room wid
him, muddy boots and all; but no sight of Elizabeth was to be
seen.

'Where's your missus?' says he to one of the maids of honour
that was dustin' the chimbley-piece.

'She's not out of her bed yet,' says the maid, with a toss of her
head; 'but if you write your message on the slate beyant, I'll see—'
but before she had finished, Essex was up the second flight and
knockin' at the Queen's bedroom door.

'Is that the hot wather?' says the Queen.

'No; it's me—Essex. Can you see me?'

'Faith, I can't,' says the Queen. 'Howld on till I draw the bed
curtains. Come in, now,' says she, 'and say your say, for I can't
have you stoppin' long you young Lutharian.'

'Bedad, yer Majesty,' says Essex, droppin' on his knees before
her (the delutherer he was), 'small blame to me if I am a Lutharian,
for you have a face on you that would charum a bird off a bush.'

'Hold your tongue, you young reprobate,' says the Queen,
blushing up to her curl papers wid delight, 'and tell me what
improvements you med in Ireland.'

'Faith I taught manners to O'Neill,' cries Essex.

'He had a bad masther then,' says Elizabeth, looking at his dirty boots; 'couldn't you wipe yer feet before ye desthroyed me carpets, young man?'

'Oh, now,' says Essex, 'is it wastin' me time shufflin' about on a mat you'd have me, when I might be gazin' on the loveliest faymale the world ever saw.'

'Well,' says the Queen, 'I'll forgive you this time, as you've been so long away, but remimber in future, that Kidderminster isn't oilcloth. Tell me,' says she, 'is Westland Row station finished yet?'

'There's a side wall or two wanted yet, I believe,' says Essex.

'What about the Loop Line?' says she.

'Oh, they're gettin' on with that,' says he, 'only some people think the girders is a disfiguremint to the city.'

'Is there any talk about the esplanade from Sandycove to Dunlary?'

'There's talk about it, but that's all,' says Essex, ''twould be an odious fine improvement to house property, and I hope they'll see to it soon.'

'Sorra much you seem to have done beyant spending me men and me money. Let's have a look at that threaty I see stickin' out of your pocket.'

Well, when the Queen read the terms of Hugh O'Neill, she just gave him one look, and jumping from off the bed, put her head out of the window, and called out to the policeman on duty—'Is the Head below?'

'I'll tell him you want him, ma'am,' says the policeman.

'Do,' says the Queen.

'Hullo,' says she, as a slip of paper dropped out of the dispatches. 'What's this! "Lines to Mary." Ho! ho! me gay fella, that's what you've been up to, is it?'

> Mrs Brady's
> A widow lady,
> And she has a charming daughter I adore;
> She's such a darlin'
> She's like a starlin',
> And in love with her I'm getting more and more.
> Her name is Mary,

She's from Dunlary;
And her mother keeps a little candy store.

'That settles it,' says the Queen. 'It's the gaoler you'll serenade next.'

When Essex heard that, he thrimbled so much that the button of his cuirass shook off and rowled under the dressin' table.

'Arrest that man!' says the Queen when the Head-constable came to the door. 'Arrest that thrater,' says she, 'and never let me set eyes on him again.'

And, indeed, she never did, for soon after that he met with his death from the blow of an axe he got when he was standin' on Tower Hill.

GAS FROM A BURNER

James Joyce

One of Percy French's most prominent admirers was the great Dublin-born writer James Joyce (1882–1941), who caricatured him in Finnegans Wake as 'Parsee French' as well as making several references to 'Phil the Fluter's Ball', 'Are Ye Right There, Michael?', 'Abdullah Bulbul Ameer', and various other of the 'troubadour's' familiar songs. Small wonder, then, that Joyce himself should have enjoyed writing parody. Apart from the elements of this to be found in his three great books, he also wrote a parody on the Irish theatre movement, 'The Day of the Rabblement' (1901); 'The Holy Office' (1904), accusing an Irish literary coterie of hypocrisy and self-deception; and 'Gas From a Burner' (1912), a biting condemnation of censorship which he originally printed at his own expense.

The lampoon had its origins in 1909 when Joyce signed a contract for the publication of his book, Dubliners, with George Roberts, the manager of Maunsel & Co in Dublin. Almost at once, Roberts began to have great doubts about the use of real names in the book, and so began a saga which lasted for three years in which he attempted to get Joyce to change certain passages. Joyce resisted this attempt at censorship, but when the two men reached an impasse which even solicitors representing them could not resolve, the author withdrew his work and took it elsewhere. A few days after leaving Dublin, he wrote the following parody which is ostensibly spoken by George Roberts, and was issued at his own expense in Paris. To add insult to injury, it has subsequently transpired that Joyce composed the first draft of 'Gas From a Burner' on the back of his contract with Maunsel & Co—an action that Swift, another of his influences, would surely have approved!

*   *   *

Ladies and gents, you are here assembled
To hear why earth and heaven trembled
Because of the black and sinister arts
Of an Irish writer in foreign parts.
He sent me a book ten years ago.
I read it a hundred times or so,
Backwards and forwards, down and up,
Through both ends of a telescope.
I printed it all to the very last word
But by the mercy of the Lord
The darkness of my mind was rent
And I saw the writer's foul intent.
But I owe a duty to Ireland:
I hold her honour in my hand,
This lovely land that always sent
Her writers and artists to banishment
And in a spirit of Irish fun
Betrayed her own leaders, one by one.
'Twas Irish humour, wet and dry,
Flung quicklime into Parnell's eye;
'Tis Irish brains that save from doom
The leaky barge of the Bishop of Rome
For everyone knows the Pope can't belch
Without the consent of Billy Walsh.
O Ireland my first and only love
Where Christ and Caesar are hand and glove!
O lovely land where the shamrock grows!
(Allow me, ladies, to blow my nose)
To show you for strictures I don't care a button
I printed the poems of Mountainy Mutton
And a play he wrote (you've read it I'm sure)
Where they talk of 'bastard', 'bugger' and 'whore'
And a play on the Word and Holy Paul
And some woman's legs that I can't recall
Written by Moore, a genuine gent
That lives on his property's ten per cent:
I printed mystical books in dozens:
I printed the table-book of Cousins
Though (asking your pardon) as for the verse
'Twould give you a heartburn on your arse:

I printed folklore from North and South
By Gregory of the Golden Mouth:
I printed poets, sad, silly and solemn:
I printed Patrick What-do-you-Colm:
I printed the great John Milicent Synge
Who soars above on an angel's wing
In the playboy shift that he pinched as swag
From Maunsel's manager's travelling-bag.
But I draw the line at that bloody fellow,
That was over here dressed in Austrian yellow,
Spouting Italian by the hour
To O'Leary Curtis and John Wyse Power
And writing of Dublin, dirty and dear,
In a manner no blackamoor printer could bear.
Shite and onions! Do you think I'll print
The name of the Wellington Monument,
Sydney Parade and Sandymount tram,
Downes's cakeshop and Williams's jam?
I'm damned if I do—I'm damned to blazes!
Talk about *Irish Names of Places*!
It's a wonder to me, upon my soul,
He forgot to mention Curly's Hole.
No, ladies, my press shall have no share in
So gross a libel on Stepmother Erin.
I pity the poor—that's why I took
A red-headed Scotchman to keep my book.
Poor sister Scotland! Her doom is fell;
She cannot find any more Stuarts to sell.
My conscience is fine as Chinese silk:
My heart is as soft as buttermilk.
Colm can tell you I made a rebate
Of one hundred pounds on the estimate
I gave him for his Irish Review.
I love my country—by herrings I do!
I wish you could see what tears I weep
When I think of the emigrant train and ship.
That's why I publish far and wide
My quite illegible railway guide.
In the porch of my printing institute
The poor and deserving prostitute

Plays every night at catch-as-catch-can
With her tight-breeched British artilleryman
And the foreigner learns the gift of the gab
From the drunken draggletail Dublin drab.
Who was it said: Resist not evil?
I'll burn that book, so help me devil.
I'll sing a psalm as I watch it burn
And the ashes I'll keep in a one-handled urn.
I'll penance do with farts and groans
Kneeling upon my marrowbones.
This very next lent I will unbare
My penitent buttocks to the air
And sobbing beside my printing press
My awful sin I will confess.
My Irish foreman from Bannockburn
Shall dip his right hand in the urn
And sign crisscross with reverent thumb
Memento homo upon my bum.

TALE TOLD IN DESTINY BAY

Donn Byrne

*Donn Byrne (1889–1928) was a flamboyant character who mixed
with high society on both sides of the Atlantic, but frequently
parodied the attitudes and morals of these men and women in his
novels and short stories. A man of great charm and wit, he was
born Brian Oswald Donn-Byrne and raised in Dublin, although he
educated himself largely by travelling around the world, taking jobs
wherever and whenever the opportunity arose. He was, for instance,
a cowhand in South America, a garage worker in New York and
a bartender in Europe. His first literary works were short, humorous
articles for some of the little Dublin magazines that appeared—
often all too briefly—during the early years of the century, and then
he turned to longer works of fiction for the popular monthly journals
published in London and New York. His novel,* Messer Marco
Polo *(1921) enabled him to become a full-time writer, and* Hang-
man's House, *published five years later, demonstrated his versatil-
ity. Even when living abroad, Donn Byrne frequently returned to
his Irish past for subject-matter, and the following brief tale is one
of several parodies he wrote about Irish social attitudes in which
native quick-wittedness is seen to have the last word over even the
most imposing sophisticate . . .*

*   *   *

Now when the High Hat Magician saw himself settled for the night
in the turf-cutter's cabin, a wave of kindliness came over him, and
he decided he'd show the turf-cutter some of the marvels of his
art. So he chucks a handful of powder on the fire, and a great
wave of blue smoke fills the little house. And in the heart of the
blue cloud, you could see as it were Dublin city: coaches rolling

up to the Houses of Parliament; merchants on Cork Hill counting spade guineas taken in the easiness of trade; bucks ruffling it down Bachelors' Walk; three-card-trick men at every corner; Dean Swift with his two wives; ladies of quality with Negro pages; King Billy on a white horse.

'What place might that be?' asks the turf-cutter.

' 'Tis Dublin,' says the High Hat Magician, 'the grandest capital on any sod.'

'Now is that a true picture of Dublin?' says the turf-cutter.

'It is,' says the High Hat Magician. ' 'Tis a picture made up out of old memories and natural genius.'

The turf-cutter gives a kick to his wife, drowsy on the pile of heather. 'Up, woman, and put the ass in the cart, for we're off to Dublin!'

'Are we off now, strong darling?'

'This very minute,' says the turf-cutter.

'For God's sake,' says the High Hat Magician, 'what about the supper you promised me? My two grilled trout, my soda bread with butter, my India tea, and the slug of whiskey to open the throttle, and the slug of whiskey to close it.'

'Oh,' says the turf-cutter, 'use your natural genius.'

THE TAILOR'S 'BUSHT'

Eric Cross

In the introduction to 'The Clan Thomas' there was an allusion to Eric Cross's The Tailor and Ansty, *a book of gusty zest and humour that tells the story of Tim Buckley, a tailor of Inchigeela, and his eloquent wife, Ansty. It is a work that has earned Cross comparison with James Boswell and his life of the wit and conversationalist, Dr Johnson. Certainly, the book did not deserve the ban placed upon it in 1942 by the Irish Censorship Board, but such was the ridicule heaped upon them as a result of the decision that the ban was lifted soon afterwards. Notwithstanding this, the book's reputation as slyly parodying aspects of Irish life has persisted.*

The author, Eric Cross (c. 1905–1980), was born the son of an Irish mother and English father in Newry, County Down, and worked for years as a research chemist, only rarely employing his undoubted gifts as a humorist in collections such as the notable Silence is Golden *(1978). The tale of 'The Tailor's "Busht"' is all about the visit of a sculptor to the Tailor's cottage in order to make a bust of the old man, and his comical reaction . . .*

* * *

I felt that strongly the time the Tailor's 'busht' was being made. For among the Tailor's many friends is Seamus Murphy, the sculptor, and when he proposed making this bust, the Tailor agreed on the spot.

'Damn it man, it was ever said that two heads are better than one and the one I have now I have had for seventy-five years and it is getting the worse for wear. Of course I'll have a new one!'

All the apparatus and materials were assembled and the Tailor inspected them with the interest of a fellow craftsman. Ansty ignored the business in the beginning. Her only interest in it was her resentment of the invasion of the 'Room'—'with all the ould clay and mortar to make a new divil'—and making fresh disorder of her disorder. The 'Room' at last justified the Tailor's name for and did become for a while what he calls it—'The Studio'. For an hour or so each day he posed and talked and commented. The measurements interested him and he linked this part of the business with his own craft.

'Many's the time that I have measured a man's body for a new suit of clothes but I never thought that the day would come when I would be measured myself for a new head.'

'I think that we will have a rest for a while,' suggested Seamus during one session.

'The divil a rest do I need. Do you know that I feel it less than I did the time the whole of my body was making before I was born. There is a considerable improvement in this method. A man can smoke and take his ease and chat away for himself.'

The news soon spread that the Tailor's 'image' was being made. Even The Sheep, on his weekly visit, mentioned it.

'I did hear tell, Tailor, that you are in the way of having your "image" made. I don't know. But I *did* hear tell.'

'Faith, I am,' agreed the Tailor, 'and a good strong one too. It is going to be made in bronze—the hardest metal that ever was. It was the metal that the Tuathaa de Danaans brought to Ireland with them and it will last for hundreds of years.'

'Indeed!' exclaimed The Sheep, settling down a little further on his stick. 'Tell me, Tailor,' he asked, with a show of interest, 'how will that be done?'

'Yerra, man alive. It's easy enough. You stick your head into a pot of stirabout and when it is cold you pull out your head and melt the metal and pour it into the hole your head made. Then you eat up the stirabout and you find your new head inside the pot.'

'Indeed!' grunted The Sheep. 'Indeed, that's wonderful enough.' The Sheep settled a little more securely on his stick to absorb and digest this new information. After a while he came out of his shell again. 'They tell me that it is unlucky for a man to have his image made, Tailor. Would this be like a photograph, now, could you tell me?'

The Sheep had always refused to stand for his photo.

'Th'anam o'n diabhal! Unlucky! It isn't half so unlucky as going to bed. Many a man had twins as the result of going to bed and, anyway, most people die in bed. If they had real sense they would keep out of bed and then the death would not catch them so easily.'

'Yes. Yes. I suppose that is true,' unreadily assented The Sheep and left very shortly after in case the Tailor might add another to his already great load of fears.

Ansty's interest was awakened when the clay began to take form. Then she was, in the beginning, afraid of it. She removed her cream pans from the Room to a cupboard under the stairs. Whatever curse may fall upon the place as the result of this latest prank of 'himself' the cream must be preserved from harm at all costs. But in spite of her fear, she could not resist a sally. From the safe distance of the doorway she watched the operation once or twice.

'Look at my divil! You'd think to look at him and the mug of him that he was a statoo in a chapel.'

Familiarity with the sight of the 'image' gradually made her contemptuous. But Old Moore did not like the idea at all. In the beginning it was mysterious to him and he could not understand it. When the image was taking form it roused all Old Moore's religious scruples.

'It isn't right, Tailor. It isn't right, I tell you. It's a graven image and it is against the commandments. The church is against it and all the popes.'

'Yerra, what harm! What harm can there be in a head? Didn't you make a couple of small lads, whole and entire, body, head, legs and all, with Nora, and you talk about an old head.'

Then 'Bydam Tighe' came in and he almost scratched his own head off in puzzlement at it. He could not understand it all.

'Bydam, Tailor, I hear that you are having a new head made.'

'That's true enough, Tighe. A brand-new head that will last a hundred years, made of bronze, the hardest substance there is. It won't be affected by the heat or the cold or the sun or the rain.'

'Bydam, that's queer. I never heard of that before.'

'It's a new patent, Tighe. They have got a new method of making people because the young people nowadays are failing at the job and the population of the country is going down.'

'Bydam, I didn't hear that.'

'There are a lot of new wonders in the world nowadays, Tighe. There's aeroplanes and cars and wireless and now this new way of making people.'

'Bydam, I have heard it said that wonders will never cease.'

'True for you, Tighe. Wonders will never cease so long as women kiss donkeys.'

Tighe disappeared to brush the road for a while. Then he came back to redden his pipe and to have another look at the Tailor's own head. He did not know that the 'image' was in the other room.

'Bydam, I was thinking, Tailor, will you be able to use it? Will you be able to talk and smoke and see with it?'

'Th'anam o'n diabhal! What the hell do you think that I am having it made for? Do you think that I want to become a dummy? I tell you that when I have this head I will be a different man. You have often heard tell that you can't put a young head on old shoulders. Well, this is what it is. I was thinking of having it the other way at first. Having a new body fitted to my old head. But the expense for the bronze was too much so I am starting with the head first. Then the new brains would not be so good as the old ones I thought. But then I thought that the old ones had done a power of thinking in their time and it would be better after all to start with the head.'

Tighe was lost in wonderment for a while.

'Bydam, Seamus Murphy must be a clever man.'

'Clever! I should think he is. He's as good as Daniel O'Connell and Owen Roe put together. They were good enough in the old-fashioned way but before he's finished with this business he'll have the whole of Ireland populated again. It is a much quicker way than the way you had of going about the business, Tighe.'

'Bydam, it must be. I must talk to herself about it tonight,' and Tighe went back to 'the most useless bloody job in the whole world', in the Tailor's opinion, brushing the road.

The daily sessions continued with interest and much verbal assistance from the Tailor. He remembered a story about a man who made a statue—but the story will not bear repetition.

'I think that if you tighten your mouth it would be better, Tailor,' suggested Seamus.

'True for you, Seamus. It is the loose tongue that does all the harm in the world. I remember a man by the name of ——' and it was a quarter of an hour before he stopped talking and the mouth was tight enough for the work to proceed.

He has one tooth left in his head. It is a very large canine which is completely useless but of which he is very proud. It even has a name. He has referred to it always as 'The Inchcape Rock'.

'I tell you that the tooth has enjoyed itself. It was no fun in its day when it had all its companions. They were the boys for you. Many's the half gallon of porter that has swirled around that, and many is the pig that it has made mincemeat of.'

'I am going to tackle your hair now, Tailor.'

'Fire away, Seamus, my boy. Fire away. I have forgotten how many there are of them, but they are all numbered, according to "the Book". But one wrong here or there won't make any difference. The divil a bit.'

Now and again Ansty peered into the room to see what progress was being made.

'Will you look at my ould shtal? Will you look at the puss on him? You'd think that he was all cream, sitting up there looking like a statoo in the chapel and divil doing nothing all the time but planning his lies and shtories.'

'You'd better get yourself tidied up a bit,' commanded the Tailor in the midst of one of her commentaries.

'Whyfore should I get tidied?' she asked with surprise.

'We'll have to go and see the priest when this is done.'

'For what, you divil?'

'Th'anam o'n diabhal! Don't be asking questions but do as you are told. We will have to go and get married again. You were only married to the old head and you will have to be married to the new head now or we will be living in sin.'

'Hould, you divil!'

The day for the plaster-casting arrived. The Tailor discovered all manner of possibly useful things for the job in Cornucopia— the butter-box he sits on. When at last the job was done he complimented Seamus. 'A damn neat job. It could not have been done better if I had done it myself.' The cast was trimmed and carried away for the metal casting. Then Seamus brought it back to Garrynapeaka and the whole valley was invited to the exhibition of 'The Tailor's New Skull'. It was placed on the stand in the dim light of the Studio with a dark cloth behind it. The door was closed. The guests were assembled. The stout and the beer and the whiskey were opened and all was expectancy. The occasion was graced by the presence of His Reverence—'The Saint'—another old friend of the Tailor's, whom Ansty calls 'the biggest divil in Ireland after himself', with a complete lack of reverence for the cloth. The Saint made a speech on the marvels of this new wonder and opened the Studio door with a string, revealing 'The Tailor's New Skull'.

There was the rapt silence of wonder for a moment. Then Ansty, who was bored with the whole affair and what seemed to her to be a quite unnecessary amount of fuss about nothing at all and who had bustled and pushed through the crowd, ripped the silence asunder:

'How are the hens by ye, Johnny Mac?'

Ansty's inconsequential remark brought the assembly back to earth. The Sheep had been gazing, with eyes agog, first at the Tailor and then at the image, scarcely able to believe what he saw. 'It's devilish. It's devilish, I tell you, Tailor.' He grunted assent with his own remark and hastened away from the house with his drink only half finished. Tighe was stirred to expression.

'Bydam!' he gasped, 'Bydam, but . . . do you know . . . but it greatly resembles the Tailor!' The Tailor himself hopped up to it and gave it a crack with his knuckles. 'There you are. A fine head. There's a head will wear out several bodies and it will break the jaws of any flea or midge that tries to bite it!'

'Look at him, will you? Look at my ould shtal,' breaks in Ansty, seeing a chance of pricking the Tailor's latest balloon, 'my ould devil of the two heads and the one he has already is no use by him. It's another bottom he needs for the one he has he's nearly worn out, sitting on it in the corner all day long, and shmoking and planning lies.'

'Wouldn't you like a bust of yourself done, Mrs Buckley?' asks the Saint, sweetly, almost certain of the reply.

'Busht! Busht!' Ansty snorts with contempt. 'If you want a match for that ould devil you can make a busht of my backside!

'And to think that Seamus made a busht of that ould devil as though he was a saint in a church. The man must be half cracked. As cracked as himself. Glory be! And to think that he wouldn't settle the leak in the chimney for me! And he with the good mortar and plaster, making a "*busht*"!'

THE SAUCEPAN

Lynn Doyle

Probably no Irish author has written better parodies of small-town life—or created a more wholly believable but imaginary community—than Lynn Doyle in his nine books about Ballygullion. The novels and stories about this place in County Down were drawn extensively from Doyle's own experiences as a bank manager, and there is obviously much of himself in Ballygullion's banker, Mr Wildridge. Other great favourites with readers were Mr Anthony, the solicitor, and Patrick Murphy, the narrator of the uproarious stories.

Lynn Doyle, the name on all these tales, was actually a pen-name which Leslie Alexander Montgomery (1873–1961) felt necessary to at least partially disguise his identity. Born in Downpatrick, he had invented the name while appearing as a young man with the Ulster Literary Theatre, a company set up in friendly rivalry to the Irish Literary Theatre. As his friend Sean MacMahon has explained, 'It was judicious in a respectable community to use a cover for one's play-acting, and Montgomery, as a bank official in Ulster, could not risk overt association with rogues and vagabonds so he signed his first full-length play, Love and Land *(1914) with the code name, "Lynn C. Doyle", which in time was used without the "C".' It was, however, for his Ballygullion books—the first published in 1908, the last in 1957—that Doyle became famous, although he was fascinated by Irish history, in particular by the United Irishmen of 1798, and wrote several tales on this theme. In 'The Saucepan', Doyle combines Ballygullion and the Battle of the Boyne in a story which he once selected for a collection entitled* My Funniest Story. *Time has done nothing to alter his verdict . . .*

*   *   *

The childher about Ballygullion is just like the childher everywhere else, they're terrible fond of imitatin' their eldhers. An' whenever the Orangemen marches out of the town on the twelfth of July, an' you're beginnin' to think ye'll get a bit of peace for your ears till they're comin' home again, out comes every wee fellow that can get hould of an ould tin can, an' batthers about till folks is near deaved.

I need hardly tell you, too, that them that stays behind in Bally-gullion on the twelfth is not of the persuasion that's likely to thole* it the best.

However, it's like Christmas, an' only comes once a year; an' as the one day does it, they put up wi' it the best way they can.

But about four or five years ago a lot of wee boys took the notion that it was a pity not to have more of a good thing; an' a party of Orangemen settin' out on the thirteenth for the sham fight at Scarva, nothin' would do the childher but they'd have a sham fight of their own at home.

It might ha' done all right, an' lasted to this day, if they'd kept it among their own sort; but wee Billy Black's son, that started the idea, thought it would give a kind of reality to the whole affair if they had some of the other side to do King James's men. An' so it did, an' a thrifle more than some of them expected.

There wasn't much throuble gettin' up the sides.

Wee Black's army was easy gathered, for most of them had got a holiday, an' wi' the other fellows keen to keep up the honour of the Irish, an' maybe seein' a chance of gettin' their own back afther all they'd tholed the day before, enough of them mitched from school to make up brave an' near as many to fight for King James.

The two armies took up their positions on each side of the wee river at the bottom of Ballygullion, both of them rigged out in great style, wi' belts an' wooden swords an' paper helmets on them. Billy Black's wee fellow, as bein' the one that got up the fun, couldn't be kept out of bein' King William, especially as he'd borrowed ould John Linchey's donkey to do the white horse; an' Murray the pawnbroker's son got doin' Schomberg on account of an ould horse-pistol an' a handful of caps he had stole out of the father's shop.

---

* Put up with, tolerate.

There was a deal of wranglin' an' disputin' about who was to be who on the other side. The biggest rush was for Pathrick Sarsfield, but when big Jacky McGra, the blacksmith's son, buttoned up his coat an' swore if anybody else wanted to be Pathrick Sarsfield he'd blacken his eye for him, they all turned their attention to who'd be King James. The wrestlin' an' wranglin' riz near as big as if it had been the rale thing, an' for a while it looked as if they were goin' to have a battle without waitin' for the enemy at all; till wee Sonny Morrison comin' up with a shield made out of a three-gallon pot lid, an' his mother's best saucepan on his head for a helmet, he was made King on the spot. An' troth, as it turned out, like ould King James himself, he had no great luck of the crown.

The leadin' men bein' once picked, the battle begun with a deal of spunk on both sides. For a good while it was fought at long range wi' balls of clay out of the river banks. Wee Brown, the rector's son, that was doin' Walker of Derry, got a clay ball in the pit of his stomach that give him the colic from that till Christmas; an' Pathrick Sarsfield got one in the face that made a sore differs to his side, for the battle was all over before he got the gutthers scooped out of his eye. But barrin' this, an' a terrible spoilin' of good clothes, there was no great harm done.

Then there riz a bit of a difference in the Orange Army. Schomberg kept blazin' away caps on the horse-pistol so like the rale thing that every boy on his side was fair green wi' envy, an' King William, seein' he was bein' made as good as nobody by it, rides up till him an' insists that it was time he died accordin' to the arrangement before they started.

Schomberg was no way willin' to do this, but his caps bein' at an end he makes a blarge wi' the last of them that near blew one of the ears off the ass, an' lies down dead in the clay at the edge of the river. His mother warmed him for that later on.

When the ass comes to afther the dazin' of the shot he gives his ears one shake, lets a couple of skreighs out of him between a squeal an' a hee-haw, an' intil the river, teeth an' heels busy, an' King William afther near goin' out over the tail makes the best of it, shouts to his men to come on, an' puts the ass at the opposite bank.

For a minit or two it looked as if it was to be the ould story over again. King James an' his men stood up manful again' the rest of the army, but they couldn't hould out again' the ass. The squealin' an' bitin' an' kickin' of him was somethin' lamentable, an' if King William could ha' sat him at all the battle was as good as won.

But a bad shot from his own side takin' the ass very threacherous in the rear, he clean forsook his colours altogether, rid himself of poor William wi' an exthra lift of his hind-end, an' away as if the divil was afther him, an' never stopped, barrin' for thrippin' every now an' then on the bridle, till he reached home.

This was great heartenin' for King James's men.

Down the bank they come with a rush, throwin' clay balls an' blowin' peas an' leatherin' round them wi' sticks, King James himself at the head of them doin' desperate execution with a four-foot length of garden hose he had stole out of Major Donaldson's garden, an' would ha' won the battle with his own hand only for the time he lost unwindin' it from round his neck every time he missed his blow.

As it was, him an' his men were well through the river an' the battle the same as ended, when, makin' a mighty spang up the bank, he puts his foot on Schomberg's face as he lay there dead.

'Twas an unlucky step for James.

Divil a word says Schomberg good or bad, but lepps to his feet an' fetches the butt end of the horse-pistol down on King James's helmet wi' both hands; an' the next minit the saucepan was sittin' on poor King James's shouldhers, an' him yellin' melia murdher from the inside; for the rim had had a difference wi' his nose on its way down, an' the nose had come badly out of it.

The battle was over in the clappin' of your hands.

Schomberg takes one look at what he'd done, dhrops the horse-pistol, an' off home for his life; an' both armies gathers young King James thryin' to quiet him, for the gowls of him inside the saucepan was like nothin' earthly, an' they were afeared of some of their mothers comin' down on them.

None of them thought very much of it at the first, for they deemed it wouldn't be much harder to get the saucepan off than it had been to get it on. But when they had worked at it for a quarther of an hour, an' near wrung King James's neck, an' still nothin' comin' of it, they begun to slip away quietly by ones an' twos, till at the last there was only about half a dozen or so left.

By this time King James begin to see that he was of some importance, an' stopped cryin' an' commenced to put on airs, an' was content enough to let the saucepan stay where it was. But the others was too uneasy in their minds to hear of that, an' when Pathrick Sarsfield come up from the rear they were as glad to see him as ever the Irishmen was at the Boyne.

'Here's big Jacky McGra,' sez one. 'Aye, here's Jacky,' sez another; 'he'll have it off in no time.' An' Jacky, bein' a big lusty fellow wi' a fair conceit of himself an' some experience of handlin' tools, was much of the same opinion himself.

'Stan' back an' gimme a chap at it,' sez he. 'If a horse-pistol put it on, sure it can take it off again.'

So they stood back an' let him at it.

Maybe it was the dirt in his eye, or maybe he was a bit nervous, but the first lick he took he missed the rim of the saucepan by about an inch, an' near put the rings of his backbone out of joint wi' the twist he give himself; an' the next blow takin' King James about the shoulder-blade an' startin' him on a worse gowl than ever, the whole party took to their heels an' off, thinkin' they had finished him, an' left him to make his way home the best he could.

More by good luck than good guidin', poor wee Sonny gropes his way up ontil the road. The mother's house was only a step or two away then, an' he got the length of it without breakin' his neck.

But och! the Boyne itself was nothin' to the row that riz when he did.

At the first fright of seein' the saucepan walk in an' sit down cryin' by the fire the mother dhrops the pot she was liftin' an' makes for the room door without a word, she was that frightened.

But when she made out 'twas wee Sonny was inside the saucepan, an' afther tuggin' at it till she was tired couldn't get him out of it, between cryin' an' lamentin', an' scoldin' at them that had put the saucepan on him, an' shoutin' at himself because he didn't take it off, she riz the very divil's own row; an' happenin' to be passin' by on my way intil Ballygullion I steps in to see who was bein' killed.

For a minit or two I couldn't for the life of me make out what was wrong; but when I did come at it nothin' but the disthress the poor crather of a mother was in would ha' kept me from laughin'.

First she'd start to tell me a bit more of the story, an' then in the middle of it break out roarin' an' cryin' that her wee son was ruined an' desthroyed, an' then all at once she'd get mad at the wee fellow for bringin' himself intil the scrape, an' would make at him wi' her hand up till she'd mind that his ears was well protected by the saucepan; an' wi' that she'd burst intil another tanthrum wi' the vexation that she couldn't get at him—all the time the saucepan hoppin' about with its hands up to save itself, every time she took a run-race at it, an' liftin' a cup or a plate off the dhresser every other minit wi' the handle. The divil a such a circus ye ever seen.

'Hould on, Mary, hould on,' sez I, at the last. 'Have ye thried all ye can to get it off him?'

'Thried is it, Misther Murphy,' sez she, breakin' out in a fresh roar. 'If I pulled an' ounce harder I'd a' had the ears off the child.

'An' 'deed small pity too if I did,' sez she, gettin' mad again, an' takin' a race at him. 'I've a big mind to pull it off him ears an' all, the—'

'Wait now, Mary, wait a minit,' sez I, gettin' between her an' the wee chap. 'Put on your shawl an' come up wi' me to the docthor's till we see what can be done. For if the child's head swells in it you'll never get it off him till they trail him to the graveyard by the handle.'

'You're right, Misther Murphy, you're right,' sez she, all in a splutther. 'Sure I might ha' thought of that before if my head hadn't been near turned. Come on, ye wee heart-scald ye, an' if I don't warm your lugs when the saucepan comes off them, my name's not Morrison. Gimme your hand.' An' she out wi' him with a tug that near pulled the arm off him, an' up the road.

When we got intil the surgery down come ould Dr Dickson chewin' the last bite of his dinner he'd put in his mouth, an' lookin' mighty cross at bein' disturbed.

'What's wrong now, Mrs Morrison?' sez he, feelin' for his glasses. 'What's this!' sez he, as he puts them on an' sees the saucepan. 'How'd he get this on his head? How'd ye get your head in this, boy?' sez he very sharp, bendin' down his ear to the child.

'Spake up an' tell the docthor,' sez the mother, bendin' down to the other ear—unlucky enough, as it happened, for the wee fellow turnin' round sharp to the mother's voice, fetches the docthor a welt on the bridge of the nose wi' the handle of the saucepan that knocked his eyeglasses intil the fendher an' starred one eye like a shop-windy with a stone through it.

'Away out of this, you an' your brat,' roars the docthor, dancin' round in a rage wi' the glasses in his hand. 'I'll charge ye wi' these, mind ye; I'll charge ye wi' these. I'll put them down in the bill—I'll—'

'Och, charge me what ye like, docthor dear,' sez the poor woman, half-cryin', 'only take the pot off his head for the love of God, or—'

'Take the pot off his head,' sez the docthor, still in a rage. 'How the divil would I take the pot off his head, barrin' I take the head off him wi' the handsaw an' them prise it off wi' a cold chisel. This is a job for a blacksmith,' sez he, feelin' round the boy's neck; 'take him away out of this.'

'Fetch him up to the blacksmith, Pat,' sez he to me. 'Ye aye like to have your finger in every pie.'

'But, docthor,' sez the mother, 'could ye not do *somethin'*? Could ye not pour somethin' on the pot would melt it?'

'I could,' sez he, 'only ye could put all would be left of the pot an' his head in a naggin bottle when I'd done. Away out of this, ye ould fool ye,' sez he, openin' the door, and pushin' the child out. 'Take him to the blacksmith's, an' he'll have the thing off his head in half an hour with a file. Here, come back,' sez he—he was a kindly man for all his short temper—'wait will I make yez up a pot of ointment. The child'll be bruised.

'Never mind, Pat,' sez he, as I went to call the boy back. 'Let him dandher on down the road. I'll not be more than a minit, if ye'll wait till I get my dinner over.'

So the mother an' I sits down for a bit, waitin' on the docthor, an' while we were there wee Sonny wandhers on down the road till he come to the wall between it an' the schoolhouse; an' just as he come fornent the schoolhouse itself, the masther happened to be lookin' out of the windy.

The masther, as everybody knowed, was no teetotaller, an' the twelfth of July comin' in at the end of the holidays, he had wound up wi' a terrible burst wi' one or two Orangemen he met comin' home from the field—just to show, as he said, that there was one broadminded man in this benighted counthry.

I'll say this for the wee man, he was no way bigoted about who he took a dhrink wi'. There's a deal of the same kind of broadmindedness about Ballygullion.

But anyway, whether the masther's mind had been broader than usual, or whether Michael Casshidy's twelfth of July whiskey didn't lie kindly on a Catholic stomach, the wee man was in a mortial bad way this day, an' wi' the thrimmle in his hand had put as many ins an' outs in the map of Ireland he'd been dhrawin' on the blackboard as would ha' bothered the best pilot on the coast. So thinkin' to steady his nerves a bit he went to the schoolroom windy for a mouthful of fresh air.

The first thing his eyes fell on was the saucepan; 'twas all he could see, for the wall.

'Who's been puttin' rubbish on the school wall?' sez he very cross. 'Here, Mickey McQuillan, run out an' take that thing away.'

'What thing, sir?' sez Mickey, comin' forward.

Just at that minit the saucepan begins to move. The masther takes a hard look at it, an' turns very pale.

'Mickey,' sez the masther, very quiet, 'do ye see a saucepan out there?'

'Where, sir?' sez Mickey, all in a flusther wi' the eye of the whole school on him.

'Out there, on the wall,' sez the masther, very short. 'Don't ye see it, ye gomeril!'

'Yes, sir; oh yes, sir,' sez Mickey in a hurry, though divil a thing he saw, good, bad, or betther, an' small blame to him; for the sash of the windy was a good two inches higher than his head, though the masther was too flusthered to notice that.

The saucepan stopped an' turned round, wi' Sonny Morrison turnin' his head to listen for the mother, an' then it began to move on again, very slow.

'Do ye see it movin', Mickey?' sez the masther in a kind of an off-hand way, as if it was nothin' much to him. 'Don't say it's movin',' sez he, breaking out very fierce.

'No, sir,' sez Mickey, edgin' away from the cane in the wee man's hand, 'it's not movin' at all, sir.'

The masther looks hard at the saucepan again, an' there, sure enough, it was walkin' along the wall.

'Mickey,' sez he, takin' a sthrong grip of himself, an' spakin' very slow an' quiet, 'are ye *sure* it's not movin'—positive?'

'Yes, sir,' sez Mickey, very anxious to please him, 'positive, sir.' An' wi' that the saucepan passes out of sight, with a desperate waggle of the handle through wee Sonny thrippin' on a stone.

'Holy Biddy,' sez the masther to himself, turnin' very white, an' thrimmlin' all over, 'this is terrible, this is terrible altogether. 'Twas that last glass in Michael's, or maybe the half pint I took home.

'I deserve it,' sez he, very bitther, 'I deserve it. This is what comes of dhrinkin' holiday whiskey—me that knows what good liquor is, too.

'But what's to be done at all,' sez he, dhroppin' down on a seat wi' his head in his hands. 'There's nothin' for it but the docthor,' sez he, startin' up again.

'Boys,' sez he, turnin' round to them all starin' at him, 'the school is dismissed. I'm not feelin' just at myself.

'Never mind me,' sez he, as one or two of them made to go over till him, 'I'll just sit down a minit or two an' then go home. Gather up your books an' slates quietly—*quietly!*' he roars as young Rafferty dhrops a slate wi' a clatther that made the wee man jump six inches straight up from the chair. 'An' if there's any—any rubbish on the school wall as you're goin' past, dhrive it—I mean, take it away.'

So the childher gathers up their bits of things, an' slips out very quiet, leavin' him sittin' there lookin' hard at the blackboard, an' ready to jump out of the windy if it as much as budged.

In the meantime Mrs Morrison an' me had been sittin' at the docthor's, she still lookin' down the road an' gettin' fidgetier every minit as she watched the wee chap stumblin' along; till at last when he thripped over the stone at the schoolhouse she could thole no longer, but down the road afther him, tellin' me to wait for the ointment.

The docthor kept me a brave while waitin', what wi' laughin' at the idea of the wee chap in the saucepan, an' then pickin' up his glasses an' gettin' angry when he looked at the wreck of them; an' at last when I did get out, who should I meet but the wee masther comin' up the road, desperate white an' shook-lookin'.

'What's wrong wi' ye, masther?' sez I; for, troth, 'twas sthrange to see the same wee man without a bit of a twinkle in his eyes. 'Has anythin' happened, that you're lookin' so glum?'

'Pat,' sez he, lookin' at me very hard, 'ye take a dhrop of dhrink like meself—maybe less, maybe less,' as he seen me goin' to say somethin', 'but still a brave dhrop. Tell me, did ye ever see anythin'—anythin' movin' about?' sez he, moistenin' his lips.

'Not that I mind,' sez I. 'I niver thried just that hard. But I've heard of people that did, customers of Michael's mostly, about a holiday or a fair day.'

'Did ye ever see a saucepan walkin' along a wall?' sez he, bendin' forward an' spakin' undher his breath.

I spotted the whole thing in a flash, but still kept my face straight. 'Never,' sez I; 'I never even heard of such a thing.'

'Well, I saw one walk along the schoolhouse wall a wee while ago,' sez the masther, lookin' back at the wall, an' then turnin' his head away very quick. 'Right along the wall it walked, from one end of it to the other, an' when it come to the far end it stopped an' wagged its tail at me. Pat,' sez he, 'I've got them, I've got them bad.'

'Tut,' sez I, 'ye'll be all right in a day or two. It might ha' been far more serious. A saucepan's not as bad as a snake,' sez I, to cheer him up; for I seen he was badly shook, an' I didn't want the thing to go too far.

'It's worse,' sez he, 'far worse. I could work wi' a snake. Sure St Pathrick banished them long ago,' sez he, wi' the wee'st bit of a twinkle in his eye, 'an' if I seen one I'd know 'twas only imagination. But when the kitchen utensils comes out an' prances up an' down the open sthreet in broad daylight it's time somethin' was done. An' all, mind ye, on less whiskey, spread over a whole day an' a deal of the night, than I've had many a time between my dinner an' my tea.

'I'm a done man, Pat,' sez he, lookin' at me very melancholy. 'I'm goin' down the hill fast. The last of the MacDermotts is goin' to end his days little betther than a teetotaller.'

'Ye should go up an' see the docthor,' sez I.

'It's just where I'm goin' this very minit,' sez he. 'Tell me, though, Pat,' sez he, cockin' his eye at me very anxious, 'he wouldn't want me to take the pledge, d'ye think? For troth, if he did, I'd rather thole. The remedy would be worse than the disease.'

'He'd never think of it,' sez I. 'Sure he's been livin' in Ballygullion too long.'

'Come on back wi' me then, Pat,' sez he, 'an' we'll hear what he says.'

But when the docthor heard the case, wi' all the winkin' I did, an' I near give meself paralysis of the right side of my face, he could hardly contain himself. He'd never ha' kept in if he hadn't seen the chance of a lifetime to straighten the masther up.

'There's no use disguisin' it, Misther MacDermott,' sez he, lookin' very solemn, 'this is a very serious business.'

'Divil a doubt of it,' sez the masther. 'The cold thrimmles is runnin' down my backbone this minit. Ye should tell that servant of yours to shut the kitchen door when she comes to open for anybody at the front. There was a wicked-lookin' ould saucepan sittin' upon a shelf that near turned me back again, an' me in the very hall.'

I could see by this the masther was comin' round a bit.

'Don't make a joke of if, Misther MacDermott,' sez the docthor. 'You're on the verge of a nervous breakdown, an' maybe of insanity,' sez he, very slow an' weighty. 'There's only one thing can save ye.'

'What's that, docthor?' sez the masther. But I could see by his face he knowed right well.

'You'll have to abstain from all intoxicatin' liquors for some time,' sez the docthor. 'Nothin' else is of any good.'

'How much do I owe ye, docthor?' sez the wee man, gettin' up. 'I'd rather face the saucepans. Maybe I'll get used to them in time.'

'Ye owe me nothin',' sez the docthor. 'I'll take no money from a dyin' man. It's my duty to tell ye it's very unlikely, if ye persist in your present way of livin', that ye'll be alive this day month. Good bye, Misther MacDermott,' sez he, houldin' out his hand.

The cold sweat broke on the wee man. First he looked at me an' then at the docthor, but we were both as solemn as judges, though I'd ha' given half-a-crown for a good laugh.

'How long would do, docthor?' sez he, in desperation. 'I'll face it for a while. 'Twould be a pity for me to go off before the school examinations, an' lose my result fees.'

'Three months,' sez the docthor, 'at the very least.'

'Ye might as well say years, docthor,' sez the wee man. 'It couldn't be done at all. Sure I might as well die of the horrors as the drouth. When are the Ballygullion Races, Pat?' sez he to me.

'This day four weeks, masther,' sez I.

'Very well, docthor,' sez he. 'I'll take the pledge for four weeks short of a day, an' divil an hour longer, should the kitchen range come out an' dance a polka in front of me.'

'It's no manner of use,' sez the docthor. 'Ye wouldn't ha' lost the taste for dhrink by that time.'

'An who tould ye I wanted to lose the taste for it?' sez the masther very sharp, 'a man wi' the gift of dhrinkin' whiskey that I have. What would become of Michael Casshidy if I lost the taste for dhrink? He'd be in the poor-house in a twelve-month. Sure he whitewashed the whole premises an' repainted the signboard out of my last quarther's salary. Ye have no considheration for the public institutions of the town at all, docthor. Four weeks, short of a day, as I said—or nothin'.'

There was no use aimin' too high an' missin' altogether, so afther arguin' a bit more the docthor give in an' bound the masther over for the time he said, wi' me for a witness; an' the wee man an' I goes back down the road.

There wasn't a word spoke. The masther walked wi' his head down, an' the tall hat on the back of his head, as miserable-lookin' as if the whole of his friends was dead an' buried; an' as for me I aye kept wondherin' what he'd do or say when he found out how he'd been thricked. I hadn't long to wait.

Just as we come to the schoolhouse, who should we meet but Long Tammas McGorrian, in a great hurry.

'Masther,' sez he, all out of breath, 'I wish ye'd step up to the blacksmith's an' see what ye could do wi' Sonny Morrison'—('Now for it!' sez I)—'he's got his head fixed in a saucepan,' goes on Tammas.

'What's that ye say, Tammas?' sez the masther, all thrimmlin'. 'What's that about a saucepan?'

'The wee fellow's got his head fixed in a saucepan, God knows how,' sez Tammas, 'an' has been walkin' about all mornin' an' can't get it off. The blacksmith has it by the handle in a vise, an' has creeshed the child's head well an' wants him to pull hard enough to get out; but he won't, for all we can do. Maybe you could persuade him. He'd be afeared of you.'

But the masther said nothin' for a minit or two, but leaned up agin the wall.

'Four weeks,' sez he till himself, very low an' bitther, 'four weeks, wantin' a day. Oh, Holy Biddy, an' me passin' Michael Casshidy's twice every day at the very least. Wait a minit, Tammas,' sez he, leppin' up, 'wait till I get my cane, an' if I don't have him out of it, should he leave the whole side of his head behind him, he'll not sit down aisy from this to the Ballygullion races anyway.' An' he intil the schoolroom like a ragin' lunatic.

But he fumbled a while at the gate, wi' the splutther he was in, an' I just had time to explain matters to Tammas.

'Run, Tammas, run now,' sez I. 'You're longer in the legs than I am. If the wee fellow isn't out before the masther comes, the blacksmith himself won't be able to save him. Run, man!'

Away goes Tammas like a hare, an' me afther him all I was fit, to see the fun. But before I reached the forge the masther was near on top of me.

I could hear the shouts of Tammas, an' the rest of them inside. 'Pull, sonny, pull; he's comin'!'

'Pull, ye boy ye,' shouts Tammas; 'here he's at the door. By the mortial, he's got ye!'

But that minit wee Sonny gives a last wrestle an' a yell, an' out of the saucepan an' through the backdoor just as the masther in at the front one wi' the cane swishin' round him like a flail. One or two of us got in front of the masther, but we needn't ha' bothered ourselves. If the real King James only run as hard from the Boyne as Sonny Morrison did from the blacksmith's shop, it's small wondher he was the first of his men to get to Dublin.

TOM GERAGHTY'S IMAGINATION

Donagh MacDonagh

From a tale of small-town life we move to a parody of the Irish legal system by an author as intimately acquainted with his subject as the previous contributor. Donagh MacDonagh (1912–1968) was a lawyer who worked for much of his life on the Western Circuit of Ireland where, by his own account, he had a 'lean but colourful career' culminating in 1947 in his appointment as a Justice of the District Court. He was the son of Thomas MacDonagh, one of the seven signatories of the proclamation of the Republic, who was shot in 1916. The older man was also an enthusiastic writer, and encouraged Donagh to take a Master's degree which he passed with honours with a treatise on the poetry of T. S. Eliot.

Although the law became his life, MacDonagh used the times when he was not occupied at the Bar writing plays such as the very successful Happy as Larry, *several volumes of poetry and innumerable short stories—mostly humorous and many inspired by the world of law and lawyers. He possessed a rich Irish brogue and was a frequent broadcaster recounting stories of Irish life, and although 'Tom Geraghty's Imagination' was not published until shortly after his death, readers who remember the author on the radio might well hear his voice again as he recounts the following amusing story of love and the effects of drink . . .*

*   *   *

The prisoner was impressed by the size and ugliness of the place even before the great door was swung open by a warder, and when he entered and saw a gate within, and another beyond, he realised that he must be a dangerous criminal indeed.

The two Civic Guards who had accompanied him from

Ballyhoney looked strange and inimical in these steely surround-
ings, no longer the country lads who had given him tea and cigarettes on their journey. As they mentioned to the warder the big
word that was tied like a label around his neck they assumed
discipline and importance.

He was taken from them, led through gates with large locks,
through doors, through corridors; his name—Myles Mongan—
was inscribed in books, his fingers smeared with black and rolled
on paper; he was stared at, whispered of; strange hands gripped
his biceps and led him on, and after a considerable time he was
brought to a cell where he was at long last left alone.

He sat on the small bed there, not thinking particularly, but
feeling bewildered. He was a man of fifty-two, rugged, hairy,
upright in bearing, brown-faced and healthy, a tinker descended
from generations of tinkers, a landless, homeless man, adrift on
the roads of Ireland.

Three days before at the fair of Ballyhoney, he had sold a horse;
he and his wife Mary had gone to Gallagher's public house for a
drink. The drink supplied by Mr Gallagher to tinkers on fair days
had, as he said, 'a lift to it'. At 10.45 p.m. in the course of an
argument, the purport of which was now obscure to him, Myles
Mongan had struck his wife an almighty blow which brought her
head into violent contact with a spiked railing, and he had soon
afterwards been informed by the law that he was a murderer.

This did not seem sensible to him. He had been fond of his
wife, had frequently struck her in the past without any legal consequences. That this unfortunate dispute should be a matter of interest to gentlemen so exalted and busy as the Attorney-General
surprised him further.

The door of his cell opened and a tall, well-made, red-faced
man entered, a warder with a mug of tea.

'You'll be Mongan,' he stated. Mongan nodded. 'Well, don't
look so sour about it. You'd think nobody ever done a murder
before. If I'd a pound for every man I saw go to the gallows!'

Mongan found this approach refreshing. Since the unlucky blow
he had been regarded with fear and distrust by all he had met, as
though sending the soul of his wife to eternity had dehumanised
his own soul for ever.

'Aye, there's a lot of them come here the same way—no sperrit
left, no pride, do you know; but after a few days it's wonderful

the way they begin to perk up; getting self-important, do you see, with all the short timers staring at them. It won't be long till you're the cock of the walk here. Sure there's nobody in the same class since they hanged poor Cleneghan last week, God rest his soul.'

'Amen,' said Mongan piously.

'There's a couple of big black-market fellows and an embezzler, and a couple of manslaughters, company directors they call themselves, but between you and me and the bedpost their noses will be sadly out of joint by this time tomorrow. Was it poison?'

'Oh, God forbid.'

'I'm glad. Sure, poison is only a mean, tricky kind of a murder. It was the wife, I believe?'

'It was, God be good to her,' Mongan said, and the warder raised his cap. 'I don't know rightly how it began. A bit of a push I gave her and her head hit something. God knows, the law is a queer yoke.'

'It's true for you. You'll have a good solicitor and barrister engaged, I'll warrant.'

'Yerra, where would I get the money for the like of them? I've nothing between myself and the scaffold this minute only the mercy of God.'

This was what the warder had been playing for. He was an ex-policeman named Tom Geraghty, a kindly man enough, fond of his bottle, willing to do a good turn if he was sure of recompense, venal in small matters, honest in great. He had for some years had a working arrangement with a solicitor of a repute which could not be termed dubious, since there was no doubt about it, and a barrister of small practice. This had been greatly to their mutual advantage. Many rural persons brought to the great prison on capital or other serious charges were unaware of the paternal interest taken in them by the State, and it was Tom Geraghty's practice to inform them of their rights. Mongan seemed a suitable subject.

'When a man has his neck in a noose, saving your presence, there's only one thing that's any use to him,' he said.

'A good confession and a firm purpose of amendment?' said Mongan helpfully.

'Arrah, you're not that far gone at all, man. No. The thing a man in that condition needs more than anything else is a good solicitor and a good counsel. Do I make myself clear?'

'You should have great experience in such matters,' said Mongan.

'I have. And a man that was wanting a good solicitor, the best solicitor, and a good counsel, the best counsel, couldn't go further than certain men that I could mention if I had a mind to.'

'I wouldn't doubt you.'

'Now, there's a very eminent solicitor by the name of,' he paused impressively, 'by the name of James Francis Xavier Connors. You've heard of him?' Mongan mendaciously nodded his head. 'He has an office the size of the Kingsbridge Railway Station and a staff of clerks the like of a bank. Now, he'd be the man I'd engage.'

'I've no doubt you would. But didn't I tell you I haven't a tosser.'

In careful reply to which, Geraghty explained the system by which solicitor and counsel are assigned to those unable to pay for their defence, explained that in addition to enjoying the confidence of the eminent solicitor J. F. X. Connors, he had the good fortune to be acquainted with Seymour Moynihan the distinguished ornament of the Irish Bar. With these two men assisting him Morgan might already consider himself a free tinker, with the roads of Ireland waiting impatiently for his familiar tread.

Mongan rose from the bed and shook Geraghty warmly and gratefully by the hand.

James Francis Xavier Connors had been admitted a solicitor in the year 1910, but he had not built what his obituary would describe as a 'large and lucrative practice'. Indeed, if building be the correct metaphor, it might be said that his practice resembled a diminutive and semi-ruinous mud-cabin. His palatial offices spread their ample carpets only in the mind of Tom Geraghty, and his most usual fee for appearing in the courts of inferior jurisdiction was the sum of two shillings and sixpence, or two bottles of stout, whichever was the more readily forthcoming. He was unimpressive in physique, and the fact that he had not, as yet, misappropriated any of his clients' money was due principally to the fact that none had been entrusted to him. His Court manner was pompous and consciously hollow, and such triumphs as he won were probably the result of a kind of contemptuous pity from the bench.

Only when dealing in matters of life and death was he in a

position to instruct counsel and his choice on such occasions was invariably Seymour Moynihan, a man who had 'drunk himself out of the finest practice in Ireland', who 'could have been Chief Justice today if he'd watched his step'. In this, as in most myths, there was some truth. He had been young, hopeful and brilliant, who now was old, bitter and drunken. He had been an orator in the great *nisi prius* tradition; now his periods were ornate and sententious, trying to the judge, ludicrous to the jury, laughable to the press. A settled melancholy and the ineffectual anodyne of drink had produced this broken Cicero.

Seeing this curious pair appear in court for assignment, many a judge had found time to wonder at the gullibility of men, facing the uncertain gulf of eternity, entrusting their lives to so precarious a bridge.

Myles Mongan, to whom a small market-town was a metropolis, found nothing odd about his proposed solicitor and counsel when they were introduced to him by Tom Geraghty. The shine at elbow and shoulder-blade, the missing button, the frayed cuff had no message for him since he had no standard of comparison, and when Seymour Moynihan, large and heavy and old, filled the cell with his rich, alcoholic voice it seemed that here indeed was the great counsellor of Tom Geraghty's imagination.

The barrister took Mongan step by step through his story, counted with him the numbers of drinks he had received from Mr Gallagher, elicited a statement of regard and esteem for the deceased, and warned him to keep a silent tongue in his head at the preliminary investigations at the District Court.

'And do not allow this gloomy environment to weigh upon your spirits or tempt you to the sin of despair,' he said in departing. 'Mr Connors and I, you may be assured, my dear Mongan, will have nothing but your interests at heart until we have restored you to liberty and the pursuit of those itinerant joys from which you have been illiberally and, if I may say so, so improperly—ah—subducted.' And he followed his stomach from the cell, leaving as comfort to Myles Morgan a cloud of unfamiliar words and the familiar aroma of Irish whiskey.

Depositions were taken at the District Court at Ballyhoney, drab proceedings in a drab and dreary room. To Myles Mongan it was unreal. His life was among whey-headed women, piebald horses, the long-toothed rain, and as he sat daily in the little courthouse his thoughts were of the feckless days of cart and caravan, and when he was returned for trial to the Central Criminal Court it meant little to him, except that the two brilliant lawyers could now watch his interests more closely.

The two brilliant lawyers were duly assigned to his defence, a copy of the Depositions and the Indictment was made available to them, and they happily prepared for a lengthy murder trial, in the course of which every one of the ninety-seven witnesses who were being brought from Ballyhoney would be exhaustively cross-examined.

Two days before the case was listed for hearing, young Mr Maguire, of the Chief State Solicitor's Office, telephoned to Mr Connors.

'This is about the Mongan case,' he said. 'I've been talking to the Attorney.'

'Yes?' said Mr Connors.

'Between ourselves, and under your hat, he doesn't think the murder rap will stand up, and after reading the Depositions I'm inclined to agree with the old man for once.'

'Yes,' said Mr Connors.

'So, off the record and all that, we'll be prepared to accept a plea to manslaughter. Will you get in touch with the big man and tell him?'

J. F. X. Connors gave a mumble into the telephone, hung up in disgust and put on his worn overcoat to go to the Law Library.

Walking rapidly down the wintry Quays he reviewed the situation. A murder trial with an almost inevitable acquittal at the end of a week or ten days had been an excellent proposition from the point of view of both business and prestige. His name and Moynihan's would have been on the front page of the newspapers each evening, and a suitable cloud of dust and smoke would have disguised the fact that the outcome of the trial was predestined.

The fees allowed by the State on assignment were not gaudy, yet more than either he or Moynihan could hope to earn by other means—they represented, in fact, cases of whiskey, crates of stout, shelves of good food. Now, through the irresponsible whim of the Attorney-General, all this was to be exchanged for the familiar shallows and miseries. A mere plea of Guilty to Manslaughter carried a fee as parsimonious and unimaginative as the crime itself. Ah, for the brave generosity of Murder!

He rushed through the gowned crowd into the Law Library, had Seymour Moynihan called, and told him of the shabby trick proposed by the Attorney-General. Seymour Moynihan, who always wore his wig and gown whether he was briefed or not, so as to give the impression that he was working, pulled irritably at his linen bands.

'The thing is palpably absurd,' he said. 'Monstrous in fact. Are we to allow poor Mongan to go through life branded as a criminal, bearing the mark of Cain on his innocent brow? Nay. Not so. We have a duty to our client, a duty to society itself. Mongan shall not live so marked and branded. Never shall it be said that Seymour Moynihan failed to break a lance in defence of the right. Think of the fee, Connors. Think of the fee if we plead. Four-four. Monstrous. Ring that young man, Connors, and tell him we fight. Not for us the primrose path of *nolle prosequi*.' And Mr Connors, thinking deeply of the diminutive fee of four guineas, went away to ring Mr Maguire at the Chief State Solicitor's Office.

The case opened at Green Street Courthouse on a churlish February day. The wind, still sea-salt after its passage over the city roof-tops, encircled the harsh old building, and Myles Mongan in the great dock in the centre of the Courthouse was grateful in his tinker's heart for the central heating.

Leading for the State was Newsome Kennedy, an undistinguished, but reliable Senior, who was accompanied by a brand-new Junior in a shiny white wig. Neither was so impressive as Seymour Moynihan, looking in his aged wig and gown like a grandfather seagull.

On the bench was Mr Justice Brennan, a new political appointment whose Bar practice had been entirely on the Chancery side. It was his first criminal trial and his first experience of criminal matters outside the covers of the textbooks. The ninety-seven witnesses for the State were called, and proved what everyone soon knew, that Myles Mongan had struck his wife in a drunken rage at the fair of Ballyhoney, and that in falling she struck her head on a spiked railing and subsequently died.

Examination in chief and cross-examination went interminably on, the jury nodded sleepily in the heat, Myles Mongan was called and told his story, the white-wigged junior closed for the State and Seymour Moynihan—who, fearing a premature conclusion, had deliberately refrained from asking for a Direction at the close of the State case—closed for the defence.

Then His Lordship summed up at agonising length, reading from his notebook everything the ninety-seven witnesses had said. He addressed the jury on the law, he made profound observations on the sanctity of human life, and he dismissed them to their deliberations.

Twenty-three minutes later they returned with a verdict of Guilty.

Then there was trouble and great commotion. The Attorney-General rang the Chief State Solicitor; the Chief Commissioner of the Civic Guards rang the Attorney-General; the Chief State Solicitor rang Newsome Kennedy asking why the charge had not been reduced, this one rang that one and that one rang another.

However it was at last agreed that Messrs Moynihan and Connors must never again be assigned to a criminal case; it was agreed that Mr Newsome Kennedy and his juvenile junior must never again prosecute in a criminal case; it was agreed that Mr Justice Brennan must never again adjudicate in a criminal case, but at the end of all this agreement one obstinate fact remained. Mr Myles Mongan, itinerant tinsmith, had been condemned to death in due form.

Seymour Moynihan was disbarred, James Francis Xavier Connors was struck from the rolls, Tom Geraghty was sacked. Myles Mongan, knowing nothing of his interference in these distinguished lives, played Forty-five in the condemned cell.

In granting his application for leave to appeal, kindly arranged for him by the Attorney-General, their three Lordships of the Court of Criminal Appeal had some rather harsh things to say about the framing of the Indictment, the trial, and their learned brother Brennan J. They left the readers of the daily news-sheets with the impression that Myles Mongan was the victim of some gigantic and inhuman conspiracy, that he was entitled as of right to the large sum which was soon collected by popular subscription, that he was well away from the world of uniforms and gowns and wigs and ensnaring documents; and who will say that this was wrong?

A month later Myles Mongan had a new caravan and a new wife. Once again it was fair day in Ballyhoney; once again the tinkers were there with their piebald horses and their whey-headed children, their tubed hunters and their pewter florins.

Once again Myles Mongan sold a horse and once again he and his wife went to drink at Gallagher's public house where the drink has 'a lift to it'. Once again he and his wife reeled into the street at closing time, arguing about a matter of little importance, and once again he raised his hand to administer a disciplinary blow.

As he did so, however, a memory of Dublin, of the great lawyers, of the small black silk square on the judge's wig, cut through the thickening drink cloud, and he turned slow, dazed eyes on his wife.

Her face was young and fresh under her tow-coloured hair, and her figure was sweet and new. Might not a man be fond of his wife, and yet strike her, without the Attorney-General interfering? He reached into his pocket and taking a half-full whiskey bottle from it pushed it towards her. 'Drink up, Annie girl,' he said, 'drink up, and don't let me be hitting you. Those lawyer fellows take a queer view of a blow.'

Side by side in the moonlight they drank from the bottle until it was empty, and then went singing back to the new caravan.

THE WHITE IRISH SOCIETY

Patrick Campbell

The Anglo-Irish language has probably been subject to more parodies than any other in the world. In truth, many of the nation's leading humorists have been happy to take advantage of this fact from time to time, but none have made quite such a career out of it as the 3rd Baron Glenavy, better known to one and all as Patrick Campbell (1913–1980). Although renowned as a comic writer, Paddy Campbell also turned a slight speech impediment into a 'badge of personality'—to quote the critic Maurice Richardson— which made him an enormously popular television personality.

Born in Dublin, Campbell discovered his talent for humour while working on the Irish Times. *During the Second World War he served in the Irish Navy, thereafter rejoining his newspaper and initiating a weekly column, 'The Irishman's Diary', in which he commented in his own unique style on the foibles of human nature—not the least of them, his own. The best of his comic essays and stories are to be found in collections such as* A Short Trot With a Cultured Mind *(1952) and the story of his Dublin newspaper days,* My Life and Easy Times *(1967). 'The White Irish Society' was originally published in 1965 and offers another of Campbell's wonderful tongue-in-cheek looks at Irish customs and the language in particular.*

*   *   *

We, of the White Irish Society for the Abolition of Discrimination against St Patrick's Day, hereby make our annual protest against gross and malicious provocation by organised groups of British nationals, who once again sought to turn this day of quiet prayer and meditation into a—into a sort of a class of a hooley, wit'

buckets of shtout runnin' in the gutthers an' fellas gettin' belted—
A'hem.

The *agents provocateurs* were out early, at their dirty work. The BBC, if you please—though you'd think them eejits had throubles enough of their own without trying to stir it up for decent, law-abidin' people. Where was I, Joe? Good for you . . .

The *agents provocateurs* were out early, at their disagreeable task an' if there's any bowsie here present that thinks we're all Paddy the Slob from Ballydehob an' can't speak French with the best of them let him stand up now or for ever—

I'm *goin'* easy, Joe. Sairtinly. Well, in that case why don't you come an' thry it yourself, yah big, ugly-lookin' bosthoon yah—
A'hem.

The *agents provocateurs* of the BBC fell to their unlovely work betimes, interrupting a musical programme of their own folk songs—'Yeah, Yeah, Yeah', 'Doo-wadda Doo-wadda', and the like—to announce that the weather forecast would be read, in honour of St Patrick's Day, by one Seamus O'Kelly.

For a moment we had some hope that a genuine and sincere tribute was about to be paid to our great Saint—until we heard the voice of this alleged O'Kelly.

My dear—absolutely *grotty*. A drag. Practically 'the mist that does be on the bog'. That weary old kick. You know?

What's that, Joe. You don't know. But you do know I'm gettin' soft. That I'm going' over to th'other side. Hold him fellas! Dhrag the jacket over his head till I give him a belt of me—
Your pardon.

This alleged Seamus O'Kelly, after giving us—as I have said—some of the more watery passages from the works of J. M. Synge, mercifully returned then to read the correct weather report in the normal accents of Chorley Wood, but the damage had been done, the gauntlet had been thrun down, the coat-tail thrailed . . .

What one means to say is that with the very first weather report from the BBC, a subject neutral enough in all conscience, the direct and provocative suggestion had been made that there was something special about St Patrick's Day, that it was, in fact, an occasion for humour, for parody, for the singling out of the entire Irish nation as figures of fun. Nor did the BBC leave it at that. The very next piece of folk music they played was a record of Bing

Crosby singing a song about the St Patrick's Day parade in New York.

The first couple of lines of this travesty of Irish culture contained the words 'colleen', 'bejabers' and 'shillelagh', and went on into the 'Hannigan, Rattigan, Carrigan, Flanagan, Dooley and Tooley and Burke and Mahone' recitative, presumably being an attempt to reproduce extracts from the Dublin telephone book.

As a song of praise to St Patrick on his Day it was too trivial to bear contemplation. As a weapon of discrimination, however, it was as brutal a blow as we of the White Irish Society have ever received. Not only did the BBC try to discriminate against the Irish in the British Isles, but they endeavoured to extend the smear to the United States of America as well, to indicate that Apartheid for the Irish was virtually world-wide . . .

Will yah shut up, Joe. I *am* gettin' on wit' it, amn't I? What's your hurry, annyway? They aren't open yet, are they? An' I can tell you there's no use in scratchin' on the back door of Mooney's in this sufferin' counthry before openin' time. Shure, they're hide-bound here wit' legislation . . . An' you, too. An' your big git of a brother . . .

Excuse me.

All day long, then, on this day of quiet prayer and meditation, the provocation went on, the *agents provocateurs* continued with their deadly work. Irishmen accosted everywhere in the public streets.

'Hello, there, Pat—why aren't you drowning the shamrock? I thought you'd be half-seas over by now.' And this as early as midday!

We countered it, we of the White Irish Society, with resistance as passive as we could muster, with the tongue rather than the sword. We adjured our tormenters to go and have a bark at themselves, rather than letting them have the skelp across the kisser they deserved. I mean, it's more than flesh and blood can stand havin' to listen to these thin-blooded, pasty-faced, Puritan English fellas thryin' to dhrive us decent, abstemious Irish to dhrink just to bring a bitta colour into their own miserable little . . .

All right, Joe, I'm comin', amn't it? What's your hurry? Haven't we got all day and night . . . ?

4

LEG PULLS

Satirical Tales

'A Tale of a Churn', by Alfred Croquil from *The Reliques of Father
Prout* by Francis Mahony.

A MODEST PROPOSAL

Jonathan Swift

The great pioneer of satire in Ireland was undoubtedly Jonathan Swift (1667–1745), although there had been a few anonymous earlier pieces of verse that might just fit this category, such as 'The Land of Cokaygne' and a curious manuscript entitled 'A Satire on the People of Kildare' which is actually about the inhabitants of Dublin! Swift himself was born in Dublin, the son of English parents, and was educated at Kilkenny Grammar School and Trinity College, Dublin, where he got into several scrapes and only obtained his degree by 'special grace'.

Swift was able to obtain a post as a secretary, and this work soon brought him into contact with the larger world which he was to lampoon so brilliantly. He first came to public attention in 1704 with A Tale of a Tub, *which satirised religious dissension, and he built a reputation as a brilliantly caustic political pamphleteer. In 1726 he published* Gulliver's Travels, *which remains to this day one of the world's most famous satires with its jibes aimed at politics, religion and science.*

Although Swift certainly hated much about Ireland, he campaigned vigorously on behalf of Irish trade and the nation's poor. A Modest Proposal *was published in 1729 with the sub-heading, 'For Preventing the Children of poor People in Ireland, from being a Burden to their Parents or Country, and for Making them Beneficial to the Public'. Sir Walter Scott, who was responsible for editing the first collection of Swift's writings, noted in 1824 that a foreign author was said to have considered the Proposal as serious, 'and to have quoted it as an instance of the extremity under which Ireland laboured, that a man of letters had seriously recommended to the rich to feed upon the children of the poor'. The importance of this celebrated satire has been broadly recognised by modern scholars, including James M. Cahalan, who says, 'In its wildly apt fantasy and humble, pleading voice, Swift's* Proposal *looks ahead to some of the best Irish novels with irony at their core, such as Eimar O'Duffy's Cuanduine trilogy and Flann O'Brien's* The Poor Mouth.'

*   *   *

It is a melancholy object to those who walk through this great town, or travel in the country, when they see the streets, the roads, and cabin-doors, crowded with beggars of the female sex, followed by three, four, or six children, all in rags, and importuning every passenger for an alms. These mothers, instead of being able to work for their honest livelihood, are forced to employ all their time in strolling to beg sustenance for their helpless infants; who, as they grow up, either turn thieves for want of work, or leave their dear native country to fight for the Pretender in Spain, or sell themselves to the Barbadoes.

I think it is agreed by all parties, that this prodigious number of children in the arms, or on the backs, or at the heels of their mothers, and frequently of their fathers, is, in the present deplorable state of the kingdom, a very great additional grievance; and, therefore, whoever could find out a fair, cheap, and easy method of making these children sound, useful members of the commonwealth, would deserve so well of the public, as to have his statue set up for a preserver of the nation.

But my intention is very far from being confined to provide only for the children of professed beggars; it is of a much greater extent, and shall take in the whole number of infants at a certain age, who are born of parents in effect as little able to support them, as those who demand our charity in the streets.

As to my own part, having turned my thoughts for many years upon this important subject, and maturely weighed the several schemes of our projectors, I have always found them grossly mistaken in their computation. It is true, a child, just dropped from its dam, may be supported by her milk for a solar year, with little other nourishment; at most, not above the value of two shillings, which the mother may certainly get, or the value in scraps, by her lawful occupation of begging; and it is exactly at one year old that I propose to provide for them in such a manner, as, instead of being a charge upon their parents, or the parish, or wanting food and raiment for the rest of their lives, they shall, on the contrary, contribute to the feeding, and partly to the clothing, of many thousands.

There is likewise another great advantage in my scheme, that it will prevent those voluntary abortions, and that horrid practice of women murdering their bastard children, alas, too frequent among us! Sacrificing the poor innocent babes, I doubt more to avoid the expense than the shame, which would move tears and pity in the most savage and inhuman breast.

The number of souls in this kingdom being usually reckoned one million and a half, of these I calculate there may be about two hundred thousand couple whose wives are breeders; from which number I subtract thirty thousand couple, who are able to maintain their own children (although I apprehend there cannot be so many, under the present distresses of the kingdom); but this being granted, there will remain a hundred and seventy thousand breeders. I again subtract fifty thousand, for those women who miscarry, or whose children die by accident or disease within the year. There only remain a hundred and twenty thousand children of poor parents annually born. The question therefore is, How this number shall be reared and provided for? Which, as I have already said, under the present situation of affairs, is utterly impossible by all the methods hitherto proposed. For we can neither employ them in handicraft or agriculture; we neither build houses (I mean in the country) not cultivate land: they can very seldom pick up a livelihood by stealing, till they arrive at six years old, except where they are of towardly parts; although I confess they learn the rudiments much earlier; during which time they can, however, be properly looked upon only as probationers; as I have been informed by a principal gentleman in the county of Cavan, who protested to me, that he never knew above one or two instances under the age of six, even in a part of the kingdom so renowned for the quickest proficiency in that art.

I am assured by our merchants, that a boy or a girl before twelve years old is no saleable commodity; and even when they come to this age they will not yield above three pounds, or three pounds and half-a-crown at most, on the exchange; which cannot turn to account either to the parents or kingdom, the charge of nutriment and rags having been at least four times that value.

I shall now, therefore, humbly propose my own thoughts, which I hope will not be liable to the least objection.

I have been assured by a very knowing American of my acquaintance in London, that a young healthy child, well nursed, is, at a year old, a most delicious, nourishing, and wholesome food, whether stewed, roasted, baked, or boiled; and I make no doubt that it will equally serve in a fricassee or a ragout.

I do therefore humbly offer it to public consideration, that of the hundred and twenty thousand children already computed, twenty thousand may be reserved for breed, whereof only one-fourth part to be males; which is more than we allow to sheep, black-cattle, or swine; and my reason is, that these children are seldom the fruits of marriage, a circumstance not much regarded by our savages, therefore one male will be sufficient to serve four females. That the remaining hundred thousand may, at a year old, be offered in sale to the persons of quality and fortune through the kingdom; always advising the mother to let them suck plentifully in the last month, so as to render them plump and fat for a good table. A child will make two dishes at an entertainment for friends; and when the family dines alone, the fore or hind quarter will make a reasonable dish, and, seasoned with a little pepper or salt, will be very good boiled on the fourth day, especially in winter.

I have reckoned, upon a medium, that a child just born will weigh twelve pounds, and in a solar year, if tolerably nursed, will increase to twenty-eight pounds.

I grant this food will be somewhat dear, and therefore very proper for landlords, who, as they have already devoured most of the parents, seem to have the best title to the children.

Infants' flesh will be in season throughout the year, but more plentifully in March, and a little before and after: for we are told by a grave author, an eminent French physician, that fish being a prolific diet, there are more children born in Roman Catholic countries about nine months after Lent, than at any other season; therefore, reckoning a year after Lent, the markets will be more glutted than usual, because the number of Popish infants is at least three to one in this kingdom; and therefore it will have one other collateral advantage, by lessening the number of Papists among us.

I have already computed the charge of nursing a beggar's child (in which list I reckon all cottagers, labourers, and four-fifths of the farmers) to be about two shillings per annum, rags included; and I believe no gentleman would repine to give ten shillings for the carcass of a good fat child, which, as I have said, will make four dishes of excellent nutritive meat, when he has only some particular friend, or his own family, to dine with him. Thus the squire will learn to be a good landlord, and grow popular among his tenants; the mother will have eight shillings net profit, and be fit for work till she produces another child.

Those who are more thrifty (as I must confess the times require) may flay the carcass; the skin of which, artificially dressed, will make admirable gloves for ladies, and summer-boots for fine gentlemen.

As to our city of Dublin, shambles may be appointed for this purpose in the most convenient parts of it, and butchers we may be assured will not be wanting; although I rather recommend buying the children alive, than dressing them hot from the knife, as we do roasting pigs.

A very worthy person, a true lover of his country, and whose virtues I highly esteem, was lately pleased, in discoursing on this matter, to offer a refinement upon my scheme. He said, that many gentlemen of this kingdom, having of late destroyed their deer, he conceived that the want of venison might we well supplied by the bodies of young lads and maidens, not exceeding fourteen years of age, nor under twelve; so great a number of both sexes in every country being now ready to starve for want of work and service; and these to be disposed of by their parents, if alive, or otherwise by their nearest relations. But, with due deference to so excellent a friend, and so deserving a patriot, I cannot be altogether in his sentiments; for as to the males, my American acquaintance assured me, from frequent experience, that their flesh was generally tough and lean, like that of our schoolboys, by continual exercise, and their taste disagreeable; and to fatten them would not answer the charge. Then as to the females, it would, I think, with humble submission, be a loss to the public, because they soon would become breeders themselves: and besides, it is not improbable that some scrupulous people might be apt to censure such a practice (although indeed very unjustly) as a little bordering upon cruelty; which, I confess, has always been with me the strongest objection against any project, how well soever intended.

But in order to justify my friend, he confessed that this expedient was put into his head by the famous Psalmanazar, a native of the island Formosa, who came from thence to London about twenty years ago; and in conversation told my friend, that in his country, when any young person happened to be put to death, the executioner sold the carcass to persons of quality as a prime dainty; and that in his time the body of a plump girl of fifteen, who was crucified for an attempt to poison the emperor, was sold to his imperial majesty's prime minister of state, and other great mandarins of the court, in joints from the gibbet, at four hundred crowns. Neither indeed can I deny, that if the same use were made of several plump young girls in this town, who, without one single groat to their fortunes, cannot stir abroad without a chair, and appear at playhouse and assemblies in foreign fineries which they never will pay for, the kingdom would not be the worse.

Some persons of a desponding spirit are in great concern about that vast number of poor people, who are aged, diseased, or maimed; and I have been desired to employ my thoughts, what course may be taken to ease the nation of so grievous an encumbrance. But I am not in the least pain upon that matter, because it is very well known, that they are every day dying, and rotting, by cold and famine, and filth and vermin, as fast as can be reasonably expected. And as to the young labourers, they are now in almost as hopeful a condition: they cannot get work, and consequently pine away for want of nourishment, to a degree, that if at any time they are accidentally hired to common labour, they have not strength to perform it; and thus the country and themselves are happily delivered from the evils to come.

I have too long digressed, and therefore shall return to my subject. I think the advantages by the proposal which I have made, are obvious and many, as well as of the highest importance.

For first, as I have already observed, it would greatly lessen the number of Papists, with whom we are yearly over-run, being the principal breeders of the nation, as well as our most dangerous enemies; and who stay at home on purpose to deliver the kingdom to the Pretender, hoping to take their advantage by the absence of so many good Protestants, who have chosen rather to leave their country, than stay at home and pay tithes against their conscience to an Episcopal curate.

Secondly, the poorer tenants will have something valuable of their own, which by law may be made liable to distress, and help to pay their landlord's rent; their corn and cattle being already seized, and money a thing unknown.

Thirdly, whereas the maintenance of a hundred thousand children, from two years old and upward, cannot be computed at less than ten shillings a piece per annum, the nation's stock will be thereby increased fifty thousand pounds per annum, beside the profit of a new dish introduced to the tables of all gentlemen of fortune in the kingdom, who have any refinement in taste. And the money will circulate among ourselves, the goods being entirely of our own growth and manufacture.

Fourthly, the constant breeders, beside the gain of eight shillings sterling per annum by the sale of their children, will be rid of the charge of maintaining them after the first year.

Fifthly, this food would likewise bring great custom to taverns; where the vintners will certainly be so prudent as to procure the best receipts for dressing it to perfection, and, consequently, have their houses frequented by all the fine gentlemen, who justly value themselves upon their knowledge in good eating: and a skilful cook, who understands how to oblige his guests, will contrive to make it as expensive as they please.

Sixthly, this would be a great inducement to marriage, which all wise nations have either encouraged by rewards, or enforced by laws and penalties. It would increase the care and tenderness of mothers toward their children, when they were sure of a settlement for life to the poor babes, provided in some sort by the public, to their annual profit or expense. We should see an honest emulation among the married women, which of them could bring the fattest child to the market. Men would become as fond of their wives during the time of their pregnancy, as they are now of their mares in foal, their cows in calf, their sows when they are ready to farrow; nor offer to beat or kick them (as is too frequent a practice) for fear of a miscarriage.

Many other advantages might be enumerated. For instance, the addition of some thousand carcasses in our exportation of barrelled beef; the propagation of swine's flesh, and improvement in the art of making good bacon, so much wanted among us by the great destruction of pigs, too frequent at our table; which are no way comparable in taste or magnificence to a well-grown, fat, yearling child, which, roasted whole, will make a considerable figure at a lord mayor's feast, or any other public entertainment. But this, and many others, I omit, being studious of brevity.

Supposing that one thousand families in this city would be constant customers for infants' flesh, beside others who might have it at merry-meetings, particularly at weddings and christenings, I compute that Dublin would take off annually about twenty thousand carcasses; and the rest of the kingdom (where probably they will be sold somewhat cheaper) the remaining eighty thousand.

I can think of no one objection, that will possibly be raised against this proposal, unless it should be urged, that the number of people will be thereby much lessened in the kingdom. This I freely own, and it was indeed one principal design in offering it to the world. I desire the reader will observe, that I calculate my remedy for this one individual kingdom of Ireland, and for no other that ever was, is, or I think ever can be, upon earth. Therefore let no man talk to me of other expedients: of taxing our absentees at five shillings a pound: of using neither clothes, nor household-furniture, except what is our own growth and manufacture: of utterly rejecting the materials and instruments that promote foreign luxury: of curing the expensiveness of pride, vanity, idleness, and gaming in our women: of introducing a vein of parsimony, prudence, and temperance: of learning to love our country, in the want of which we differ even from Laplanders, and the inhabitants of Topinamboo: of quitting our animosities and factions, nor acting any longer like the Jews, who were murdering one another at the very moment their city was taken: of being a little cautious not to sell our country and conscience for nothing: of teaching landlords to have at least one degree of mercy toward their tenants: lastly, of putting a spirit of honesty, industry, and skill into our shopkeepers; who, if a resolution could now be taken to buy only our negative goods, would immediately unite to cheat and exact upon us in the price, the measure, and the goodness, nor could ever yet be brought to make one fair proposal of just dealing, though often and earnestly invited to it.

Therefore I repeat, let no man talk to me of these and the like expedients, till he has at least some glimpse of hope, that there will be ever some hearty and sincere attempt to put them in practice.

But, as to myself, having been wearied out for many years with offering vain, idle, visionary thoughts, and at length utterly despairing of success, I fortunately fell upon this proposal; which, as it is wholly new, so it has something solid and real, of no expense and little trouble, full in our own power, and whereby we can incur no danger in disobliging England. For this kind of commodity will not bear exportation, the flesh being of too tender a consistence to admit a long continuance in salt, although perhaps I could name a country, which would be glad to eat up our whole nation without it.

After all, I am not so violently bent upon my own opinion as to reject any offer proposed by wise men, which shall be found equally innocent, cheap, easy, and effectual. But before something of that kind shall be advanced in contradiction to my scheme, and offering a better, I desire the author, or authors, will be pleased maturely to consider two points. First, as things now stand, how they will be able to find food and raiment for a hundred thousand useless mouths and backs. And, secondly, there being a round million of creatures in human figure throughout this kingdom, whose whole subsistence put into a common stock would leave them in debt two millions of pounds sterling, adding those who are beggars by profession, to the bulk of farmers, cottagers, and labourers, with the wives and children who are beggars in effect; I desire those politicians who dislike my overture, and may perhaps be so bold as to attempt an answer, that they will first ask the parents of these mortals, whether they would not at this day think it a great happiness to have been sold for food at a year old, in the manner I prescribe, and thereby have avoided such a perpetual scene of misfortunes, as they have since gone through, by the oppression of landlords, the impossibility of paying rent without money or trade, the want of common sustenance, with neither house nor clothes to cover them from the inclemencies of the weather, and the most inevitable prospect of entailing the like, or greater miseries, upon their breed for ever.

I profess, in the sincerity of my heart, that I have not the least personal interest in endeavouring to promote this necessary work, having no other motive than the public good of my country, by advancing our trade, providing for infants, relieving the poor, and giving some pleasure to the rich. I have no children by which I can propose to get a single penny; the youngest being nine years old, and my wife past child-bearing.

A TALE OF A CHURN

Francis Mahony

The tradition of satire which Swift inaugurated was enthusiastically taken up by other writers, but it was not until some years later that the pioneer himself became the subject of sustained attack. Pre-eminent among those who lampooned the great man was Francis Mahony (1804–1866), a former Irish priest who signed his work as 'Father Prout'. Perhaps sensitive about the satires Swift had directed at religion, Mahony replied with a number of squibs including 'Dean Swift's Madness' and 'A Tale of a Churn', which is clearly intended as a jibe at Swift's famous satire of 1704.

Mahony, who was born at Cork, became a Jesuit priest but forsook his calling for journalism and poetry. He is probably best remembered for the nostalgic 'Bells of Shandon' and a collection of his works, The Reliques of Father Prout *(1836), which Vivian Mercier has described as full of 'audacious and sometimes libellous pranks'. The tale which follows is just such a prank—a story allegedly told by Swift's long-lost child, in which he recounts the amusing adventures that befell him after he was abandoned . . .*

* * *

Some are born, says the philosophic Goldsmith, with a silver spoon in their mouth, some with a wooden ladle; but wretched I was not left even that miserable implement as a stock-in-trade to begin the world. Moses lay ensconced in a snug cradle of bulrushes when he was sent adrift; but I was cast on the flood of life with no equipage or outfit whatever; and found myself, to use the solemn language of my Lord Byron,

Sent afloat
With nothing but the sky for a great coat.

But stop, I mistake. I *had* an appendage round my neck—a trinket, which I still cherish, and by which I eventually found a clue to my real patronage. It was a small locket of my mother Stella's hair, of raven black (a distinctive feature in her beauty, which had especially captivated the Dean): around this locket was a Latin motto of my gifted father's composition, three simple words, but beautiful in their simplicity—'PROUT STELLA REFULGES!' So that, when I was taken into the 'Cork Foundling Hospital', I was at once christened 'Prout', from the adverb that begins the sentence, and which, being the shortest word of the three, it pleased the chaplain to make my future patronymic.

Of all the singular institutions in Great Britain, philanthropic, astronomic, Hunterian, ophthalmic, obstetric, or zoological, the 'Royal Cork Foundling Hospital', where I had the honour of matriculating, was then, and is now, decidedly the oddest in principle and the most comical in practice. Until the happy and eventful day when I managed, by mother-wit, to accomplish my deliverance from its walls (having escaped in a *churn*, as I will recount presently), it was my unhappy lot to witness and to endure all the varieties of human misery. The prince of Latin song, when he wishes to convey to his readers an idea of the lower regions and the abodes of Erebus, begins his affecting picture by placing in the foreground the souls of infants taken by the mischievous policy of such institutions from the mother's breast, and perishing by myriads under the infliction of a mistaken philanthropy:

> *Infantumque animae flentes in lumine primo:*
> *Quos dulcis vitae exsortes, et ab ubere raptos,*
> *Abstulit atra dies, et funere mersit acerbo.*

The inimitable and philosophic Scarron's translation of this passage in the *Æneid* is too much in my father's own style not to give it insertion:

> *Lors il entend, en ce lieu sombre,*
> *Les cris aigus d'enfants sans nombre.*
> *Pauvres bambins! ils font grand bruit,*
> *Et braillent de jour et de nuit—*
> *Peut-être faute de nourrice? &c. &c.*

But if I had leisure to dwell on the melancholy subject, I could a tale unfold that would startle the Legislature, and perhaps arouse the Irish secretary to examine into an evil crying aloud for redress and suppression. Had my persecutor, the hard-hearted coppersmith, Woods, had any notion of the sufferings he entailed on Swift's luckless infant, he would never have exposed me as an *enfant trouvé*; he would have been satisfied with plunging my father into a madhouse, without handing over his child to the mercies of a foundling hospital. Could he but hear my woeful story, I would engage to draw 'copper' tears down the villain's cheek.

Darkness and mystery have for the last half-century hung over this establishment; and although certain returns have been moved for in the House of Commons, the public knows as little as ever about the fifteen hundred young foundlings that there nestle until supplanted, as death collects them under his wings, by a fresh supply of victims offered to the Moloch of Ψευδο-philanthropy. Horace tells us, that certain proceedings are best not exhibited to the general gaze —

Nec natos coram populo Medea trucidet.

Such would appear to be the policy of these institutions, the only provision which the Legislature has made for Irish pauperism.

My sagacious father used to exhort his countrymen to burn every article that came from England, except coals; and in 1729 he addressed to the 'Dublin Weekly Journal' a series of letters *on the use of Irish coals* exclusively. But it strikes me that, as confessedly we cannot do without the English article in the present state of trade and manufactures, the most mischievous tax that any Irish seaport could be visited with, would be a tonnage on so vital a commodity to the productive interests of the community. Were this vile impost withdrawn from Cork, every class of manufacture would hail the boon; the iron foundry would supply us at home with what is now brought across the Channel; the glassblower's furnace would glow with inextinguishable fires; the steam engine, that giant power, as yet so feebly developed among us, would delight to wield on our behalf, its energies unfettered, and toil unimpeded for the national prosperity; new enterprise would inspirit the capitalist; while the humble artificer at the forge would learn the tidings with satisfaction—

Relax his ponderous strength, and lean to hear.

Something too much of this. But I have felt it incumbent on me to place on record my honest conviction of the impolicy of the tax itself, and of the still greater enormity of the evil which it goes to support. To return to my own history.

In this 'hospital', which was the first *alma mater* of my juvenile days, I graduated in all the science of the young gypsies who swarmed around me. My health, which was naturally robust, bore up against the fearful odds of mortality by which I was beset; and although I should have ultimately, no doubt, perished with the crowd of infant sufferers that shared my evil destiny, still, like that favoured Grecian who won the good graces of Polyphemus in his anthropophagous cavern, a signal privilege would perhaps have been granted me: Prout would have been the last to be devoured.

But a ray of light broke into my prison-house. The idea of escape, a bold thought! took possession of my soul. Yet how to accomplish so daring an enterprise? How elude the vigilance of the fat door-keeper, and the keen eye of the chaplain? Right well did they know the muster-roll of their stock of urchins, and often verified the same:

Bisque die numerant ambo pecus, alter et haedos.

Heaven, however, soon granted what the porter denied. The milk-man from Watergrasshill, who brought the supplies every morn and eve, prided himself particularly on the size and beauty of his churn—a capacious wooden recipient which my young eye admired with more than superficial curiosity. Having accidentally got on the wagon, and explored the capacious hollow of the machine, a bright angel whispered in my ear to secrete myself in the cavity. I did so; and shortly after, the gates of the hospital were flung wide for my egress, and I found myself jogging onward on the high road to light and freedom! Judge of my sensations! Milton has sung of one who, 'long in populous city pent', makes a visit to Highgate, and, snuffing the rural breeze, blesses the country air: my rapture was of a nature that defies description. To be sure, it was one of the most boisterous days of storm and tempest that ever vexed the heavens; but secure in the churn, I chuckled with joy, and towards evening fell fast asleep. In my subsequent life I have often dwelt with pleasure on that joyous escape; and when in my course of studies I met with the following beautiful elegy of Simonides, I could not help applying it to myself, and translated it accordingly. There have been versions by Denman, the *Queen's* solicitor; by Elton, by W. Hay, and by Doctor Jortin; but I prefer my own, as more literal and more conformable to genuine Greek simplicity.

The Lament of Stella
By Father Prout

> While round the churn, 'mid sleet and rain,
> It blew a perfect hurricane,
> Wrapt in slight garment to protect her,
> Methought I saw my mother's spectre,
> Who took her infant to her breast—
> Me, the small tenant of that chest—
> While thus she lulled her babe: 'How cruel
> Have been the Fates to thee, my jewel!
> But, caring naught for foe or scoffer,
> Thou sleepest in this milky coffer,
> Cooper'd with brass hoops weather-tight,
> Impervious to the dim moonlight.
> The shower cannot get in to soak
> Thy hair or little purple cloak;
> Heedless of gloom, in dark sojourn,
> Thy face illuminates the churn!
> Small is thine ear, wee babe, for hearing,
> But grant my prayer, ye gods of Erin!
> And may folks find that this young fellow
> Does credit to his mother *Stella*.'

THE GRIDIRON

Samuel Lover

*According to a critical essay by W. B. Yeats, Samuel Lover (1797–
1868) was the man who popularised the cliché figure of the amiable
and gormless bosthoon familiar in many Anglo-Irish works of fiction. While this has given him a rather negative reputation among
some critics, Lover was undoubtedly a man of great comic talent.
He deliberately chose to satirise elements of Irish life in such a way
that although his work was very popular in England—where much
of it first appeared in* Bentley's Miscellany, *edited for a time by
Charles Dickens—he was always in danger of being attacked by
the Irish nationalist press.*

*Born in Dublin, Lover actually first earned a reputation as a
marine painter and miniaturist, before turning to storytelling and
drama. His biggest success was undoubtedly* Handy Andy *(1842),
the story of Andy Rooney, a fellow who has 'the most singularly
ingenious knack of doing everything the wrong way'. Apart from
satirising a number of peasant characters, the book also lampooned
the exploits of the aristocrats and landlords such as Squire O'Grady
of 'Neck-or-Nothing Hall'. The success of this book brought its
author to London, where in 1844 he started a humorous entertainment called 'Irish Evenings', which was a hit both in England and
America. Many of Lover's stories are anecdotal in tone, and among
these 'The Gridiron' is certainly one of the best, as well as being
told in much the same rollicking manner as* Handy Andy . . .

*   *   *

A certain old gentleman in the west of Ireland, whose love of the
ridiculous quite equalled his taste for claret and fox-hunting, was
wont, upon certain festive occasions when opportunity offered, to

amuse his friends by drawing out one of his servants who was exceedingly fond of what he termed his 'thravels', and in whom a good deal of whim, some queer stories, and, perhaps more than all, long and faithful services, had established a right of loquacity.

He was one of those few trusty and privileged domestics, who, if his master unheedingly uttered a rash thing in a fit of passion, would venture to set him right.

If the square said, 'I'll turn that rascal off,' my friend Pat would say, 'Throth you won't, sir'; and Pat was always right, for if any altercation arose upon the subject-matter in hand, he was sure to throw in some good reason, either from former service—general good conduct—or the delinquent's 'wife and childher', that always turned the scale.

But I am digressing. On such merry meetings as I have alluded to, the master, after making certain 'approaches', as a military man would say, as the preparatory steps in laying siege to some extravaganza of his servant, might, perchance, assail Pat thus:

'By the by, Sir John' (addressing a distinguished guest), 'Pat has a very curious story, which something you told me today reminds me of. You remember, Pat' (turning to the man, evidently pleased at the notice paid to himself)—'you remember that queer adventure you had in France?'

'Throth I do, sir,' grins forth Pat.

'What!' exclaims Sir John, in feigned surprise. 'Was Pat ever in France?'

'Indeed he was,' cries mine host; and Pat adds, 'Ay, and farther, plase your honour.'

'I assure you, Sir John,' continues mine host, 'Pat told me a story once that surprised me very much, respecting the ignorance of the French.'

'Indeed!' rejoins the baronet. 'Really, I always supposed the French to be a most accomplished people.'

'Throth, then, they're not, sir,' interrupts Pat.

'Oh, by no means,' adds mine host, shaking his head emphatically.

'I believe, Pat, 'twas when you were crossing the Atlantic?' says the master, turning to Pat with a seductive air, and leading into the 'full and true account'—(for Pat had thought fit to visit North Amerikay, for 'a raison he had', in the autumn of the year ninety-eight).

'Yes, sir,' says Pat, 'the broad Atlantic,' a favourite phrase of his, which he gave with a brogue as broad almost as the Atlantic itself.

'It was the time I was lost in crassin' the broad Atlantic, comin' home,' began Pat, decoyed into the recital; 'whin the winds began to blow, and the sae to rowl, that you'd think the *Colleen Dhas* (that was her name) would not have a mast left.

'Well, sure enough, the masts went by the board at last, and the pumps was choaked (divil choak them for that same), and av coorse the wather gained an us, and throth, to be filled with water is neither good for man or baste; and she was sinkin' fast, settlin' down, as the sailors calls it, and faith I never was good at settlin' down in my life, and I liked it then less nor ever. Accordingly we prepared for the worst, and put out the boat, and got a sack o' bishkits, and a cashk o' pork, and a kag o' wather, and a thrifle o' rum aboord, and any other little mathers we could think iv in the mortial hurry we wor in—and, faith, there was no time to be lost, for my darlint, the *Colleen Dhas*, went down like a lump o' lead, afore we wor many sthrokes o' the oar away from her.

'Well, we dhrifted away all that night, and next mornin' we put up a blanket an the ind av a pole as well as we could, and thin we sailed illigant, for we dar'n't show a stitch o' canvas the night before, bekase it was blowin' like murther, savin' your presence, and sure it's the wondher of the world we worn't swallyed alive by the ragin' sae.

'Well, away we wint for more nor a week, and nothin' before our two good-looking eyes but the canophy iv heaven, and the wide ocean—the broad Atlantic—not a thing was to be seen but the sae and the sky: and though the sae and the sky is mighty purty things in themselves, throth they're no great things whin you've nothin' else to look at for a week together—and the barest rock in the world, so it was land, would be more welkim.

'And then, sure enough, throth, our provisions began to run low, the bishkits, and the wather, and the rum—throth that was gone first of all—God help uz!—and oh! it was thin that starvation began to stare us in the face. "Oh, murther, murther, captain, darlint," says I, "I wish we could see land anywhere," says I.

'"More power to your elbow, Paddy, my boy," says he, "for sitch a good wish, and, throth, it's myself wishes the same."

'"Oh," says I, "that it may plaze you, sweet queen in heaven—

supposing it was only a dissolute island," says I, "inhabited wid Turks, sure they wouldn't be such bad Christhans as to refuse uz a bit and a sup."

'"Whisht, whisht, Paddy," says the captain; "don't be talkin' bad of any one," says he; "you don't know how soon you may want a good word put in for yourself, if you should be called to quarthers in th' other world all of a suddent," says he.

'"Thrue for you, captain, darlint," says I—I called him darlint, and made free wid him, you see, bekase disthress makes uz all equal—"thrue for you, captain, jewel—God betune uz and harm, I owe no man any spite"—and, throth, that was only thruth.

'Well, the last bishkit was sarved out, and, by gor, the wather itself was all gone at last, and we passed the night mighty cowld. Well, at the brake o' day the sun riz most beautiful out o' the waves, that was as bright as silver and as clear as cryshthal.

'But it was only the more crule upon uz, for we wor beginnin' to feel terrible hungry; when all at wanst I thought I spied the land—by gor, I thought I felt my heart up in my throat in a minnit, and "Thundher and turf, captain," says I, "look to leeward," says I.

'"What for?" says he.

'"I think I see the land," says I. So he ups with his bring-'um-near (that's what the sailors call a spy-glass, sir), and looks out, and, sure enough, it was.

'"Hurrah!" says he, "we're all right now; pull away, my boys," says he.

'"Take care you're not mistaken," says I; "maybe it's only a fog-bank, captain, darlint," says I.

'"Oh no," says he, "it's the land in airnest."

'"Oh, then, whereabouts in the wide world are we, captain?" says I; "maybe it id be in Roosia or Proosia, or the Garman Oceant," says I.

'"Tut, you fool," says he, for he had that consaited way wid him—thinkin' himself cleverer nor any one else—"tut, you fool," says he; "that's France," says he.

'"Tare an ouns," says I, "do you tell me so? And how do you know it's France it is, captain, dear?" says I.

'"Bekase this is the Bay o' Bishky we're in now," says he.

'"Throth, I was thinkin' so myself," says I, "by the rowl it has;

for I often heerd av it in regard o' that same"; and, throth, the likes av it I never seen before nor since, and, with the help o' God, never will.

'Well, with that my heart begun to grow light, and when I seen my life was safe, I began to grow twice hungrier nor ever—so says I, "Captain, jewel, I wish we had a gridiron."

'"Why, then," says he, "thundher and turf," says he, "what put a gridiron into your head?"

'"Bekase I'm starvin' with the hunger," says I.

'"And sure, bad luck to you," says he, "you couldn't ate a gridiron," says he, "barrin you wor a pelican o' the wilderness," says he.

'"Ate a gridiron!" says I. "Och, in throth, I'm not such a gommoch all out as that, anyway. But sure if we had a gridiron we could dress a beefsteak," says I.

'"Arrah! but where's the beefsteak?" says he.

'"Sure, couldn't we cut a slice aff the pork?" says I.

'"By gor, I never thought a' that," says the captain. "You're a clever fellow, Paddy," says he, laughin'.

'"Oh, there's many a thrue word said in joke," says I.

'"Thrue for you, Paddy," says he.

'"Well, then," says I, "if you put me ashore there beyant" (for we were nearin' the land all the time), "and sure I can ask thim for to lind me the loan of a gridiron," says I.

'"Oh, by gor, the butther's comin' out o' the stirabout in airnest now," says he. "You gommoch," says he, "sure I towld you before that's France—and sure they're all furriners there," says the captain.

'"Well," says I, "and how do you know but I'm as good a furriner myself as any o' thim?"

'"What do you mane?" says he.

'"I mane," says I, "what I towld you, that I'm as good a furriner myself as any o' thim."

'"Make me sinsible," says he.

'"By dad, maybe that's more nor me, or greater nor me, could do," says I; and we all began to laugh at him, for I thought I'd pay him off for his bit o' consait about the Garman Oceant.

'"Lave off your humbuggin," says he, "I bid you, and tell me what it is you mane at all, at all."

' "Parly-voo frongsay?" says I.

' "Oh, your humble sarvant," says he. "Why, by gor, you're a scholar, Paddy."

' "Throth, you may say that," says I.

' "Why, you're a clever fellow, Paddy," says the captain, jeerin' like.

' "You're not the first that said that," says I, "whether you joke or no."

' "Oh, but I'm in airnest," says the captain. "And do you tell me, Paddy," says he, "that you spake Frinch?"

' "Parly-voo frongsay?" says I.

' "By gor, that bangs Banagher, and all the world knows Banagher bangs the devil. I never met the likes o' you, Paddy," says he. "Pull away, boys, and put Paddy ashore, and maybe we won't get a good bellyfull before long."

'So, with that, it was no sooner said nor done—they pulled away and got close into shore in less than no time, and run the boat up in a little creek; and a beautiful creek it was, with a lovely white sthrand, an illigant place for ladies to bathe in the summer; and out I got, and it's stiff enough in my limbs I was afther bein' cramped up in the boat, and perished with the cowld and hunger; but I conthrived to scramble an, one way or the other, towards a little bit iv a wood that was close to the shore, and the smoke curlin' out of it, quite timpting like.

' "By the powdhers o' war, I'm all right," says I; "there's a house there"—and sure enough there was, and a parcel of men, women, and childher, ating their dinner round a table quite convainent. And so I wint up to the dure, and I thought I'd be very civil to thim, as I heerd the Frinch was always mighty p'lite intirely—and I thought I'd show them I knew what good manners was.

'So I took off my hat, and making a low bow, says I, "God save all here," says I.

'Well, to be sure, they all stopt ating at wanst, and begun to stare at me, and faith they almost looked me out of countenance— and I thought to myself it was not good manners at all—more be token from furriners, which they call so mighty p'lite; but I never minded that, in regard of wantin' the gridiron; and so says I, "I beg your pardon," says I, "for the liberty I take, but it's only bein' in disthress in regard of ating," says I, "that I make bowld no

throuble yez, and if you could lind me the loan of a gridiron,"
says I, "I'd be entirely obleeged to ye."

'By gor, they all stared at me twice worse nor before, and with
that, says I (knowing what was in their minds), "Indeed it's thrue
for you," says I; "I'm tathered to pieces, and God knows I look
quare enough, but it's by raison of the storm," says I, "which
dhruv us ashore here below, and we've all starvin'," says I.

'So then they began to look at each other agin, and myself,
seeing at wanst dirty thoughts was in their heads, and that they
tuk me for a poor beggar comin' to crave charity—with that, says
I, "Oh! not at all," says I, "by no manes; we have plenty o' mate
ourselves, there below, and we'll dhress it," says I, "if you would
be plased to lind us the loan of a gridiron," says I, makin' a low
bow.

'Well, sir, with that, throth, they stared at me twice worse nor
ever, and faith I began to think that maybe the captain was wrong,
and that it was not France at all, at all; and so says I—"I beg
pardon, sir," says I, to a fine ould man, with a head of hair as
white as silver—"maybe I'm undher a mistake," says I, "but I
thought I was in France, sir; aren't you furriners?" says I—'Parly-
voo frongsay?"

'"We, munseer," says he.

'"Then would you lind me the loan of a gridiron," says I, "if
you plase?"

'Oh, it was thin that they stared at me as if I had siven heads;
and faith myself began to feel flusthered like, and onaisy—and
so, says I, making a bow and scrape agin, "I know it's a liberty I
take, sir," says I, "but it's only in the regard of bein' cast away,
and if you plase, sir," says I, "Parly-voo frongsay?"

'"We, munseer," says he, mighty sharp.

'"Then would you lind me the loan of a gridiron?" says I, "and
you'll obleege me."

'Well, sir, the old chap begun to munseer me, but the divil a
bit of a gridiron he'd gie me; and so I began to think they were
all neygars, for all their fine manners; and, throth, my blood began
to rise, and says I, "By me sowl, if it was you was in disthress,"
says I, " and if it was to ould Ireland you kem, it's not only the
gridiron they'd give you if you ax'd it, but something to put an it
too, and a dhrop of dhrink into the bargain, and cead mille failte."

'Well, the word cead mille failte seemed to stchreck his heart, and the ould chap cocked his ear, and so I thought I'd give him another offer, and make him sinsible at last; and so says I, wanst more, quite slow, that he might undherstand—"Parly—voo—frongsay, munseer?"

'"We, munseer," says he.

'"Then lind me the loan of a gridiron," says I, "and bad scran to you."

'Well, bad win' to the bit of it he'd gi' me, and the ould chap begins bowin' and scrapin', and said something or other about a long tongs.

'"Phoo!—the devil sweep yourself and tongs," says I, "I don't want a tongs at all, at all; but can't you listen to raison," says I—"Parly-voo frongsay?"

'"We, munseer."

'"Then lind me the loan of a gridiron," says I, "and howld your prate."

'Well, what would you think but he shook his owld noddle, as much as to say he wouldn't; and so says I, "Bad cess to the likes o' that I ever seen—throth if you were in my country, it's not that-a-way they'd use you; the curse o' the crows on you, you ould sinner," says I; "the divil a longer I'll darken your dure."

'So he seen I was vexed, and I thought, as I was turnin' away, I seen him begin to relint, and that his conscience throubled him; and says I, turnin' back, "Well, I'll give you one chance more—you owld thief—are you a Chrishthan at all, at all?—are you a furriner," says I, "that all the world calls so p'lite? Bad luck to you; do you undherstand your own language—Parly-voo frongsay?" says I.

'"We, munseer," says he.

'"Then, thundher and turf," says I, "will you lind me the loan of a gridiron?"

'Well, sir, the divil resave the bit of it he'd gi' me—and so with that, "The curse o' the hungry on you, you owld negardly villain," says I; "the back o' my hand and the sowl o' my foot to you; that you may want a gridiron yourself yet," says I; "and wherever I go, high and low, rich and poor shall hear o' you," says I; and with that I lift them there, sir, and kem away—and in throth it's often since that I thought that it was remarkable.'

LISHEEN RACES, SECOND-HAND

Edith Somerville & Martin Ross

The literary partnership of Edith Somerville (1858–1949) and her second cousin 'Martin Ross'—whose real name was Violet Florence Martin (1862–1915)—produced some of the best satires contrasting native Irish culture with the bemused and often bewildered Anglo-Irish gentry and assured their leading position in the pantheon of great Irish humorous writers. The two ladies, who themselves came from landed Anglo-Irish stock (Edith from Castlehaven, West Cork, and Violet from Ross in County Galway), began writing together in 1889, drawing their inspiration from the people and places they knew so intimately. Their first collaboration, An Irish Cousin, *appeared in 1889, but it was the comic masterpiece,* Some Experiences of an Irish R.M. *(1899), about the hilarious adventures of the Englishman, Major Sinclair Yeates, a resident magistrate in the West of Ireland, which made the names of Somerville and Ross internationally famous. In the stories, all recounted by the Major, he was frequently outwitted by the very people over whom he was supposed to sit in judgement. This was followed by two equally amusing sequels,* Further Experiences of an Irish R.M. *(1908) and* In Mr Knox's Country *(1915), which appeared in the year of Violet's death.*

In 'Lisheen Races, Second-Hand', first published in the Badminton Magazine *and one of partnership's sharpest satires, a visiting Englishman, Leigh Kelway, is shown just how hopelessly naïve his countrymen are about the country they govern . . .*

*   *   *

It may or may not be agreeable to have attained the age of thirty-eight, but, judging from old photographs, the privilege of being nineteen has also its drawbacks. I turned over page after page of an ancient book in which were enshrined portraits of the friends of my youth, singly, in David and Jonathan couples, and in groups in which I, as it seemed to my mature and possibly jaundiced perception, always contrived to look the most immeasurable young bounder of the lot. Our faces were fat, and yet I cannot remember ever having been considered fat in my life; we indulged in low-necked shirts, in 'Jemima' ties with diagonal stripes; we wore coats that seemed three sizes too small, and trousers that were three sizes too big; we also wore small whiskers.

I stopped at last at one of the David and Jonathan memorial portraits. Yes, here was the object of my researches; this stout and earnestly romantic youth was Leigh Kelway, and that fatuous and chubby young person seated on the arm of his chair was myself. Leigh Kelway was a young man ardently believed in by a large circle of admirers, headed by himself and seconded by me, and for some time after I had left Magdalen for Sandhurst, I maintained a correspondence with him on large and abstract subjects. This phase of our friendship did not survive; I went soldiering to India, and Leigh Kelway took honours and moved suitably on into politics, as is the duty of an earnest young Radical with useful family connections and an independent income. Since then I had at intervals seen in the papers the name of the Honourable Basil Leigh Kelway mentioned as a speaker at elections, as a writer of thoughtful articles in the reviews, but we had never met, and nothing could have been less expected by me than the letter, written from Mrs Raverty's Hotel, Skebawn, in which he told me he was making a tour in Ireland with Lord Waterbury, to whom he was private secretary. Lord Waterbury was at present having a few days' fishing near Killarney, and he himself, not being a fisherman, was collecting statistics for his chief on various points connected with the Liquor Question in Ireland. He had heard that I was in the neighbourhood, and was kind enough to add that it would give him much pleasure to meet me again.

With a stir of the old enthusiasm I wrote begging him to be my guest for as long as it suited him, and the following afternoon he arrived at Shreelane. The stout young friend of my youth had changed considerably. His important nose and slightly prominent teeth remained, but his wavy hair had withdrawn intellectually from his temples; his eyes had acquired a statesmanlike absence of expression, and his neck had grown long and bird-like. It was his first visit to Ireland, as he lost no time in telling me, and he and his chief had already collected much valuable information on the subject to which they had dedicated the Easter recess. He further informed me that he thought of popularising the subject in a novel, and therefore intended to, as he put it, 'master the brogue' before his return.

During the next few days I did my best for Leigh Kelway. I turned him loose on Father Scanlan; I showed him Mohona, our champion village, that boasts fifteen public houses out of twenty buildings of sorts and a railway station; I took him to hear the prosecution of a publican for selling drink on a Sunday, which gave him an opportunity of studying perjury as a fine art, and of hearing a lady, on whom police suspicion justly rested, profoundly summed up by the sergeant as 'a woman who had th' appairance of having knocked at a back door.'

The net result of these experiences has not yet been given to the world by Leigh Kelway. For my own part, I had at the end of three days arrived at the conclusion that his society, when combined with a notebook and a thirst for statistics, was not what I used to find it at Oxford. I therefore welcomed a suggestion from Mr Flurry Knox that we should accompany him to some typical country races, got up by the farmers at a place called Lisheen, some twelve miles away. It was the worst road in the district, the races of the most grossly unorthodox character; in fact, it was the very place for Leigh Kelway to collect impressions of Irish life, and in any case it was a blessed opportunity of disposing of him for the day.

In my guest's attire next morning I discerned an unbending from the role of cabinet minister towards that of sportsman; the outlines of the notebook might be traced in his breast pocket, and traversing it was the strap of a pair of field-glasses, and his light grey suit was smart enough for Goodwood.

Flurry was to drive us to the races at one o'clock, and we walked to Tory Cottage by the short cut over the hill, in the sunny beauty of an April morning. Up to the present the weather had kept me in a more or less apologetic condition; any one who has entertained a guest in the country knows the unjust weight of responsibility that rests on the shoulders of the host in the matter of climate, and Leigh Kelway, after two drenchings, had become sarcastically resigned to what I felt he regarded as my mismanagement.

Flurry took us into the house for a drink and a biscuit, to keep us going, as he said, till 'we lifted some luncheon out of the Castle Knox people at the races,' and it was while we were thus engaged that the first disaster of the day occurred. The dining-room door was open, so also was the window of the little staircase just outside it, and through the window travelled sounds that told of the close proximity of the stable-yard; the clattering of hoofs on cobble stones, and voices uplifted in loud conversation. Suddenly from this region there arose a screech of the laughter peculiar to kitchen flirtation, followed by the clank of a bucket, the plunging of a horse, and then an uproar of wheels and galloping hoofs. An instant afterwards Flurry's chestnut cob, in a dogcart, dashed at full gallop into view, with the reins streaming behind him, and two men in hot pursuit. Almost before I had time to realise what had happened, Flurry jumped through the half-opened window of the dining-room like a clown at a pantomime, and joined in the chase; but the cob was resolved to make the most of his chance, and went away down the drive and out of sight at a pace that distanced every one save the kennel terrier, who sped in shrieking ecstasy beside him.

'Oh merciful hour!' exclaimed a female voice behind me. Leigh Kelway and I were by this time watching the progress of events from the gravel, in company with the remainder of Flurry's household. 'The horse is desthroyed! Wasn't that the quare start he took! And all in the world I done was to slap a bucket of wather at Michael out the windy, and 'twas himself got it in place of Michael!'

'Ye'll never ate another bit, Bridgie Dunnigan,' replied the cook, with the exulting pessimism of her kind. 'The Master'll have your life.'

Both speakers shouted at the top of their voices, probably because in spirit they still followed afar the flight of the cob.

Leigh Kelway looked serious as we walked on down the drive. I almost dared to hope that a note on the degrading oppression of Irish retainers was shaping itself. Before we reached the bend of the drive the rescue party was returning with the fugitive, all, with the exception of the kennel terrier, looking extremely gloomy. The cob had been confronted by a wooden gate, which he had unhesitatingly taken in his stride, landing on his head on the farther side with the gate and the cart on top of him, and had arisen with a lame foreleg, a cut on his nose, and several other minor wounds.

'You'd think the brute had been fighting the cats, with all the scratches and scrapes he has on him!' said Flurry, casting a vengeful eye at Michael, 'and one shaft's broken and so is the dashboard. I haven't another horse in the place; they're all out at grass, and so there's an end of the races!'

We all three stood blankly on the hall-door steps and watched the wreck of the trap being trundled up the avenue.

'I'm very sorry you're done out of your sport,' said Flurry to Leigh Kelway, in tones of deplorable sincerity; 'perhaps, as there's nothing else to do, you'd like to see the hounds—?'

I felt for Flurry, but of the two I felt more for Leigh Kelway as he accepted this alleviation. He disliked dogs, and held the newest views on sanitation, and I knew what Flurry's kennels could smell like. I was lighting a precautionary cigarette, when we caught sight of an old man riding up the drive. Flurry stopped short.

'Hold on a minute,' he said; 'here's an old chap that often brings me horses for the kennels; I must see what he wants.'

The man dismounted and approached Mr Knox, hat in hand, towing after him a gaunt and ancient black mare with a big knee.

'Well, Barrett,' began Flurry, surveying the mare with his hands in his pockets, 'I'm not giving the hounds meat this month, or only very little.'

'Ah, Master Flurry,' answered Barrett, 'it's you that's pleasant! Is it give the like o' this one for the dogs to ate! She's a vallyble strong young mare, no more than sixteen years of age, and ye'd sooner be lookin' at her goin' under a side-car than eatin' your dinner.'

'There isn't as much meat on her as 'd fatten a jackdaw,' said Flurry, clinking the silver in his pockets as he searched for a matchbox. 'What are you asking for her?'

The old man drew cautiously up to him.

'Master Flurry,' he said solemnly, 'I'll sell her to *your* honour for five pounds, and she'll be worth ten after you give her a month's grass.'

Flurry lit his cigarette; then he said imperturbably, 'I'll give you seven shillings for her.'

Old Barrett put on his hat in silence, and in silence buttoned his coat and took hold of the stirrup leather. Flurry remained immovable.

'Master Flurry,' said old Barrett suddenly, with tears in his voice, 'you must make it eight, sir!'

'Michael!' called out Flurry with apparent irrelevance, 'run up to your father's and ask him would he lend me a loan of his side-car.'

Half-an-hour later we were, improbable as it may seem, on our way to Lisheen races. We were seated upon an outside-car of immemorial age, whose joints seemed to open and close again as it swung in and out of the ruts, whose tattered cushions stank of rats and mildew, whose wheels staggered and rocked like the legs of a drunken man. Between the shafts jogged the latest addition to the kennel larder, the eight-shilling mare. Flurry sat on one side, and kept her going at a rate of not less than four miles an hour; Leigh Kelway and I held on to the other.

'She'll get us as far as Lynch's anyway,' said Flurry, abandoning his first contention that she could do the whole distance, as he pulled her on to her legs after her fifteenth stumble, 'and he'll lend us some sort of a horse, if it was only a mule.'

'Do you notice that these cushions are very damp?' said Leigh Kelway to me, in a hollow undertone.

'Small blame to them if they are!' replied Flurry. 'I've no doubt but they were out under the rain all day yesterday at Mrs Hurley's funeral.'

Leigh Kelway made no reply, but he took his notebook out of his pocket and sat on it.

We arrived at Lynch's at a little past three, and were there confronted by the next disappointment of this disastrous day. The door of Lynch's farmhouse was locked, and nothing replied to our knocking except a puppy, who barked hysterically from within.

'All gone to the races,' said Flurry philosophically, picking his way round the manure heap. 'No matter, here's the filly in she shed here. I know he's had her under a car.'

An agitating ten minutes ensued, during which Leigh Kelway and I got the eight-shilling mare out of the shafts and the harness, and Flurry, with our inefficient help, crammed the young mare into them. As Flurry had stated that she had been driven before, I was bound to believe him, but the difficulty of getting the bit into her mouth was remarkable, and so also was the crab-like manner in which she sidled out of the yard, with Flurry and myself at her head, and Leigh Kelway hanging on to the back of the car to keep it from jamming in the gateway.

'Sit up on the car now,' said Flurry when we got out on to the road; 'I'll lead her on a bit. She's been ploughed anyway; one side of her mouth's as tough as a gad!'

Leigh Kelway threw away the wisp of grass with which he had been cleaning his hands, and mopped his intellectual forehead; he was very silent. We both mounted the car, and Flurry, with the reins in his hand, walked beside the filly, who, with her tail clasped in, moved onward in a succession of short jerks.

'Oh, she's all right!' said Flurry, beginning to run, and dragging the filly into a trot; 'once she gets started—' Here the filly spied a pig in a neighbouring field, and despite the fact that she had probably eaten out of the same trough with it, she gave a violent side spring, and broke into a gallop.

'Now we're off!' shouted Flurry, making a jump at the car and clambering on; 'if the traces hold we'll do!'

The English language is powerless to suggest the view-halloo with which Mr Knox ended his speech, or to do more than indicate the rigid anxiety of Leigh Kelway's face as he regained his balance after the preliminary jerk, and clutched the back rail. It must be said for Lynch's filly that she did not kick; she merely fled, like a dog with a kettle tied to its tail, from the pursuing rattle and jingle behind her, with the shafts buffeting her dusty sides as the car swung to and fro. Whenever she showed any signs of slackening, Flurry loosed another yell at her that renewed her panic, and thus we precariously covered another two or three miles of our journey.

Had it not been for a large stone lying on the road, and had the filly not chosen to swerve so as to bring the wheel on top of it, I dare say we might have got to the races; but by an unfortunate coincidence both these things occurred, and when we recovered from the consequent shock, the tyre of one of the wheels had come off, and was trundling with cumbrous gaiety into the ditch. Flurry stopped the filly and began to laugh; Leigh Kelway said something startlingly unparliamentary under his breath.

'Well, it might be worse,' Flurry said consolingly as he lifted the tyre on to the car; 'we're not half a mile from a forge.'

We walked that half-mile in funereal procession behind the car; the glory had departed from the weather, and an ugly wall of cloud was rising up out of the west to meet the sun; the hills had darkened and lost colour, and the white bog cotton shivered in a cold wind that smelt of rain.

By a miracle the smith was not at the races, owing, as he explained, to his having 'the tooth-aches', the two facts combined producing in him a morosity only equalled by that of Leigh Kelway. The smith's sole comment on the situation was to unharness the filly, and drag her into the forge, where he tied her up. He then proceeded to whistle viciously on his fingers in the direction of a cottage, and to command, in tones of thunder, some unseen creature to bring over a couple of baskets of turf. The turf arrived in process of time, on a woman's back, and was arranged in a circle in a yard at the back of the forge. The tyre was bedded in it, and the turf was with difficulty kindled at different points.

'Ye'll not get to the races this day,' said the smith, yielding to a sardonic satisfaction; 'the turf's wet, and I haven't one to do a hand's turn for me.' He laid the wheel on the ground and lit his pipe.

Leigh Kelway looked pallidly about him over the spacious empty landscape of brown mountain slopes patched with golden furze and seamed with grey walls; I wondered if he were as hungry as I. We sat on stones opposite the smouldering ring of turf and smoked, and Flurry beguiled the smith into grim and calumnious confidences about every horse in the country. After about an hour, during which the turf went out three times, and the weather became more and more threatening, a girl with a red petticoat over her head appeared at the gate of the yard, and said to the smith:

'The horse is gone away from ye.'

'Where?' exclaimed Flurry, springing to his feet.

'I met him walking wesht the road there below, and when I thought to turn him he commenced to gallop.'

'Pulled her head out of the headstall,' said Flurry, after a rapid survey of the forge. 'She's near home by now.'

It was at this moment that the rain began; the situation could scarcely have been better stage-managed. After reviewing the position, Flurry and I decided that the only thing to do was to walk to a public house a couple of miles farther on, feed there if possible, hire a car, and go home.

It was an uphill walk, with mild generous raindrops striking thicker and thicker on our faces; no one talked, and the grey clouds crowded up from behind the hills like billows of steam. Leigh Kelway bore it all with egregious resignation. I cannot pretend that I was at heart sympathetic, but by virtue of being his host I felt responsible for the breakdown, for his light suit, for everything, and divined his sentiment of horror at the first sight of the public house.

It was a long, low cottage, with a line of dripping elm-trees overshadowing it; empty cars and carts round its door, and a babel from within made it evident that the racegoers were pursuing a gradual homeward route. The shop was crammed with steaming countrymen, whose loud brawling voices, all talking together, roused my English friend to his first remark since we had left the forge.

'Surely, Yeates, we are not going into that place?' he said severely; 'those men are all drunk.'

'Ah, nothing to signify!' said Flurry, plunging in and driving his way through the throng like a plough. 'Here, Mary Kate!' he called to the girl behind the counter, 'tell your mother we want some tea and bread and butter in the room inside.'

The smell of bad tobacco and spilt porter was choking; we worked our way through it after him towards the end of the shop, intersecting at every hand discussions about the races.

'Tom was very nice. He spared his horse all along, and then he put into him—' 'Well, at Goggin's corner the third horse was before the second, but he was goin' wake in himself.' 'I tell ye the mare had the hind leg fasht in the fore.' 'Clancy was dipping in the saddle.' ''Twas a dam nice race whatever—'

We gained the inner room at last, a cheerless apartment, adorned with sacred pictures, a sewing-machine, and an array of supplementary tumblers and wineglasses; but, at all events, we had it so far to ourselves. At intervals during the next half-hour Mary Kate burst in with cups and plates, cast them on the table and disappeared, but of food there was no sign. After a further period of starvation and of listening to the noise in the shop, Flurry made a sortie, and, after lengthy and unknown adventures, reappeared carrying a huge brown teapot, and driving before him Mary Kate with the remainder of the repast. The bread tasted of mice, the butter of turf-smoke, the tea of brown paper, but we had got past the critical stage. I had entered upon my third round of bread and butter when the door was flung open, and my valued acquaintance, Slipper, slightly advanced in liquor, presented himself to our gaze. His bandy legs sprawled consequentially, his nose was redder than a coal of fire, his prominent eyes rolled crookedly upon us, and his left hand swept behind him the attempt of Mary Kate to frustrate his entrance.

'Good-evening to my vinerable friend, Mr Flurry Knox!' he began, in the voice of a town crier, 'and to the Honourable Major Yeates, and the English gintleman!'

This impressive opening immediately attracted an audience from the shop, and the doorway filled with grinning faces as Slipper advanced farther into the room.

'Why weren't ye at the races, Mr Flurry?' he went on, his roving eye taking a grip of us all at the same time; 'sure the Miss Bennetts and all the ladies was asking where were ye.'

'It'd take some time to tell them that,' said Flurry, with his mouth full; 'but what about the races, Slipper? Had you good sport?'

'Sport is it? Divil so pleasant an afternoon ever you seen,' replied Slipper. He leaned against a side table, and all the glasses on it jingled. 'Does your honour know O'Driscoll?' he went on irrelevantly. 'Sure you do. He was in your honour's stable. It's what we were all sayin'; it was a great pity your honour was not there, for the likin' you had to Driscoll.'

'That's thrue,' said a voice at the door.

'There wasn't one in the Barony but was gethered in it, through and fro,' continued Slipper, with a quelling glance at the interrupter; 'and there was tints for sellin' porther, and whisky as pliable as new milk, and boys goin' round the tints outside, feeling for heads with the big ends of their blackthorns, and all kinds of recreations, and the Sons of Liberty's piffler and dhrum band from Skebawn; though faith! there was more of thim runnin' to look at the races than what was playin' in it; not to mintion different occasions that the bandmasther was atin' his lunch within in the whisky tint.'

'But what about Driscoll?' said Flurry.

'Sure it's about him I'm tellin' ye,' replied Slipper, with the practised orator's watchful eye on his growing audience. ''Twas within in the same whiskey tint meself was, with the bandmasther and a few of the lads, an' we buyin' a ha'porth o' crackers, when

I seen me brave Driscoll landin' into the tint, and a pair o' thim long boots on him; him that hadn't a shoe nor a stocking to his foot when your honour had him picking grass out o' the stones behind in your yard. "Well," says I to meself, "we'll knowk some spoort out of Driscoll!"

' "Come here to me, acushla!" says I to him; "I suppose it's some way wake in the legs y'are," says I, "an' the docthor put them on ye the way the people wouldn't thrample ye!"

' "May the divil choke ye!" says he, pleasant enough, but I knew by the blush he had he was vexed.

' "Then I suppose 'tis a left-tenant colonel y'are," says I; "yer mother must be proud out o' ye!" says I, "an' maybe ye'll lend her a loan o' thim waders when she's rinsin' yer bauneen in the river!" says I.

' "There'll be work out o' this!" says he, lookin' at me both sour and bitther.

' "Well indeed, I was thinkin' you were blue moulded for want of a batin'," says I. He was for fightin' us then, but afther we had him pacificated with about a quarther of a naggin o' sperrits, he told us he was goin' ridin' in a race.

' "An' what'll ye ride?" says I.

' "Owld Bocock's mare," says he.

' "Knipes!" says I, sayin' a great curse; "is it that little staggeen from the mountains; sure she's somethin' about the one age with meself," says I. "Many's the time Jamesy Geoghegan and meself used to be dhrivin' her to Macroom with pigs an' all soorts," says I; "an' is it leppin' stone walls ye want her to go now?"

' "Faith, there's walls and every vari'ty of obstackle in it," says he.

' "It'll be the best o' your play, so," says I, "to leg it away home out o' this."

' "An' who'll ride her, so?" says he.

' "Let the divil ride her," says I.'

Leigh Kelway, who had been leaning back seemingly half asleep, obeyed the hypnotism of Slipper's gaze, and opened his eyes.

'That was now all the conversation that passed between himself and meself,' resumed Slipper, 'and there was no great delay afther that till they said there was a race startin' and the dickens a one at all was goin' to ride only two, Driscoll, and one Clancy. With that then I seen Mr Kinahane, the Petty Sessions clerk, goin' round clearin' the coorse, an' I gethered a few o' the neighbours, an' we walked the fields hither and over till we seen the most of th' obstackles.

'"Stand aisy now by the plantation," says I; "if they get to come as far as this, believe me ye'll see spoort," says I, "an' 'twill be a convanient spot to encourage the mare if she's anyway wake in herself," says I, cuttin' somethin' about five foot of an ash sapling out o' the plantation.

'"That's yer sort!" says Owld Bocock, that was thravellin' the racecoorse, peggin' a bit o' paper down with a thorn in front of every lep, the way Driscoll 'd know the handiest place to face her at it.

'Well, I hadn't barely thrimmed the ash plant—'

'Have you any jam, Mary Kate?' interrupted Flurry, whose meal had been in no way interfered with by either the story or the highly scented crowd who had come to listen to it.

'We have no jam, only thraycle, sir,' replied the invisible Mary Kate.

'I hadn't the switch barely thrimmed,' repeated Slipper firmly, 'when I heard the people screechin', an' I seen Driscoll an' Clancy comin' on, leppin' all before them, an' Owld Bocock's mare bellusin' an' powdherin' along, an' bedad! whatever obstackle wouldn't throw *her* down, faith, she'd throw *it* down, an' there's the thraffic they had in it.

'"I declare to me sowl," says I, "if they continue on this way there's a great chance some one o' thim 'll win," says I.

'"Ye lie!" says the bandmasther, bein' a thrifle fulsome after his luncheon.

'"I do not," says I, "in regard of seein' how soople them two boys is. Ye might observe," says I, "that if they have no convanient way to sit on the saddle, they'll ride the neck o' the horse till such time as they gets an occasion to lave it," says I.

'"Arrah, shut yer mouth!" says the bandmasther; "they're puckin' out this way now, an' may the divil admire me!" says he, "but Clancy has the other bet out, and the divil such leatherin' and beltin' of Owld Bocock's mare ever you seen as what's in it!" says he.

'Well, when I seen them comin' to me, and Driscoll about the length of the plantation behind Clancy, I let a couple of bawls.

'"Skelp her, ye big brute!" says I. "What good's in ye that ye aren't able to skelp her?"'

The yell and the histrionic flourish of his stick with which Slipper delivered this incident brought down the house. Leigh Kelway was sufficiently moved to ask me in an undertone if 'skelp' was a local term.

'Well, Mr Flurry, and gintlemen,' recommenced Slipper, 'I declare to ye when Owld Bocock's mare heard thim roars she sthretched out her neck like a gandher, and when she passed me out she give a couple of grunts, and looked at me as ugly as a Christian.

'"Hah!" says I, givin' her a couple o' dhraws o' th' ash plant across the butt o' the tail, the way I wouldn't blind her; "I'll make ye grunt!" says I, "I'll nourish ye!"'

'I knew well she was very frightful of th' ash plant since the winter Tommeen Sullivan had her under a side-car. But now, in place of havin' any obligations to me, ye'd be surprised if ye heard the blaspheemious expressions of that young boy that was ridin' her; and whether it was over-anxious he was, turnin' around the way I'd hear him cursin', or whether it was some slither or slide came to Owld Bocock's mare, I dunno, but she was bet up agin the last obstackle but two, and before ye could say "Schnipes," she was standin' on her two ears beyond in th' other field! I declare to ye, on the vartue of me oath, she stood that way till she reconnoithered what side would Driscoll fall, an' she turned about then and rolled on him as cosy as if he was meadow grass!'

Slipper stopped short; the people in the doorway groaned appreciatively; Mary Kate murmured 'The Lord save us!'

'The blood was dhruv out through his nose and ears,' continued Slipper, with a voice that indicated the cream of the narration, 'and you'd hear his bones crackin' on the ground! You'd have pitied the poor boy.'

'Good heavens!' said Leigh Kelway, sitting up very straight in his chair.

'Was he hurt, Slipper?' asked Flurry casually.

'Hurt is it?' echoed Slipper in high scorn; 'killed on the spot!' He paused to relish the effect of the denouement on Leigh Kelway. 'Oh, divil so pleasant an afthernoon ever you seen; and indeed, Mr Flurry, it's what we were all sayin', it was a great pity your honour was not there for the likin' you had for Driscoll.'

As he spoke the last word there was an outburst of singing and cheering from a car-load of people who had just pulled up at the door. Flurry listened, leaned back in his chair, and began to laugh.

'It scarcely strikes one as a comic incident,' said Leigh Kelway, very coldly to me; 'in fact, it seems to me that the police ought—'

'Show me Slipper!' bawled a voice in the shop; 'show me that dirty little undherlooper till I have his blood! Hadn't I the race won only for he souring the mare on me! What's that you say? I tell ye he did! He left seven slaps on her with the handle of a hay-rake—'

There was in the room in which we were sitting a second door, leading to the back yard, a door consecrated to the unobtrusive visits of so-called 'Sunday travellers'. Through it Slipper faded away like a dream, and, simultaneously, a tall young man, with a face like a red-hot potato tied up in a bandage, squeezed his way from the shop into the room.

'Well, Driscoll,' said Flurry, 'since it wasn't the teeth of the rake he left on the mare, you needn't be talking!'

Leigh Kelway looked from one to the other with a wilder expression in his eye than I had thought it capable of. I read in it a resolve to abandon Ireland to her fate.

At eight o'clock we were still waiting for the car that we had been assured should be ours directly it returned from the races. At half-past eight we had adopted the only possible course that remained, and had accepted the offers of lifts on the laden cars that were returning to Skebawn, and I presently was gratified by the spectacle of my friend Leigh Kelway wedged between a roulette table and its proprietor on one side of a car, with Driscoll and Slipper, mysteriously reconciled and excessively drunk, seated, locked in each other's arms, on the other. Flurry and I, somewhat similarly placed, followed on two other cars. I was scarcely surprised when I was informed that the melancholy white animal in the shafts of the leading car was Owld Bocock's much-enduring steeplechaser.

The night was very dark and stormy, and it is almost superfluous to say that no one carried lamps; the rain poured upon us, and through wind and wet Owld Bocock's mare set the pace at a rate that showed she knew from bitter experience what was expected from her by gentlemen who had spent the evening in a public house; behind her the other two tired horses followed closely, incited to emulation by shouting, singing, and a liberal allowance of whip. We were a good ten miles from Skebawn, and never had the road seemed so long. For mile after mile the half-seen low walls slid past us, with occasional plunges into caverns of darkness under trees. Sometimes from a wayside cabin a dog would dash out to bark at us as we rattled by; sometimes our cavalcade swung aside to pass, with yells and counter-yells, crawling carts filled with other belated racegoers.

I was nearly wet through, even though I received considerable shelter from a Skebawn publican, who slept heavily and irrepressibly on my shoulder. Driscoll, on the leading car, had struck up an approximation to the 'Wearing of the Green', when a wavering star appeared on the road ahead of us. It grew momently larger; it came towards us apace. Flurry, on the car behind me, shouted suddenly—

'That's the mail car, with one of the lamps out! Tell those fellows ahead to look out!'

But the warning fell on deaf ears.

'When laws can change the blades of grass
From growing as they grow—'

howled five discordant voices, oblivious of the towering proximity of the star.

A Bianconi mail car is nearly three times the size of an ordinary outside-car, and when on a dark night it advances, Cyclops-like, with but one eye, it is difficult for even a sober driver to calculate its bulk. Above the sounds of melody there arose the thunder of heavy wheels, the splashing trample of three big horses, then a crash and a turmoil of shouts. Our cars pulled up just in time, and I tore myself from the embrace of my publican to go to Leigh Kelway's assistance.

The wing of the Bianconi had caught the wing of the smaller car, flinging Owld Bocock's mare on her side and throwing her freight headlong on top of her, the heap being surmounted by the roulette table. The driver of the mail car unshipped his solitary lamp and turned it on the disaster. I saw that Flurry had already got hold of Leigh Kelway by the heels, and was dragging him from under the others. He struggled up hatless, muddy, and gasping, with Driscoll hanging on by his neck, still singing the 'Wearing of the Green'.

A voice from the mail car said incredulously, '*Leigh Kelway!*' A spectacled face glared down upon him from under the dripping spikes of an umbrella.

It was the Right Honourable the Earl of Waterbury, Leigh Kelway's chief, returning from his fishing excursion.

Meanwhile Slipper, in the ditch, did not cease to announce that 'Divil so pleasant an afthernoon ever ye seen as what was in it!'

DONALD DUDLEY THE BASTARD CRITIC

Amanda McKittrick Ros

In a nation full of characters as well as great humorous writers there can still be few more extraordinary figures than Amanda McKittrick Ros (1860–1939), who has been described as 'the world's worst novelist', although she herself regarded her work as without peer and spent much of her life in an obsessional pursuit of all those who criticised her. Born in County Down, she was a schoolteacher before marrying the stationmaster of Larne in County Antrim and embarking on her literary career. In 1897 she published Irene Iddesleigh, *in which she gave full rein to her talent for alliteration and malapropism. This romance between young Helen of Crow Cottage, Ballynahinch, and Lord Rasberry, with its idiosyncratic spelling and unconventional punctuation, so bemused the English critic (and noted humorist) Barry Pain that he described it as 'a book without meaning' and added, 'The most stupendous and monumental characteristic in it, perhaps, is its absence of any sense of humour.' Amanda Ros was incandescent with rage at Pain and others who similarly ridiculed her book, and thereafter began a campaign which was eventually to embroil six firms of lawyers in legal proceedings against critics 'for being facetious about my work' and other lawyers 'because they have fleeced me in my legal proceedings'. So wholeheartedly did she direct her energies to this cause, that she wrote only two more novels,* Delina Delaney *and* Helen Huddleson, *which did not appear in print until after her death.*

Although all the leading English and American critics refused to take her work seriously, Mrs Ros did attract a small coterie of admirers, including Aldous Huxley, Osbert Sitwell, Mark Twain and E. V. Lucas, who actually founded an 'Amanda Ros Club' in

*London. In 1911, her work was the subject of a notorious skit by
F. Anstey in* Punch *which further enraged her. On several occasions
she referred to herself as 'the Notorious Boil on the tip of the Critics'
tongues', and she sought to gain some revenge on all those who
had dared to attack her in the following satire. Of it, one of Mrs
Ros's admirers, T. S. Mercer, has written, 'Donald Dudley is the
personification of the whole tribe of critics—he carries the sins of
the entire fraternity and the full measure of her wrath.' No collection
of Irish humour, intentional or otherwise, could possibly claim to
be in any way representative without a contribution from this unique
personality.*

*   *   *

Night was fast slipping towards morning. The wind howled like
the Devil's coaxing bray in horrored trim, dashing its cold damp
breath through the numerous apertures of Miss Shorthorn's apartment, made more cold from the fact that not a speck of fire or
heat was either seen or flung from the ashy handful that rested
within the rusty grate.

I sat within a kick of death, hungry, cold and sickish, while my
visitor sat on with his hands carelessly crossed over his hilly
stomach, his eyes painfully resting on me with a catlike glare.

I didn't wish to exhibit the least bit of bad breeding, though
crammed with it—for I was only a critic you know, though dawd-
ling on the very brink of resignation—by advising him of the hour.
I left this to himself.

Judging from his card or rather the scrap of paper torn from an
old pocket-book on which appeared the word 'gentleman', I came
to the conclusion he knew best when to make good his exit.

Pursing painfully his great mouth, he said in a pleasant tone,

'Mr Dudley, have you heard of "Lax", Mal Mary Marlow's
latest issue? Being a critic you are bound to.'

'Indeed, yes I have, and fairly well it's written too,' I glibly
answered.

'And criticised,' he threw in.

'Yes, I've read the criticism in a London weekly.'

'Did not *you* think it terribly torn up then?'

'Oh, to be sure I did, but if what *you* say be true, what of that?
The public, according to *your* version of criticism, are growing

absolutely indifferent in this age to our sharp-edged dross, therefore our labours are totally in vain.'

I was creeping towards curiosity to arrive at his name. Indeed
I yearned for his name and his mission.

'Mr—— I beg your pardon Mr——.'

'Devildinger,' he growled, a touch loudly.

'Mr Devildinger, if you want my opinion, you shall have it. My
idea of "Lax" is—that it is a very "lax" production for anything
in the shape of "woman" to acknowledge its authorship. Also the
author of "Lax" never meant surely to lash such a grossly immoral
tale—a well written one nevertheless—into print and sleep over
the fact that it would escape "hacking". She isn't quite so simple-
minded as all that to judge from her gift of English.'

'Then what of "Tuscha"?'

'Ah yes, "Tuscha" is damnation *itself*. Why you couldn't dinge
a page within its cursed covers, its construction is so damnably
adamant, but you must take into consideration, my dear Mr
Devildinger, that "Tuscha" is written by a man.'

'So a London "bartender" of honour insinuated if I read his
criticism aright, but I happen to have the honour of being perfectly
acquainted with "Addy Rivers", the clever writer of "Tuscha". I
in fact nursed her when a baby and that wasn't yesterday, and
have therefore a better idea of her sex than any "groping" wag of
"bribery" slum.'

'Ah, then you know the author personally of "Tuscha"?'

'Perfectly, she is hard though upon our passion-quellers—
very—don't you think so, Mr Dudley?'

'I swear I don't *think* her a hard writer but would certify the
fact that in all my varied experience on novel writing—she takes
the "bun"!'

'Whips Mal Mary Marley then you think?'

'In everything but the use of blackguardly language.'

'Then you don't admire "Lax" owing to its corrupting
tendency?'

'I certainly do not. No author, particularly a female, should
pander to those who relish filth and *that* means ninety-nine per
cent of this rotten generation.'

'As a lady, then, you don't admire Mal Mary Marlow?' he giving
me a searching glance.

'As a *lady* did you say?'

'Yes,' he shot back.

'The deuce! Mal Mary Marlow a lady! Nay, Mr Devildinger, were she a royal princess instead of the charity object of Mr Ralph Riley, she'd soil for ever and ever Amen her royal "pre" through the publication of "Lax".'

'Is that story then really true, presently afloat about her parentage? You've seen it, or rather read it, in the "Daily Dodger", I venture to say.'

'I've read it, yes, it's perfectly true, I knew her well,' I answered. 'She's the daughter of a common prostitute and sure you've only got to read "Lax" to verify the fact that her mind is strongly imbued with her mother's immoral tuitions. She was educated by one, Mr Ralph Riley—don't you know Riley of "Wormy Club", an MP for some of the Midland boroughs?'

'I do well.'

'He it is, then, who first planted Mal Mary on the soil of existence and literature.'

'Indeed! Not many men would *care* to educate a prostitute's offspring—he must have been greatly interested in her I fancy.'

'Not many, indeed,' I answered back. 'The majority of men merely bribe them for a moment's loan, then label them "cast off", but Riley, it seems, harbours the author's mother and cared for her daughter in a manner scarcely hitherto known. He doesn't deny his fatherly relation to her, although she retains her mother's name, Marlow.'

'She began writing early, did she not?' he asked, a spark of satisfaction lurking round his large rough mouth.

'At a dangerous age she began, when not more than nineteen winters blew over her slumming quarters.'

'She did not always reside, then, in "Cosy Nook"?' he then asked.

'Bless your soul—by no means—she resided with her mother in "Slobby Alley". I have often paddled the dirty, disease-giving lane, have passed the little window of her grim, poor home and never would the thought strike you that an individual existed amongst its slummy holes much better than the brute beasts—it's the last entry in the world whence you'd imagine a book to emerge is Slobby Alley. Why, Sir, you'd choke at the very sight of the long, narrow, dirty, dingy lane.'

'And do you wish me to believe, Mr Dudley, that "Thin Lips", her first attempt, issued from within the slum you refer to?'

'Yes, indeed, and her second and third too.'

His eyes now shone inquiringly as he asked.

'But where the devil has she drawn her descriptions from? Observe how she describes the "billiard-room", "smoke-room", "dining-room", "art gallery" and "library", etc., etc., of Watworth Castle, the seat of attraction for all the fast men and women in and around "Justacre".'

'Well, I suppose she makes Mr Ralph Riley's country seat "Decadence", her foundation. Her mother is his *chief* mistress there, you know, and Mal Mary, I dare say, takes an occasional "slip" over (it isn't far from Cosy Nook) when the master is from home. This is the usual thing nowadays for bastard beggarly upstarts to "ape" a pretty home, by exercising strict watch as to the movements of someone distinguished a bit and enjoying "week-day" intimacy with the chief of the servants' staff, are admitted (paper and pencil in hand) to inspect the furnishings and curios, etc., etc.'

'Is that so?'

'Quite so, I have known this sneaky means being adopted by women possessors of nothing more than a tiny "baby-linen" shop.'

Hour after hour we talked like this and I was getting tired, heart tired of this "gentleman", and wished him far enough away while I yearned both for his exit and for a couple of "spuds" I was stewing in a tin for supper. But whilst I grew weary and cold, Mr Devildinger seemed to increase in animation and heat and at one time—the hour I know not—he burst into such wild laughter as to cause the prim Miss Shorthorn to leap out of bed, rushing down to see the cause of such noise in such haste as to forget her disrobed condition.

As she entered her *sanctum sanctorum* wildly screaming, I felt as uncomfortable as if bitten with a barrel of fleas.

The night was so far advanced and I felt so hungry, cold and feeble—and quite abashed—if you believe me at the almost naked landlady standing in enraged ugliness, vociferating loudly because of the hilarity of Mr Devildinger, who continued his ha-ha-ha with as much gusto as if it had been 10 p.m., that I didn't care if the devil had me.

'What's the matter?' squealed Miss Shorthorn, turning to me

with an impish flash in her eyes—while Mr Devildinger laughed on.

'Miss Shorthorn,' I said, with a sort of innocent emphasis, 'you will excuse my friend's loud jocularity. It is rather late, I know, for his feelings to adopt such a strain, but really the subject on which we were discussing was so hideously risible that I can well understand his lengthy laugh.'

'Ha-hooch' now was heard, much to my mind as a proclamation of subsidy, and Mr Devildinger's laughter came to an end.

He looked at the frightened landlady.

'I apologise, Miss Shorthorn, for my transgression on your quiet hours, but the fact of the matter is—I can never control my passions once they are tickled—I never can.'

He gave her a look with a two-fold meaning. She bowed slightly and retired without another word. Why? I cannot define—I must leave *something* for my brother jobbers.

I felt terribly nervous as the door closed once more upon us, while Mr Devildinger, I could see, remained quite composed.

The woman with her tempting night-gown frightened my very soul within me, unduly raised by brute passion (so easily elevated in our sex, you know), in fact I never witnessed such a thing, save once at a museum and that was The Maid of Muscat in marbled magnificence, who stands in regal boldness, lifeless, soulless, calm and lovely, with one hand stretched forth as if to greet her thousands of sympathetic admirers, the other clasping to her breast the sin of her youth.

I swear to you the impression presented by my clangorous and semi-denuded landlady left me absolutely useless. I must have fainted or fallen into some abyss of apathy or other, for I recollect nothing more until midday.

I then awoke and found myself nearer to death than ever. Nothing in the world I thought could repeat the life-charge. The sensation I felt that moment would have shaken the veritable Samson.

I felt like a forgotten icicle. I tried to move my legs but not budge would they, my hands ditto. There I lay like the corpse of Croydon, save that a flicker of life still remained, for I spoke to a form bent eagerly over me.

I looked East and West in dire astonishment, the light of a fine large window puzzled me, not being privileged, owing to my very extreme poverty, to observe anything when I awoke to a sense of sight in the mornings, having only a disused waterbarrel in which to envelop my hungered emaciated compilation of sapless bone and muscle.

'Where *am* I?' I faintly asked Mr Devildinger, for I could recollect the man perfectly.

'You are with *me*, I swear you are all right, friend Dudley, don't worry or bother about anything just now.'

I felt so hungry I knew I must soon die of starvation.

'Mr Devildinger,' I said, 'Goodbye and God bless you. I can't live much longer. The result of *all this* will be a Coroner's Inquest and "Death from Starvation" the verdict.'

This was as modest a way as I could possibly put it, for although I was only a critic, yet there dwelt a sense of pride about me, empty ignorant pride I must have inherited from my father, who had the handle of his name burnished with the word Reverend.

'Mr Dudley, pardon my sense of neglect,' spake Mr Devildinger, looking alarmingly at me, 'I shall never be charged with the great sin of seeing *any* creature die of starvation again. I remember,' he continued, 'one poor fellow—a critic, too, a brother jobber of yours—dying in want whilst being driven to the Union. I chanced to see him expire and always think had I only reached him a drink of water, he might *still* have been spared.

'Oh no, Mr Dudley, you'll never die in this predicament while a crust of bread or rind of pork is obtainable or in my power to offer you.'

He went into an adjoining room, brought me a small cup of beef-tea, a slice of bread and an apple. He repeated the dose three times ere I felt creeping towards a satisfied condition. Strength I felt gradually steal into my system, and at noon I was able to sit up.

I found myself alone in the midst of a mighty room, not too liberally furnished, but comfortable beyond comparison for such a ragged, miserable being as I then felt. A cheerful fire burned beyond a silken rug on which lay a few novels, 'Lax' by Mal Mary Marlow, 'That Critic Cad' by the author of 'A Bilious Attack', 'Sweet Heaven' by Cecilia Croker, and 'The Pope's Conversion' by Priestly Pigott.

Besides these lay a cross little spaniel, ready for war should a finger touch them in his master's absence. Of this I was practically convinced. Shortly afterwards entered Mr Devildinger, a look of sadness damping his visage.

*

I was seated when Mr Devildinger returned. The little spaniel frolicked about his legs, rejoiced to see him back again, shook its tail with delight—not passion—and growled sometimes jealously as it surveyed me up and down.

Mr Devildinger sat down quite near me, poked into my health's state and all such. This ended, I began to thank this man-friend of mine for his thoughtfulness and generosity in bringing me to his comfortable quarters as I was convinced.

He then led me into an adjoining apartment, moderately comfortable, and at my disposal lay a grey tweed suit.

'Mr Dudley, allow me to present you with this. I am so struck with your aspect, I am resolved to change it somewhat.'

I thanked him from my heart, dressed myself with his permission in my new attire and felt a trifle pompous as I surveyed myself through means of a long narrow mirror, broad at will though, to suffice my vanity, for I was narrowed to nothing by long years of misery.

'This is truly a friend,' I allowed such a thought to tumble through my mind, 'as none on earth hath been and now that I've got a "rig-out", a decent one too, I can knock about and secure a crust in some shape or other. I'll "jack-up" my job of critic, for I've been in blank beggary since ever the devil tempted me to take the job.'

There is nothing I can see about it to make me like it. A critic I now was led to assure myself, was in other words 'a damned nothing'. A complication of lies. A hound of the lowest, the very lowest breed—for I was merely a bastard you know, no fault of mine.

So I concluded they were *all* bastards, for no properly begat man would accept a post where lies and bribery were its sole basis. Bum—Bum—and from that moment I swore the critics would have one less in number and be deprived as well of one of the 'literary hacks' ever prompted to accept with a bribe.

While forming this resolution, Mr Devildinger said—

'Give me your hand, old fellow!' as he viewed me mechanically in my new outfit. 'You're a thorough decent-looking chap. This I believe since I've had the express privilege of forming an acquaintance with you last night.'

A chill ran through me as he cordially shook my extension. I felt inspired in a degree with something but couldn't define, for the life of me, what that 'something' was! My nature seemed instantly changed from the tender-hearted Dudley to a strong-hearted devil. My thoughts then turned upon him, I gazed on him, nothing I could see shook my belief in him.

At that moment fine deep strains dashed against my ear, accompanied by the words I remember still—

1

Oh for a home with the devil below,
Who welcomes both rich and poor we know,
He's a capital favourite with wealthy and great,
An owner of countless tribes and estates,
A King o'er the damned, all of whom are refused
Admission above, but never abused.

2

The gate of Eternity stands ajar
For those who through life their pleasures mar,
But the door of Hell with its hinges strong
Sends forth its creaks both loud and long.
It's flung wide open, you're welcome *there*
By the Devil himself, Hell's Chief Lord Mayor.

3

Laughing and crying, preaching and prayer,
Dancing and singing, all meet you there.
Friends of your youth, foes of old age,
The actors, the players, the team of the stage,
The prince and the parson, the King and the knave,
'My lord' and 'My lady', its hot streets pave.

4

Hurrah for the King of this Hell below,
Where mostly all of our folk doth go,
Not mizzled or decked in white array
Or straining to sing a roundalay.
There you appear all naked and bare
Bereft of but one thing 'There, oh There.'

I sat for a few moments dumb-stricken as the grand unearthly strains died in my ear. Mr Devildinger sat too, eyeing me intently.

'Well, Mr Dudley, what think you of the choir?'

'Much, much, the voices are sweet and transportingly plaintive. Nothing I've ever heard or was privileged to hear could compare with the delightful harmony. I assure you there was no "artificial" harmony there, it was perfect and faultless.'

Mr Devildinger looked pleased. The dullness that visited him shortly before had now disappeared. He, like myself, seemed to be charmed with the conquering refined tones of marvellously pathetic strain. The nature I thought would be callous, the rich stream of voices wouldn't have softened with its seraph-trickle.

I sat on drowned in thought, in awe, then Mr Devildinger rose, motioning me to follow him into a chamber still as death, whose atmosphere seemed charged with the breaths of a million frosty nights. The room was in total darkness.

Mr Devildinger caught my arm and led me into its centre and freeing me from his tight grip, left me there. I then heard a door open and close gently, its muffled sound convincing me its hinges were leathern.

Down my back trickled a stream of fear, my nerves grew quite unstrung. What does this mean? I groaned aloud. Then rushed into my memory pores an advice my mother gave me and it was this—'Always seek the Lord in your hour of distress.'

Well, my hour was simply ten years, for my distress commenced ever since I joined the 'jobbing', and my throat was hoarse daily praying to the Lord and somehow he never seemed to take the least notice of me, or to offer me help in any way—and now that I view the matter in a right light, I couldn't be one bit angry with Him. He knew my trade didn't warrant a spark of sympathy, a trade, the staple feature of which was *lying, mere lying*, for I was a 'critic' you know and in the trade—the greater the liar the better chance to grow in favour with the journalists to secure a sort of living.

Now that I had my mind made up to have nothing more to do with journalists, for I was convinced that they were mere 'poking prigs' playing with the genius of a lot of 'jobbing' fools, which cost them only a tanner a day each while *this* in return filled their pockets with what gave rise to position (irrespective of pedigree), pomp and vanity illimitable.

I may safely say whilst my standing commission lasted, I dived oftener into my memory cells than I did during my whole lifetime, for promises of every conceivable description I could think would help a poor devil in a difficulty, which I stored there from out That Book years before I joined the hungry squad, and the most appropriate I could then think of was—

'Ask and ye shall receive.'

'O Lord,' I began, 'can't you give a fellow a blooming blink. I am standing here in absolute blackness, almost frozen to the floor and trembling like a palsied priest.

'It is you I wish, Dear Lord, to take into my confidence with every deference to Your Father and the Holy Ghost, and I implore of You that You oblige me with a light! A ray even or blink of any shape or form—damn the matter it's made of—I'd thank You for even a lucifer or to put it as plainly as I can—a match.

'I know, O Lord, You don't give a "rap" for the language any of Your creatures use in petitioning You a favour—whether in English, Dutch or Hebrew. For my part, I have only a *limited* knowledge of English, though mind You, I have a "smush" of French and a "smach" of Irish that, too, share my knowledge-pot.

'Something simple and plain you prefer, judging, if I read aright, your style of speech (and of which we all have a short account in the Antique Testament)'—but I broke off in disgust for there was no more glim of a blink than when I uttered the first word of my earnest prayer.

'Ah, damn such fables—it matters not a snap *who* wrote them or inspired the perpetraters'—I groaned in my hour of distress and disappointment, not failing to give the Lord a 'dig' too.

I stamped my feet like an angry schoolmaster and swore my throat sore.

'Talk about the devil,' said I to myself. But I'm as sure as I stand that had I entreated him with only one-tenth part of the anxious harangue, he'd have given ear to me long since and then and there I resolved to give him a chance.

My strength was up a bit, so I rubbed my forehead with my hand and felt heavy wrinkles drawn across it by the fingers of fear. These were supplied with the dew of agony. I wiped it off, drying my hand on the seat of my grey tweed trousers—handkerchief I hadn't for years.

Clasping my hands, I began—

'O King Devil, the rage of our nation, the English Nation I mean, the tool of the quack novelist, the beauty of our Universe, whose charming good looks are made more lovely from the fact that you are always either smiling or bordering on a "smudge".

'Would you send a poor beggar a light?'

But I hadn't time to prove to me whether or not he'd befriend me until Mr Devildinger entered, touched a tiny 'closer" and the room was a luminous area.

PRINCIPLES OF STONE-BREAKING

Patrick Kavanagh

Patrick Kavanagh (1905–1967) was also long renowned as an eccentric: a comic 'character' who lived in Dublin and loved poking fun at the Irish establishment. He was a close friend of Flann O'Brien and his novel, Tarry Flynn *(1948), a satire on Ireland's lost rural past, has been widely compared to O'Brien's master-piece,* The Poor Mouth. *Kavanagh was born the son of a poor farmer in Inniskeen, County Monaghan, and moved to Dublin, where he gained encouragement for his literary ambitions from George Russell, 'A.E.', who published the first of his highly acclaimed collections of poetry,* Ploughman and Other Poems, *in 1936. Subsequent volumes of verse, including* A Soul for Sale *(1947), caused him to be described as one of the most notable Irish poets of the century, second only to W. B. Yeats. Kavanagh's facility at writing comedy is also evident in* The Green Fool, *an autobio-graphical sequence of sketches based on his early life.*

Vivian Mercier saw Kavanagh as a descendant of Swift, and it is not hard to imagine the following amusing little squib, which Kava-nagh wrote for Lilliput *magazine in 1950, having come from the Dean's pen if he had lived two centuries later . . .*

* * *

A politician by the name of De Valera threatened on a day when he looked like going out of power that he had the health and physique to break stones for a living. It occurred to me then that some simple instructions in the craft of breaking stones would be supplying a want. The breaking of stones has been part of the disciplinary exercises of jail and workhouse, and with civilisation going the way it is these destinations are among the possibilities for many of us.

So to get down to the technical side of the business before it is too late. For the breaking of gravel a few simple implements are required: a sledge, 14 lb weight or over, for reducing the big ones to a reasonable size; a pair of wire goggles, a sack filled with straw for sitting on, and the little hammer which is used for the intimate job itself.

There are two sizes of hammers favoured by the professional—the six-ounce and the eight-ounce. One has to see too that the face of the hammer is not too broad as to lack sweetness nor yet too narrow so as to punch a hole in the stone instead of breaking it.

A most important part of the stone-breaker's equipment is handles for the hammers. The handles should be made of young ash quicks, preferably ones that grew in yellow soil, which would be the toughest and the nimblest.

The thinner the handle the better, for the object is to produce an action on the stone similar to the action of the skull-crackers used by Charlie Peace—a whale-bone and rubber rebound. To give a better grip it is necessary to tie some rags round the end of the handle.

You sit astraddle on the sack on top of the heap of stones. You hold the stone between your legs and chip it nicely round the edge. One should strike the stone in the hardest spot. If there is a patina on the stone, the hammer will sink into it, and in that case the only thing that will be broken will be the stone-breaker's heart. The worst snag in this trade is the tendency of stones to resolve themselves into unresolvable lumps about the size of number three footballs. The only thing to be done with them is bury them deep in the pile of gravel out of reach of the jailer's eye.

On the whole, stone-breaking is a pleasant philosophical job which, when one becomes adept at it, gives time for daydreams of a pleasant kind. Beware however of using a full-arm movement. It is purely a wrist action.

And that now is about all you need to know about stone-breaking, a trade which has been driven up old lanes by the mechanical stone-breaker, but which survives as a symbol of the degree of wretchedness to which man can sink.

THE MAJESTY OF THE LAW

Frank O'Connor

Sean O'Faolain considered Frank O'Connor (1903–1966) 'the finest craftsman in the art of the short story Ireland has produced'. There is certainly little argument that O'Connor is one of the great masters of this genre, but according to Vivian Mercier he is also an outstanding satirist. Writing in The Irish Comic Tradition, *Mercier says, 'O'Connor has produced a small group of short stories which form a unique comic subspecies . . . in these tales, abstractions like law and religion, sin and crime are opposed to the concrete behaviour of country people, who act and judge in accordance with tribal, familial or personal values rather than those of the impersonal church or state.'*

O'Connor was well prepared by experience to become a writer. Having been born Michael O'Donovan in terrible poverty in Cork, he had to leave school at 14 and after a few odd jobs joined the Republican forces during the Civil War and was captured. It was during his imprisonment that he improved his scanty education and began to write. Later in Dublin he met Yeats, who encouraged his work and helped him get a job as director of the Abbey Theatre. Although he later wrote two novels, several travel books and a survey of Irish literature, it was for his short stories that O'Connor became famous and remains so to this day, regarded as one of the most influential figures of the century. 'The Majesty of the Law' is a typical example from the 'unique comic subspecies' to which Mercier referred: a satire on the law in which the roles of punisher and punished are reversed . . .

*   *   *

Old Dan Bride was breaking brosna for the fire when he heard a step up the path. He paused, a bundle of saplings on his knee.

Dan had looked after his mother while the spark of life was in her, and after her death no other woman had crossed the threshold. Signs on it, his house had that look. Almost everything in it he had made with his own hands in his own way. The seats of the chairs were only slices of log, rough and round and thick as the saw had left them, and with the rings still plainly visible through the grime and polish that coarse trouser bottoms had in the course of long years imparted. Into these Dan had rammed stout knotted ash boughs which served alike for legs and back. The deal table, bought in a shop, was an inheritance from his mother, and a great pride and joy to him, though it rocked forward and back whenever he touched it. On the wall, unglazed and fly-spotted, hung in mysterious isolation a Marcus Stone print and beside the door was a calendar representing a racehorse. Over the door hung a gun, old but good and in excellent condition, and before the fire was stretched an old setter who raised his head expectantly whenever Dan rose or even stirred.

He raised it now as the steps came nearer, and when Dan, laying down the bundle of saplings, cleaned his hands thoughtfully in the seat of his trousers, he gave a loud bark, but this expressed no more than a desire to display his own watchfulness. He was half human and knew that people thought he was old and past his prime.

A man's shadow fell across the oblong of dusty light thrown over the half door before Dan looked round.

'Are you alone, Dan?' asked an apologetic voice.

'Oh, come in, come in, sergeant, come in and welcome,' exclaimed the old man, hurrying on rather uncertain feet to the door, which the tall policeman opened and pushed in. He stood there, half in sunlight, half in shadow, and seeing him so, you would have realised how dark was the interior of Dan's house. One side of his red face was turned so as to catch the light, and behind it an ash-tree raised its boughs of airy green against the sky. Green fields, broken here and there by clumps of red-brown rock, flowed downhill, and beyond them, stretched all across the horizon was the sea, flooded and almost transparent with light. The sergeant's face was fat and fresh, the old man's face, emerging from the twilight of the kitchen, had the colour of wind and sun, while the features had been so shaped by the struggle with time and the elements that they might as easily have been found impressed upon the surface of a rock.

'Begor, Dan,' said the sergeant, ' 'tis younger you're getting.'

'Middling I am, sergeant, middling,' agreed the old man in a voice which seemed to accept the remark as a compliment of which politeness would not allow him to take too much advantage. 'No complaints.'

'Faix, and 'tis as well. No wan but a born idiot would believe them. And th' ould dog don't look a day older.'

The dog gave a low growl as though to show the sergeant that he would remember this unmannerly reference to his age, but indeed he growled every time he was mentioned, under the impression that people could have nothing but ill to say of him.

'And how's yourself, sergeant?'

'Well, now, like that in the story, Dan, neither on the pig's back or at the horse's tail. We have our own little worries, but, thanks be to God, we have our compensations.'

'And the wife and care?'

'Good, glory and praise be to God, good. They were away from me with a month, the lot of them, at the mother-in-law's place in Clare.'

'Ah, do you tell me so?'

'I had a fine, quiet time.'

The old man looked about him, and then retired to the near-by bedroom from which he emerged a moment later with an old shirt. With this he solemnly wiped the seat and back of the log-chair nearest the fire.

'Take your ease, now, take your ease. 'Tis tired you must be after the journey. How did you come?'

'Teigue Leary it was that gave me a lift. Wisha, now Dan, don't you be putting yourself about. I won't be stopping. I promised them I'd be back inside an hour.'

'What hurry is on you?' asked the old man. 'Look now, your foot was on the path when I rose from putting kindling on the fire.'

'Now! Now! You're not making tea for me.'

'I am not then, but for myself, and very bad I'll take it if you won't join me.'

'Dan, Dan, that I mightn't stir, but 'tisn't an hour since I had a cup at the barracks.'

'Ah, *Dhe*, whisht, now! Whisht, will you! I have something that'll put an appetite on you.'

The old man swung the heavy kettle on to the chain over the open fire, and the dog sat up, shaking his ears with an expression of the deepest interest. The policeman unbuttoned his tunic, opened his belt, took a pipe and a plug of tobacco from his breast-pocket, and crossing his legs in easy posture, began to cut the tobacco slowly and carefully with his pocket-knife. The old man went to the dresser, and took down two handsomely decorated cups, the only cups he had, which, though chipped and handleless, were used at all only on very rare occasions: for himself, he preferred tea from a basin. Happening to glance into them, he noticed that they bore the trace of disuse and had collected a substantial share of the fine white dust which was constantly circulating within the little smoky cottage. Again he thought of the shirt, and, rolling up his sleeves with a stately gesture, he wiped them inside and out till they shone. Then he bent and opened the cupboard. Inside was a quart bottle of pale liquid, obviously untouched. He removed the cork and smelt the contents, pausing for a moment in the act as though to recollect where exactly he had noticed that particular smoky odour before. Then, reassured, he rose and poured out with a liberal hand.

'Try that now, sergeant,' he said.

The sergeant, concealing whatever qualms he might have felt at the thought of imbibing illegal whiskey, looked carefully into the cup, sniffed, and glanced up at old Dan.

'It looks good,' he commented.

'It should be.'

'It tastes good, too,' he added.

'Ah, sha,' said Dan, clearly not wishing to praise his own hospitality in his own house, ' 'tis of no great excellence.'

'You're a good judge, I'd say,' said the sergeant without irony.

'Ever since things became what they are,' said Dan, carefully guarding himself from a too direct reference to the peculiarities of the law administered by his guest, 'liquor is not what it used to be.'

'I have heard that remark made before now,' said the sergeant thoughtfully. 'I have often heard it said by men of wide experience that liquor used to be better in the old days.'

'Liquor,' said the old man, 'is a thing that takes time. There was never a good job done in a hurry.'

' 'Tis an art in itself.'

'Just so.'

'And an art takes time.'

'And knowledge,' added Dan with emphasis. 'Every art has its secrets, and the secrets of distilling are being lost the way the old songs were lost. When I was a boy there wasn't a man in the barony but had a hundred songs in his head, but with people running here, there and everywhere, the songs were lost . . . Ever since things became what they are,' he repeated on the same guarded note, 'there's so much running about the secrets are lost.'

'There must have been a power of them.'

'There was. Ask any man today that makes liquor do he know how to make it of heather.'

'And was it made of heather?' asked the policeman.

'It was.'

'Did you ever drink it yourself?'

'I did not; but I knew men that drank it. And a purer, sweeter, wholesomer drink never tickled a man's gullet. Babies they used to give it to and growing children.'

'Musha, Dan, I think sometimes 'twas a great mistake of the law to set its hand against it.'

Dan shook his head. His eyes answered for him, but it was not in nature that in his own house a man should criticise the occupation of his guest.

'Maybe so, maybe not,' he said in a non-committal tone.

'But sure, what else have the poor people?'

'Them that makes the laws have their own good reasons.'

'All the same, Dan, all the same, 'tis a hard law.'

The sergeant would not be outdone in generosity. Politeness required him not to yield to the old man's defence of his superiors and their mysterious ways.

'It is the secrets I would be sorry for,' said Dan, summing up. 'Men die, and men are born, and where one man drained another will plough, but a secret lost is lost for ever.'

'True,' said the sergeant mournfully. 'Lost for ever.'

Dan took the policeman's cup, rinsed it in a bucket of clear water beside the door and cleaned it anew with the aid of the shirt. Then he placed it carefully at the sergeant's elbow. From the dresser he took a jug of milk and a blue bag containing sugar: this he followed up with a slab of country butter and—a sign that his visitor was not altogether unexpected—a round cake of

home-made bread, fresh and uncut. The kettle sang and spat, and
the dog, shaking his ears, barked at it angrily.

'Go 'way, you brute!' growled Dan, kicking him out of his way.

He made the tea and filled the two cups. The sergeant cut himself a large slice of bread and buttered it thickly.

'It is just like medicines,' said the old man, resuming his theme
with the imperturbability of age. 'Every secret there was is lost.
And leave no one tell me a doctor is the measure of one that has
secrets from old times.'

'How could he?' asked the sergeant with his mouth full.

'The proof of that was seen when there were doctors and wise
people there together.'

'It wasn't to the doctors the people went, I'll engage.'

'It was not. And why?' . . . With a sweeping gesture the old
man took in the whole world outside his cabin. 'Out there on the
hillsides is the sure cure for every disease. Because it is written'—
he tapped the table with his thumb—'it is written by the poets
"an galar 'san leigheas go bhfaghair le ceile" ("wherever you find
the disease you will find the cure"). But people walk up the hills
and down the hills and all they see is flowers. Flowers! As if God
Almighty—honour and praise to Him!—had nothing better to do
with His time than be making ould flowers!'

'Things no doctor could cure the wise people cured.'

'Ah musha, 'tis I know it,' said Dan bitterly, ' 'tis I know it, not
in my mind but in my own four bones.'

'Do you tell me the rheumatics do be at you always?'

'They do . . . Ah, if you were living, Kitty O'Hara, or you,
Nora Malley of the Glen, 'tisn't I would be dreading the mountain
wind or the sea wind; 'tisn't I'd be creeping down with me misfortu-
nate red ticket for the blue and pink and yellow dribble-drabble
of their ignorant dispensary!'

'Why then, indeed,' said the sergeant with sudden determi-
nation, 'I'll get you a bottle for that.'

'Ah, there's no bottle ever made will cure me!'

'There is, there is. Don't talk now till you try it. My own
mother's brother, it cured him when he was that bad he wanted
the carpenter to cut the two legs off him with a hand-saw.'

'I'd give fifty pounds to be rid of it,' said Dan. 'I would and five
hundred!'

The sergeant finished his tea in a gulp, blessed himself and struck a match which he then allowed to go out as he answered some question of the old man's. He did the same with a second and third, as though titillating his appetite with delay. At last he succeeded in getting it alight, and then the two men pulled round their chairs, placed their toes side by side in the ashes, and in deep puffs, lively bursts of conversation and long long silences, enjoyed their pipes.

'I hope I'm not keeping you,' said the sergeant, as though struck by the length of his visit.

'Erra, what keep?'

'Tell me if I am. The last thing I'd like to do is to waste a man's time.'

'Och, I'd ask nothing better than to have you here all night.'

'I like a little talk myself,' admitted the policeman.

And again they became lost in conversation. The light grew thick and coloured, and wheeling about the kitchen before it disappeared became tinged with gold; the kitchen itself sank into a cool greyness with cold light upon the cups and the basins and plates upon the dresser. From the ash tree a thrush began to sing. The open hearth gathered brightness till its light was a warm, even splash of crimson in the twilight.

Twilight was also descending without when the sergeant rose to go. He fastened his belt and tunic and carefully brushed his clothes. Then he put on his cap, tilted a little to side and back.

'Well,' he said, 'that was a great talk.'

'It's a pleasure,' said Dan, 'a real pleasure, that's what it is.'

'And I won't forget the bottle.'

'Heavy handling from God to you!'

'Goodbye now, Dan.'

'Goodbye and good luck.'

Dan did not offer to accompany the sergeant beyond the door. Then he sat down in his old place by the fire. He took out his pipe once more, blew through it thoughtfully, and just as he leaned forward for a twig to kindle it he heard steps returning to the house. It was the sergeant. He put his head a little way over the half door.

'Oh, Dan,' he called softly.

'Ay, sergeant,' replied Dan, looking round, but with one hand still reaching for the twig. He could not see the sergeant's face, only hear his voice.

'I suppose you're not thinking of paying that little fine, Dan?'

There was a brief silence. Dan pulled out the lighted twig, rose slowly and shambled towards the door, stuffing it down into the almost empty bowl of the pipe. He leaned over the half door, while the sergeant with hands in the pockets of his trousers gazed rather in the direction of the laneway, yet taking in a considerable portion of the sea-line.

'The way it is with me, sergeant,' replied Dan unemotionally, 'I am not.'

'I was thinking that, Dan. I was thinking you wouldn't.'

There was a long silence during which the voice of the thrush grew shriller and merrier. The sunken sun lit up islands of purple cloud moored high above the wind.

'In a way,' said the sergeant, 'that was what brought me.'

'I was just thinking so, sergeant, it struck me and you going out the door.'

'If 'twas only the money, I'm sure there's many would be glad to oblige you.'

'I know that, sergeant. No, 'tisn't the money so much as giving that fellow the satisfaction of paying. Because he angered me, sergeant.'

The sergeant made no comment upon this and another long silence ensued.

'They gave me the warrant,' he said at last in a tone which dissociated him from all connection with the document.

'Ay, begod!' said Dan, without interest.

'So whenever 'twould be convenient to you—'

'Well, now you mention it,' said Dan, by way of throwing out a suggestion for debate, 'I could go with you now.'

'Oh, tut, tut!' protested the sergeant with a wave of his hand, dismissing the idea as the tone required.

'Or I could go tomorrow,' added Dan, warming up to the issue.

'Just as you like now,' replied the sergeant, scaling up his voice accordingly.

'But as a matter of fact,' said the old man emphatically, 'the day that would be most convenient to me would be Friday after dinner, seeing that I have some messages to do in town, and I wouldn't have me jaunt for nothing.'

'Friday will do grand,' said the sergeant with relief that this delicate matter was now practically disposed of. 'You could just walk in yourself and tell them I told you.'

'I'd rather have yourself, if 'twould be no inconvenience, sergeant. As it is, I'd feel a bit shy.'

'You needn't then. There's a man from my own parish there, a warder; one Whelan. You could say you wanted him, and I'll guarantee when he knows you're a friend of mine he'll make you as comfortable as if you were at home by your own fire.'

'I'd like that fine,' said Dan with satisfaction.

'Well, goodbye again now, Dan. I'll have to hurry.'

'Wait now, wait, till I see you to the road!'

Together the two men strolled down the laneway while Dan explained how it was that he, a respectable old man, had had the grave misfortune to open the head of another old man in such a way as to necessitate his being removed to hospital, and why it was that he could not give the old man in question the satisfaction of paying in cash for an injury brought about through the victim's own unmannerly method of argument.

'You see, sergeant,' he said, 'the way it is, he's there now, and he's looking at us as sure as there's a glimmer of sight in his wake, wandering, wathery eyes, and nothing would give him more gratification than for me to pay. But I'll punish him. I'll lie on bare boards for him. I'll suffer for him, sergeant, till he won't be able to rise his head, nor any of his children after him, for the suffering he put on me.'

On the following Friday he made ready his donkey and butt and set out. On his way he collected a number of neighbours who wished to bid him farewell. At the top of the hill he stopped to send them back. An old man, sitting in the sunlight, hastily made his way within doors, and a moment later the door of his cottage was quietly closed.

Having shaken all his friends by the hand, Dan lashed the old donkey, shouted 'hup, there!' and set out alone along the road to prison.

THE DEATH OF A SCIENTIFIC HUMANIST

Brian Friel

It seems appropriate to follow a satire on the law with one about religion, written by a man widely regarded as Ireland's most important contemporary playwright, Brian Friel (1929–). Yet Brian, who was born in Omagh, County Tyrone, began his literary career as a short story writer, and many of his tales first appeared in the columns of the prestigious US magazine, the New Yorker. *He wrote most of these in his spare time after having followed in his father's footsteps to work as a teacher in Derry City between 1950 and 1960. It was the success of his first play,* Philadelphia, Here I Come *(1964)—later filmed in 1970 and a huge hit on Broadway—that made him turn his back on fiction for drama. Several of his subsequent plays have also been box-office successes, including* The Loves of Cass Maguire *(1966) and* The Freedom of the City *(1973), so firmly establishing his reputation.*

Brian Friel's loss to short fiction has been keenly felt, however, not least because of the comparisons which have been drawn between his work and the stories of Liam O'Flaherty and Frank O'Connor. James F. Kilroy in particular believes there are strong similarities between Friel and O'Connor: both, he says, have written as many comic stories as serious ones, and 'many of the comic stories are tinged with the same ruefulness'. Kilroy also believes that the following satire on Church rules regarding burial is 'one of the finest of postwar stories'.

* * *

The only time I saw Uncle Cormac, Mother's twin brother, was in my tenth year. He was laid out in the morgue of the Bethlehem Hospital—a plump, middle-aged man with tiny hands and golden, wavy hair and a smile on his smooth face as if he were listening to an amusing story. He had been on his way to visit us when the coronary struck him. Two days previously, we learned later, he had arrived in Dublin on the freighter he had boarded in Cape Town, and had then set out for Beannafreaghan, our home, three miles outside the town of Omagh. He got the length of Omagh on a coal truck, had the attack in the Shamrock Bar, and was rushed off to the nuns in the Bethlehem Hospital, where he died shortly afterwards. He had been out of the country so long that twenty-four hours elapsed before the police were able to identify him, and I could tell from Mother's face when she entered the morgue that even she did not recognise him immediately. She kissed him on the forehead, and cried a bit, and then she and I said a decade of the Rosary with the two hefty nuns who were on guard over the remains. Then Sister Benedict, the mother superior, joined us, and Mother and she kissed, and Mother cried a bit more, and finally Sister Benedict led us to the visitors' parlour, where an elegant tea was waiting.

There was something about nuns and the velvety atmosphere of convents that knocked the spunk out of Mother and transformed her into a sweet, devout woman. Not that she was not always an ardent and pious Catholic—'Please, God, don't be too sore on those poor, stupid Protestants,' she used to pray, long before ecumenism was ever heard of—but the low-keyed, genteel presence of nuns smothered her native spirit and reduced her to a simpering, sighing caricature of herself. At home in Beannafreaghan, where Father taught school, she never left her tongue off the sisters, because they ran the town school and openly canvassed outside the town for more prosperous pupils, who would otherwise have enlisted with Father's dwindling numbers; and she knew that if Father's numbers dropped below a certain level, Canon Flanagan, the manager of both schools, would have little hesitation in closing down the Beannafreaghan building. 'Thieves!' she would say. 'Sneaky, rotten thieves, with their oh-so-nice accents and their slithery eyes! Lord, but they'll have a lot to answer for, thon gang!' This sort of talk distressed Father, whose one ambition in life was to reach retirement with a minimum of fuss and work. Yet when the nuns invited us to their annual school operetta, or to a sale of work for their hospital, or to a guest tea for their orphanage, it was Mother who insisted that we go. Those were the only occasions when she met all the grand people of the town, and I suppose she could not resist that attraction. For days she would rehearse all the cutting remarks she intended making to the nuns, but once the huge oak doors of the convent closed behind us her resolution vanished and she lisped 'Yes, Sister' and 'No, Sister' like a soapy schoolgirl. Father said she was a damned hypocrite, but I think now that she could not help herself.

During the tea, I paid no attention to what Sister Benedict and Mother were saying until I heard Mother say, with a gasp of astonishment, 'My God, Sister! What—what are you saying?'

'I would like to think there was a mistake, Mrs Cassidy,' said the nun evenly. 'But I'm afraid there wasn't. Sister Michael and Sister Pascal never left his side, and although they prayed incessantly for him, there was no change of heart.'

'But he wasn't conscious, Sister, was he? He was raving! He didn't know what he was saying!'

'I'm afraid he knew perfectly well. He actually snorted—you will forgive me saying this, Mrs Cassidy, but that's what he did, snorted like a brute beast—when I told him I had sent for Father Tobin.'

'Many a good Catholic dies without the priest,' Mother said limply.

'Perfectly right, Mrs Cassidy. But never by choice.'

'And—and what happens now, Sister?'

The nun inhaled and exhaled slowly. 'He cannot be buried in consecrated ground.'

'Just because he said he was—he was—What ever is that thing?'

' "A scientific humanist." I heard him say it myself. "None of your mumbo-jumbo for me," he said. "I'm a scientific humanist. Have been for years." And I wouldn't have been so horrified, Mrs Cassidy, if he hadn't done something then.'

'What?' breathed Mother, her mouth falling open.

'He laughed.'

'Cormac?'

'In my face.'

'At you, Sister?'

'Defiantly. It was a terrifying sound, Mrs Cassidy.'

Mother let out a wail of anguish. 'Oooh, Sister, Sister, what will we do? We're disgraced altogether! My twin brother a humanistic scientist! O God, have mercy on him and on all of us! Tell me what to do, Sister! Tell me what to do!'

With great sympathy and with a hint of pride at the extent of her theological knowledge, Sister Benedict said there was nothing could be done; the poor, misguided sinner had renounced his allegiance to his faith, had rejected the wonderful opportunity of a deathbed repentance, and must now suffer the consequences. She had already phoned Canon Flanagan, the parish priest, and he had confirmed her opinion that a Catholic burial was impossible. There was the remote possibility, she pointed out, that the unfaithful departed may have had a momentary change of heart even after that final laugh that set the features of his face forever, but no one but God himself could tell that. On the evidence available—and the Church had to act on that—it was beyond reasonable doubt that Cormac was an apostate at the time of his demise. We could pray for him, of course, and even if he were beyond prayers, their merit would be applied to some deserving soul.

'You never kept in touch with your brother after he emigrated, Mrs Cassidy?'

'No, Sister.' Mother shuddered with misery.

'Why not?'

'He kept moving about. We never knew where he was.'

'A pity. Your letters might have been lighthouses of hope in the pagan sea he was floundering in.'

'I suppose so, Sister.'

'We'll pray for you, Mrs Cassidy. We'll pray that you get the strength and the courage to bear this great cross courageously.' She caught Mother's elbow and raised her to her feet. 'You'll let us know what plans you make?'

'Yes, Sister.'

'Surely this is a lesson for all of us,' said the nun, looking straight and hard at me. 'The mills of God grind slow, but they grind exceeding fine.'

It was raining, and Mother did not utter a word during the three-mile walk to Beannafreaghan. When we got home, she brushed past Father and went straight up to her bedroom. I told him all I knew—that Uncle Cormac had snorted and laughed at the nuns, that he had refused to see Father Tobin, that he looked to be a very happy corpse, and that there was nowhere to bury him. The problem, as I saw it, was like the problem that had faced me when my pet rabbit died the previous winter. The ground was so stiff with frost that I was not able to dig a grave, and the flax dam was frozen over. After two days of desperate thought, I dropped the carcass behind the wall that surrounded the school, and for weeks the vision of Kiki, with his paws in the air and his startled eyes staring up at me, stayed with me. I now felt that we were going to be similarly burdened with Uncle Cormac, and somehow his smooth, smiling face was even more disquieting than Kiki's startled eyes.

'What does Canon Flanagan say?' was Father's only question. I told him that Canon Flanagan had ruled that burial in the Catholic cemetery was impossible.

'We're destroyed,' moaned Father. 'Utterly destroyed. Damn your Uncle Cormac anyhow! He was always a bloody wastrel!' He went to the cupboard where drinks for visiting inspectors were kept, and poured himself a glass of whiskey. He seldom drank spirits, and with every sup his face became more wry.

Mother had changed into dry clothes. She had a fresh outfit for me, too. 'Get into these,' she snapped. 'We're going out again.'

'This is terrible news, Angela,' Father cried. 'To think that Cormac would go and do a thing like—'

'Shut up!' barked Mother, pulling on a pair of Wellingtons. 'I'm not done yet with those lying thieves of nuns! If they think they have me beaten, they have another think coming to them!'

'What—what are you going to do, woman?'

'"Apostate"!' snorted Mother. 'By God, I'll apostate them! My Cormac will be buried like a gentleman, and no thieving nuns will stop me!'

'There's nothing you can do when the Canon's against you,' said Father. 'There's nothing anybody can do now.'

'Just you wait and see,' said Mother. 'He'll be buried as a good humanistic scientist should be buried. And if necessary I'll say the burial prayers over him myself!' She pulled a coat round her and made for the door. 'Are you coming?' she called to me.

'Coming,' I said.

'Make your own supper,' she said to Father. 'God knows when we'll be back.'

It was almost dark by the time we arrived in the town again. Once, on the way there, Mother spoke. 'Didn't he look nice, though?' she said very softly.

'Who?' I asked.
'Your Uncle Cormac. Wasn't he handsome?'
I said he was.
'And young-looking?'
I agreed.
'And his eyes—wouldn't they make you want to dance?'
I said that his eyes were closed.

Without slackening her speed, she put her hands round me and gave me a hug. 'Handsome as a king,' she said. 'The girls were all crazy about him. Oh, poor, poor silly Cormac!' Then she wiped her nose on the sleeve of her raincoat and brushed her hair back from her face. 'By God,' she suddenly declared to the sodden hedges, 'I'll stand by him! We'll not be beaten by those twisters of nuns! By God, we'll not!'

Ned Brady was the chirpiest undertaker in the whole of Ireland. Years ago, the relatives of one of his first jobs happened to mention to him that his cheery disposition had been a great strength to them, and that casual compliment had determined his attitude towards all subsequent work. He whistled—and on occasions of extreme grief sometimes even sang—his way through wakes and funerals. The people of Omagh did not hold this against him, because he was married to a virago. They knew that his business was his only pleasure.

Now he emerged, beaming, from his work-shop, and pumped Mother's hand enthusiastically. 'No need to tell me what has you here, Angela,' he said. 'I heard the news a while ago. Poor Cormac! If it wasn't for the bottle, he would have been Prime Minister or something. Shocking altogether.' He fell into a boxer's stance and weaved his fists before my nose. 'And how's young Cassidy? Is he chasing the girls yet, Angela, eh? Has he got a wee bit of skirt of his own out in Beannafreaghan? Aha, I wouldn't trust them tricky eyes of his, Angela, if I was you!'

'Ned,' said Mother quietly. 'I'm in trouble.'

'It'll pass. Everything passes. Nothing lasts forever. Don't tell me it's still raining?' He straightened himself and peered interestedly at the street behind us. 'Nothing but rain in this godforsaken country. Leave everything to me, Angela. I know exactly what you want—something nice but not too dear. Sure, everybody knows poor Cormac wasn't a man to gather money. And tell me, how's the boss himself doing these times?'

'The Canon says that Cormac can't be buried in his part of the cemetery, Ned,' said Mother, pitching her voice as if she were addressing a deaf person. 'You see, he wasn't a Catholic when he died.'

'Cormac? Not a Catholic?'

'He was a very holy humanistic scientist.'

'Scientific humanist,' I prompted.

'A Protestant?' Ned gasped, and immediately his mouth formed into an 'O', as if he were about to whistle.

'Certainly not!' said Mother. 'Our Cormac was always a good-living Christian gentleman. But what I want your advice about is this: Where are we going to bury him?'

'You're sure about the Canon?'

'He has already refused the nuns,' said Mother, adjusting the truth slightly.

'It's a tricky one, Angela. It is indeed. I mean to say, if he's not buried in the Catholic part, there's nothing left but the Protestant end, and, damn it all, you wouldn't put decent Cormac down with all them black Protestants, would you? I mean to say, Angela—'

'There's a strip of land between the two parts of the cemetery, isn't there?'

'Where the butcher Doherty grazes his sheep? There is surely, Angela, but—'

'And wasn't Colonel Harrington's mother buried in that strip?'

'That English pagan? True enough, she was laid there. But that was no funeral, for God's sake! Some free-thinker from Dublin reciting a ballad or something! No grief or nothing! Aw, that was the most depressing thing I ever witnessed.'

'The land belongs to the urban council, doesn't it?'

'It does. The butcher Doherty has a lease of it.'

'Then get me a plot there,' said Mother with finality. 'A single plot.'

'Angela—'

'The funeral will be tomorrow. Good night, Ned.'

'Hold on a second, Angela—'

Mother caught my elbow and led me to the door. Ned must have assumed that she was temporarily deranged with grief, because when I glanced back at him his face was set in a wild, strained smile, his fists were clenched and weaving loosely, and even before we had closed the door he had begun to sing in an uncertain baritone voice, 'You are my heart's delight . . .'

Strule Lodge, the home of Colonel Scott Harrington, was hidden in a cluster of chestnut trees at the outskirts of the town. He was known to be eccentric, very wealthy, and of uncertain morals. He answered our knock—a scruffy-looking old man in army boots and a soiled shirt. He was the tallest and thinnest man I ever saw; my eyes were level with the front of his unbuttoned trousers.

In a voice that wavered between deference and defiance, Mother told him what brought her to the Lodge: to learn the protocol for a funeral of someone who was neither Catholic nor Protestant. She understood, she said, articulating very carefully, that the Colonel had some experience of this.

When she had finished, the Colonel said, 'Thought at first you were another maid looking for a job. Come inside.'

He led us into a huge room with three chairs and straw on the floor, and stood with his back to the white marble fireplace, although there was no fire in the grate. 'Funny thing,' he said, addressing the ceiling. 'They keep coming to me for jobs, even though I have the reputation for raping every maid I ever had.'

Mother's hand tightened protectively on mine.

'The dead man is a brother?' Colonel Harrington asked.

'My only brother,' said Mother demurely.

'And what was his persuasion?'

'I beg your pardon?' said Mother.

'His creed—his belief. What was he?'

'What was he again?' Mother asked me.

'Scientific humanist,' I said.

'That's it,' said Mother. 'A devout scientific humanist.'

'Mother was a Christadelphian, Father Unitarian,' Colonel Harrington said. 'I'm nothing myself. Scientific humanist? Never heard of them. Humanist, yes. What the hell does "scientific" mean? Not that it matters. I suppose I'm a humanist myself. All thinking people are. And how can I help you?'

Mother began hesitantly to explain about Cormac's death. When she got to the snort—she described it as 'a cry of impatience'—the Colonel interrupted her.

'Ah! So you want me to conduct the service. Why not? Buried dozens of men in Mesopotamia in my day. Let's see . . . Humanist

... Scientific humanist. A bit of Whitman, I should say, and a chunk of old Shelley.'

'All I want to know, Colonel,' Mother began, 'is how to go about arranging—'

'No trouble at all,' the Colonel broke in. 'Leave it all to me. Yes, Whitman is right, and Shelley, too. I'll hunt up something suitable. What time is the funeral at?'

'I don't know yet,' said Mother. She was about to cry again.

'Nothing to cry about, woman. Death's just another experience—like new food and travel and sex.'

Mother's grip tightened on me again.

'Is Brady in charge?' the Colonel asked.

'Yes,' said Mother.

'A fool. But efficient enough. And cheap, too. So we can't complain. Let Mother off for fourteen pounds. I'll call on him tonight. Between us, we'll see to the details. Good night.'

When we got home, Father was asleep beside the kitchen fire. Mother took one look at him and then slapped him hard across the face. 'You're nothing but an old woman!' she exploded. 'A useless, cowardly, old woman! You and Cormac—two loafers, two good-for-nothing loafers! O God, protect me from useless men!'

There were about thirty mourners at the funeral, but they went no farther than the cemetery gates. Only Mother, Father, Colonel Harrington, and I followed the hearse to the graveside. Ned Brady was waiting for us there, warding off the butcher Doherty's inquisitive sheep.

In his full military uniform, the Colonel looked even taller. He held his hands behind his back and carried a cane under his arm. Beside him, Father looked shrunken and miserable. When he felt the Colonel's eyes on him, he straightened his shoulders and bared his teeth in an attempt at friendship. Mother cried quietly. She held her rosary beads in her hands and prayed in long, hissing exhalations.

The coffin was laid on the brink of the grave, and the four bearers retreated to the safety of the Catholic area.

'Let us commence,' said the Colonel.

'Fire ahead, man,' said Ned amicably. 'Nothing lasts forever. Even these sheep here are for the high jump next week, if they only had the sense to know it. Ha-ha!'

The Colonel removed his cap and handed it to Father. Then he fixed his eyes on a point in the sky directly above the gapers at the gate, stood at attention, and, in a barrack-square voice that sent the sheep fleeing in terror, began:

> 'He has outsoared the shadow of our night;
> Envy and calumny and hate and pain,
> And that unrest which men miscall delight
> Can touch him not and torture not again;
> From the contagion of the world's slow stain
> He is secure, and now can never mourn
> A heart grown cold, a head grown grey in vain.'

'Hear, hear!' said Ned.

'Very nice indeed,' murmured Father.

Mother produced a bottle of holy water from her handbag and splashed half of it over the coffin.

'With a bit of luck,' said Ned, 'we'll be home before the rain comes. Eh?'

The Colonel cleared his throat and hitched his shoulders back until his elbows were almost touching behind him. 'That was an excerpt from the great humanist Shelley,' he said. 'I shall now recite another excerpt from the same source.' He relaxed for a second, long enough to whisper to Mother, 'Some bitch stole my Whitman.' Then he went rigid again.

> 'The fountains mingle with the river,
> And the rivers with the ocean;
> The winds of heaven mix forever
> With a sweet emotion;
> Nothing in the world is single;
> All things, by a law divine,
> In one another's being mingle—
> Why not I with thine?'

We knew he had finished because he took his cap from Father and put it on. His eyes never left the sky. Now that the thunder of his voice had stopped, the countryside seemed to throb with stillness and expectancy.

'I suppose we may fire ahead now, Colonel, eh?' asked Ned, suspicious of the unnatural quiet.

'The ceremony is over,' said the Colonel.

'Man, you have a powerful voice,' said Ned warmly. 'I could listen to you roaring all day.'

Mother dropped on her knees beside the open grave. 'Eternal rest grant unto him, O Lord, and let perpetual light shine on him. May he rest in peace. Amen. Our Lady of perpetual succour, pray for him. St Jude, pray for him. St Teresa of the Little Flower, pray for him. St Joseph, pray for him.' This litany of aspirations was still spilling from her when the four bearers returned and began lowering the coffin. When it touched the bottom of the grave, the Colonel went rigid again. He looked as if he were in agony. Father moved over beside Mother and put his arm around her. Ned began to whistle. The mourners at the gate strained their necks so as not to miss a detail.

When the grave was filled, the Colonel shook Mother's hand. 'A delightful ceremony,' he said. 'It will be a pleasant memory. Goodbye.'

'Thank you, Colonel,' Mother began, but he had gone, covering the ground with huge, greedy strides.

We looked at the mound of fresh clay, and at the sheep, and at the neat rows of crosses and headstones on our left and right, and then we left, too. As we walked towards the gate, Ned had begun to sing, and the sheep were bleating, and the body of silence that the Colonel's oration had created suddenly cracked and dissipated.

A month passed before Mother mentioned the funeral or the nuns, and then she vowed that she would never set foot in the convent again. Of course she broke her vow, many times. Within that year alone, we attended a garden party to celebrate the silver jubilee of the arrival of the sisters in Omagh, and the annual operetta, and a jumble sale for the hospital. And although Mother threatened before each event to 'expose the hypocrites when all their swank friends are gathered round', she was a model of gentility and sweetness when the occasion came.

It seemed to me that her docility was caused by the extension of the Catholic portion of the graveyard. Cormac was not dead twelve months when the Canon bought the plot where he and Mrs Harrington were buried. The butcher Doherty was evicted, and the ground was consecrated. Within a week, Cormac had two neighbours, and within a month he was surrounded.

As Mother used to say wistfully, 'Our Cormac did not die in vain. The mills of God grind fine and slow, but they get there in the end.'

SHAYBO

Patrick Boyle

This last story is a satire on sexual mores which also underlines how the shackles have finally been lifted on what were once taboo subjects in Irish fiction. Contemporary writers now have the freedom of expression to explore topics that not so many years ago would have led the books or magazines in which they appeared to be banned. As Roddy Doyle demonstrated in the very first story in this book—and those who followed him have re-emphasised—the Irish have always possessed a ribald, earthy sense of humour when it comes to writing about suggestive situations, yet there can be few more outlandish places in which to set a story than the following one, which takes place in a public toilet.

Patrick Boyle (1905–1982), who was born in County Antrim and worked for 45 years as a bank manager, is, at first glance, an unlikely author to have penned this bizarre black comedy. Yet, even though he grew up in the same generation as O'Flaherty, O'Faolain and O'Connor, he brought a new voice to the Irish short story during the Sixties—with, memorably, his collection, At Night All Cats Are Grey *(1966)—in tales that have proved to be as vigorous and uncompromising as anything written by authors half his age. As well as its curious locale, 'Shaybo' is full of memorable characters and the sort of ripe speech that helped establish Patrick Boyle's work at the forefront of modern Irish humour. It also ends the collection on a note of satiric farce that is, I believe, hard to beat.*

*   *   *

You'd be right in thinking that an underground jakes is a poor place for a smoke and a chat. The more so when the sun is knocking sparks off the glass roof and stirring up a stink that would bloody near talk to you. But when you haven't the price of a packet of fags and when Shaybo Gallagher, the Corporation attendant, is a County-man of your own, a bit of hardship is neither here nor there.

'Hey!' he calls out, when he sees you stowing away. '*You're* a stranger. Come over here and tell us the news.'

Shaybo's cubby-hole is so small that there's only room for the one chair, but give the little whitterit credit, up he gets.

'Take the weight off your feet, old stock,' says he. 'It's tiring work walking the streets on a day like this.'

And on top of that, he produces the packet. A twenty Players, not long opened. Good for an hour or two of Shaybo's blethering.

'The city's choked up with yobs from the country,' he says. 'Up for the match. Oh, a shower of ignorant gulpins. They've made a hames of the joint already.'

He aims a kick at a terrier dog about to lift a leg against the door jamb.

'Hump off!'

It's a poor class of a man takes his spleen out on a brute beast. But there you are. What more can you expect from a shithouse warden?

'It'll have to be cleaned down from stem to stern,' says he. 'It is far from public conveniences these gentlemen were reared. Coming up from the Kerry mountains or the bogs of Cavan with but one thought in the heads—to rid themselves of the load of dirty black porter they've incurred in their travels. Clambering up on the seat and squatting down on their hunkers as if they were in their own haggards.'

He goes ranting on with this class of chat as though he wasn't born and bred, like many a better man, in the wilds of Donegal. Sight nor sound of a flush lavatory did he see till he came to work in the city thirty-odd years back. Damn the bit he knew what the chain was even for. Or where the used paper should go. To listen to him now, you would think he is gentry.

'Mean scuts they are too. They would stand outside an occupied cubicle for twenty minutes at a time, waiting for the customer inside to finish his business. Ducking in past him as soon as the door is opened. You can be full sure the ratepayers won't fatten on what they get by way of contributions from the crowd of country hallions heading for Croke Park.'

As he is giving out the pay, you can hear in the background the clatter of the crowd coming and going. The mutter of voices. The shuffle and stamp of impatient feet on the tiled floor. The swish of water from the pipes. And, from the closets, the odd cough or grunt or maybe even a rumbling fart as some poor bugger strives to relieve himself. A pleasant class of a commotion, one you could listen to for hours, if you've the smokes to go with it.

Shaybo is now holding forth about the way people look down on a lavatory attendant. And, God knows, you could hardly blame him. You'd see folk cringing away from him in disgust who'd find nothing bothersome in the company of a cow doctor—a man very apt at any time of the day or night to ram his arm, shoulder deep, up the backside of a brute beast.

'The truth is, it's a job like any other,' he says. 'The pay is good. The hours not too long. The work light. Granted it's not the best place to be in the real hot weather. Or when the crowds flock into the city for an All Ireland final.'

You could say that again. There's a hum rising, thick as a cloud of midges, that only cigarette smoke would disperse. Shaybo takes the hint and when the fags are lit, he says:

'You'd be surprised at the folk come in here. All classes of people. Even the clergy. Priests, Christian Brothers and the like.'

They'd be the queer asset in any public lavatory! It would be very liable to put a man off his devotions if he found a parish priest mounting the pulpit beside him and proceeding to let his dog off the chain.

The traffic had slackened a lot.

'It's the same every Sunday at this time,' says Shaybo. 'Everyone's at Croke Park, Dalymount Park, the Phoenix Park. They could be devouring pints somewhere or other. Or maybe be at the pictures. Wherever they get to, they don't come down here. A different class of a character altogether you'd find using a public convenience during a slack period. Queer-hawks of one sort or another. Slipping in here looking for company. The Guards are death on them. There's polismen smelling around this place at every hour of the day or morning. In full canonicals or in civvies. Out to plague and pester these poor angashores. And you'd wonder why. For they're a decent harmless enough lot. They may have their little weaknesses, I'll grant you that. But sure none of us is perfect. And few as quiet and civil and well-mannered as these lads.'

To hear the little pigmy giving off, you would think it is a meeting of the Sacred Heart Confraternity he is talking about instead of a gathering of blackguardly rascals intent on every manner of villainy and rascality. Take care but maybe Mister bloody Shaybo himself isn't properly battened down and shipshape. Why else would he be taking up the cudgels on behalf of a crowd of bloody half-in-halfs? Oh, he could be a dark horse, all right. Isn't he forever running to the altar rails and to evening devotions. Sure these craw-thumpers are all the same, the world over. Master hands at deception.

He gives me a nudge.

'Psst! Here's one of the regulars now. Out and in here a dozen times a day. Blondie, I call him.'

Well, the Lord knows, you couldn't mistake him. Strutting along, his hips clashing like a pair of cymbals. A tall fellow with fair wavy hair, a nose you would love to flatten and a double-breasted suit with padded shoulders and french letter fitting. A shockproof, fully automatic, twenty-two-carat bum-boy.

'Watch the antics of him,' says Shaybo.

Blondie minces down to the far end of the urinal. Stops at the hand basins. Takes out a pocket comb and starts preening himself up. Cocking his head this way and that to see what he looks like. The kind of carry-on that would give you the sick.

'Hush!' says Shaybo. 'He's watching everything in the mirror. You don't want to let him know he's taped.'

Sure enough, when you study closer, it is sticking out a mile that what Blondie is really doing at the hand basins is lamping the establishment. He stands there combing his hair, all the time grinning and grimacing into the mirror, until the last customer has emptied his bladder and gone his way rejoicing. Then he strolls across to the stall at the very end of the line, mounts the ledge and lounges there. Waiting.

'Isn't he the last word?' whispers Shaybo. 'He's the daddy of them all, I tell you.'

You would think he is talking about a prize fighter. Or a politician. Instead of a scrubby, smirking pansy.

'Someone's coming,' Shaybo mutters. 'With any sort of luck, we should have a right bit of gallery.' He leans out to look up the stairs. Ducks back immediately. 'Be cripes, it's a plain-clothes man. I'd know by the cut of his jib.'

Indeed, like Blondie, you would know him at once. Close-cropped bullet head, wattles of flesh creasing the collar of his jacket, splay feet treading cautiously: a rozzer if ever there was one. At the foot of the stairs slowing down, like you would be going into a place of worship. Sizing up the available space. Then, believe it or not, he heads straight for the only occupied stall in the tool house. A thing no decent law-abiding citizen would dream of doing. For a man is entitled to a bit of privacy on a job of this kind. Unless the jakes is packed out.

'There'll be trouble come of this,' Shaybo says, watching the rozzer take up pumping stations beside Blondie.

Flutes in their fists, they stand side by side, paying no attention—or so you'd think—to each other. But you are sorely mistaken if you think they are making proper use of the facilities provided by the Corporation. You would be fully assured of this when you see Blondie reach his free hand across in the general direction of the rozzer's fly.

'That's torn the coupon,' says Shaybo, starting off down the jakes at a run. He has rubber-soled shoes and the pair of bucks know nothing till he is upon them.

'Hey, you!' he shouts, giving the rozzer a push in the small of the back. 'Enough of that.'

The rozzer lurches forward against the slippery porcelain. Claws wildly at it with both hands, seeking purchase to push himself upright. He fails. The feet go from under him, skidding off the ledge to the floor, sending him sliding down to crash on his mouth and nose into the trough. You can say without the word of a lie that he swallows back a mouthful of porter piss that would soften the cough of a chief superintendent. To crown the poor bugger's misfortunes, doesn't the bloody spray take it into its head to start working, drenching the sleeves and shoulders of his nice new suit. You'd have broken your arse laughing at the cut of him, lying there wriggling and gasping like a freshly caught conger.

Shaybo leans over him.

'What are you supposed to be doing down there?' he shouts, above the roar of the spray. 'This is no place to be doing your barrack square exercises.'

The rozzer struggles up to his hands and knees, clear of the spray.

'What's wrong?' he asks the tiled floor. 'What's going on here?'

He shakes his head violently, scattering water all round, in an effort to clear his head. With the clatter he got, he must be just about half-conscious.

'You should be ashamed of yourself,' says Shaybo. 'Nosing your way into Corporation property on your filthy errands. Those that sent you here must have the queer dirty minds.'

The rozzer turns his head up sideways. There is a dazed expression on his face.

'Someone gave me a belt of a fist,' he says. 'When my back was turned. Gave me a bloody judas.'

Shaybo leans closer, hissing into the astonished face.

'No one hit you. Though if someone did, I wouldn't raise a hand to stop him. What right have you to come in here starting trouble. I keep a decent law-abiding establishment, I'll have you to know.'

You would find it in your heart to be proud of the little banty cock. Not since the force was started, could there have been a rozzer talked to in this fashion. Though it's to be admitted that a copper is not at his best kneeling on the floor of a piss house with his flute hanging out and him wringing wet from wallowing in the lavatory trough.

He gets to his feet and stands there swaying, gaping in bewilderment at the little circle of curious customers that's after gathering. It is worth noting that there is no sign of Blondie. Wisely enough, he has skipped it. After starting off the whole bucking rumpus.

Shaybo hasn't finished with him yet.

'Put away that truncheon of yours,' he says. 'And button up your spare. Don't you know full well, if you're conversant with your manual of instructions, that exposing your person in public is a criminal offence.'

He pauses to let that shaft penetrate.

'Whether in uniform or in plain clothes,' he finishes.

While the rozzer, red faced and all thumbs, is tucking away his paraphernalia, the crowd of earwigging gulpins mutters:

'What's the row about?'

'Didn't you hear what the man said?'

'Exposing his person, no less.'

'A drunken polisman, they say.'
'Disgraceful!'
'What's happening anyway?'
Shaybo, with flapping hands, shoos them off.
'It's all right, gentlemen,' he says. 'Everything's under control.'
For sheer brass neck and general effrontery, you must hand
it to the little weasel. Making an unprovoked attack on a law
enforcement officer, accusing him of unspeakable practices,
humiliating him before a gathering of scandalised citizens and then
calming the enraged populace with a few words of soft sawder.
Though to be strictly accurate, you have only to take a look at
the rozzer with his arms hanging the one length, the water dripping
out of his sleeves and running down his cheeks, his face twisted
with suppressed rage, to know that there is one member of the
company far from calm and reassured.
'Look!' he says, displaying his sodden jacket with the sleeves
already riding up the wrists. 'Look at the state of my clothes.'
God knows, if he weren't a plain-clothes cop—the type of creeping Jesus nobody likes—you would feel sorry for him.
'Sure it's a thing of nothing,' says Shaybo. 'The cleaners will
put it right for you in jig time.'
He takes the rozzer by the arm and leads him past the scattering
of customers now absorbed in their devotions.
At the foot of the stairs he halts.
'You'd be as well though,' says he, 'to get out of those wet duds
before you do another short arm inspection.'
He pauses.
'Elsewhere,' he adds. And there's a growl in his voice that would
do credit to a mastiff.
The rozzer shambles up the stairs without another word out of
him and Shaybo comes strutting back to his cubby-hole.
'It'll be the queer while,' says he, 'before that fellow comes
down here again on his filthy pursuits. This place would get a bad
name if that kind of carry-on were to continue.'
In the name of God, what class of a joint does the little pintle
think he is running? A convent or a crap house? He is getting too
big for his boots, Mister bloody Shaybo. He wants taking down a
peg. But if you're smoking a man's cigarettes, your hands are tied.
He is still holding forth like an outraged abbess when there's
the sound of footsteps on the stairs. Standing at the door, he has

a clear view of all comers and you can see by the look on his face that a stumer is on its way.

'And what brings *you* back?' he demands, as the tow-headed pansy puts his head round the door.

'He's gone, I see,' says Blondie, in a sour tone of voice.

'If it's your playmate you mean, I ran him out of here.'

'It's a pity you couldn't mind your own business instead of interfering in what doesn't concern you.'

'What's that?' Shaybo yelps.

You can see he is shook. But the silly slob should know that a queer the like of Blondie specialises in biting the hand that feeds him.

'I had him on the hook. You made a bags of the whole thing by butting in.'

'Do-you-do-you-do you mean . . . that you should have been allowed . . . without let or hindrance . . . to . . . to—'

'Sure, I do. I know how to handle these customers.'

'You know . . . how to handle . . . these—?'

'Yeah. It's my job.'

Shaybo takes a deep breath. Lets it out slowly through his nose.

'Well, you made a poor fist of the job here today, if I may say so. Did you not tape the class of a gentleman you were propositioning?'

'Of course I did. Isn't he a notorious character? Known in every public lavatory in the city.'

'Why did you tackle him so? You could have landed yourself in the Bridewell.'

Blondie switches a pair of lamps on Shaybo that would shrivel your soul.

'Didn't I tell you it's my job? How do you think vice in this city can be stamped out without the work of the Special Branch?'

It would make the day for you, if you were to see the cut of Shaybo. The legs must be going from under him for he is propped up against the door jamb like a sagging bolster. His face is twisted up and his eyes squeezed tight. The fingers of his locked hands are squirming furiously. There are sounds coming from his open mouth that could very well come from someone after getting a woeful kick in the fork. At length the words come.

'Special Branch?' he squeaks.

'Yes.'

'You mean . . . that all the times you came in here . . . day and daily for weeks past . . . you were on duty?'

'That's right. It was suspected at Headquarters that these premises were becoming a centre of homosexual activities.'

Shaybo's eyes are scampering around in their sockets like hunted sheep, trying to evade the expressionless face of his tormentor. He runs his tongue round his lips. Whispers hoarsely:

'Suspected . . . homosexual . . . activity?'

'Yes. That's what I was on the track of today.'

'But . . . but . . . but I don't understand. Wasn't that bullet-headed fellow a plain-clothes man? How could there be . . .'

Shaybo dries up. And no wonder. The thought of two rozzers tricking with each other's tools in a public lavatory would be enough to put you wondering what capers they would be at in the privacy of the barracks day room.

Blondie snorts.

'Plain-clothes man, how are you! Is it trying to insult the Force you are?'

'You mean—' Shaybo moistens his trembling lips. 'You mean . . . he's not . . . a policeman?'

'Of course not. He's a wretched little homo. And but for your intervention, I'd have him up on a charge of indecent behaviour.'

This is too much for Shaybo. He burst out:

'Indecent behaviour, is it? Sure no man's accoutrements would be safe with you around. Didn't I see you with my own two eyes interfering with that poor fellow who had no other errand in here but to make his water? And then you talk of bringing a charge against him. It's little short of felon setting, that's what it is. Felon setting.'

Blondie gives him the kind of look you'd give to a turning worm.

'My man,' says he, in a voice these gentlemen use when they are very liable to take out the notebook, 'any more trouble from you and I'll book you for obstructing an officer in the execution of his duty.'

Shaybo's eyebrows are up in his hair and his jaw is dangling by its own weight. There is no fight left in him. All that is wanted now is a blow of the chopper to finish him off.

Blondie squares his shoulders. Clears his throat. Swings up the blade.

'In the course of my investigations here,' says he, and you could almost hear the icicles tinkling in his voice, 'it has become evident that you have been turning a blind eye on what is happening under your nose.'

He breaks off to turn to the little group of gougers, their heads stuck out trying to catch what's being said above the swish of the pipes.

'Move along there,' he says. 'Be off about your business.'

When they are gone, he turns back to Shaybo.

'Furthermore,' says he, bringing down the chopper, 'your behaviour would lead to the belief that you are in sympathy with the activities of these immoral characters.'

Well, that's a real slaughter-house blow and no mistake. Who would ever think that that little maggot, a notorious candidate for beatification, is all the time running a class of a knocking shop instead of a gent's lavatory? The novenas will have to come thick and fast to atone for this transgression.

As Blondie turns away and moves off towards the stairs, you'd be inclined to think that the entertainment is over. But no! Shaybo starts clearing his throat, rasping and raking and hawking till he drags up a bloody great ball of phlegm that must have had roots growing down to his navel. With the force of a sling shot, he sends it cracking off the tiled floor at Blondie's heels.

'Jesus curse you!' he murmurs fervently.

Blondie stops in his tracks. Wheels round slowly. Comes back a pace.

'What was that you said?' he demands.

'My Jesus, mercy!' Shaybo spits out the words as though he is pronouncing a malediction.

'What kind of a war-cry is that?'

'It's a pious ejaculation. Entitles you to three hundred days' indulgence.'

'And what's the idea of this?' Blondie points to the green gob-bet, still quaking like a jelly.

'I'm a bit caught in the throat. It'll maybe clear up if I keep spitting.'

They stay eyeing each other while you would count ten, neither moving a muscle.

'If you take my advice,' says Blondie, at length, 'you'll mind your step in future. Or you'll be in trouble.'

His gaze swivels slowly round the empty stalls.

'Big trouble.'

He turns on his heel and starts off up the stairs again.

Not till the footsteps have died away does Shaybo's face uncoil. He opens and closes his lips, searching for spittle. Sucks up a noisy breath through his nose. Hawks deep in his throat. Spits dry.

Straightening up, he moves across to the back of the cubby-hole. Rummages around on the shelf. Picking things up and putting them down again. His legs are shaky enough, so is his voice when he says:

'Very few around for the day of a match.'

He stands there, staring into space, with not a word out of him that you'd throw to a dog, until a group of schoolboys comes trampling down, shouting and jack-acting. Then he rouses himself. Rubs his hands together briskly.

'The sun splitting the trees and not a potato washed,' he says.

He picks up a long-handled mop. Goes to the door.

'The crowd'll be along any minute now,' he says.

Leaning on the mop handle, he gazes down the length of the jakes. There is only one customer left. An old buff with a dark suit and a bowler hat. A Bank director or the like. Rushing off to a board meeting, you'd say, for he keeps glowering impatiently down at the unceasing dribble. You would cripple yourself laughing at the contortions of him when he starts stowing away. Hard put to it you'd be to say whether it is the crown jewels or a dangerous reptile that he is stuffing down the leg of his trousers, jiggling and jerking with one knee bent to make full sure the pants are slung on the usual side and the last drop shaken from Fagan. In spite of all his precautions, he moves off stiff-legged, letting the cat out of the bag, so to speak.

Shaybo is muttering to himself.

'Tck! Tck! Tck!' He shakes his head sadly. 'Blondie—of all people. You'd lose faith in human nature after the likes of that.'

ACKNOWLEDGEMENTS

The editor would like to record his thanks to Peter Berresford Ellis, W. O. G. Lofts and Brian Cleeve for their help in assembling this collection. He and the publishers are also grateful to the following authors, publishers and agents for permission to reprint copyright stories: Secker & Warburg for 'A Night in Limerick', an extract from *The Van* by Roddy Doyle; Macmillan General Books for 'A Rhinoceros, Some Ladies and a Horse' by James Stephens, 'The Corncrake' by Sean O'Casey and 'The Majesty of the Law' by Frank O'Connor; John Calder Publishers for 'Love and Lethe' by Samuel Beckett; Constable Ltd for 'The Woman Who Married Clark Gable' by Sean O'Faolain and 'Liquid Assets' by Oliver St John Gogarty; David R. Godine for 'A Ball of Malt and Madame Butterfly' by Benedict Kiely; Random House Publishers for 'Phonefun Limited' by Bernard MacLaverty, 'A Day on the Bog' by Lord Dunsany and 'I Meet a Sheik' by Brendan Behan; HarperCollins for 'The Martyr's Crown' by Flann O'Brien and 'Shaybo' by Patrick Boyle; Viking Press for 'Dan Doonan's Wake' by Spike Milligan and 'The White Irish Society' by Patrick Campbell; Reed Consumer Books for 'Tale Told in Destiny Bay' by Donn Byrne; The O'Brien Press for 'The Tailor's "Busht"' by Eric Cross; Faber for 'The Saucepan' by Lynn Doyle; Fleetway Publications for 'Tom Geraghty's Imagination' by Donagh MacDonagh and 'Principles of Stone Breaking' by Patrick Kavanagh; Victor Gollancz Ltd for 'The Death of a Scientific Humanist' by Brian Friel. Acknowledgement is also made to Twayne Publishers for permission to quote from *The Irish Short Story: A Critical History* by James F. Kilroy and *The Irish Novel: A Critical History* by James M. Cahalan. While every care has been taken to clear permission for the use of the stories in this book, in the case of any accidental infringement, copyright holders are asked to write to the editor care of the publishers.